PRAISE FOR "THE WHISPERERS' WAY"

"…remarkable and supremely informative! With authority, clarity and compassion, the author presents a guide for interacting with animals—human or nonhuman—empathically and effectively. *The Whisperer's Way* offers a wide range of approaches, each rooted in scientific evidence and presented in a readily usable manner. A powerful resource for human and animal medical professionals, psychotherapists, parents…"

~Barbara Natterson-Horowitz, MD, author of "Zoobiquity", Harvard Medical School, Harvard Department of Human Evolutionary Biology, UCLA Division of Cardiology

"The Whisperers' Way, is a skillfully written, straightforward, and transformative approach to healing troubled individuals, especially our youth, with Heart + Wisdom +Knowledge. This transformative book brings the collective wisdom of several disciplines to heal with insight and understanding without judgment. A must read!"

~Dr. Christopher Hansen, Solano County Chief Probation Officer, Lecturer Criminology & Criminal Justice Studies Sonoma State University

"… simple enough to understand and yet deep enough in philosophy, her whisperers' process is touched by layers of wisdom from her real life experiences. This book will certainly be an addition to humanity as the author shows unique ways of overcoming difficult situations ."

~Dr. Selim Sheikh DVM PhD, President, Humanity Beyond Barriers

"Sue Chan proved to me that she can transform a boy in residential care and special education classes due to hyperactivity and trauma from abandonment and abuse into a calmer child who felt safe, trusted and responsible. Her book will help others do the same."

~Russell Kusama, retired Director, Progress Ranch Residential Care Services

"Sue Chan's *The Whisperers' Way* is a timely work very much needed in understanding the evolved approaches that a variety of 'whisperers' have used successfully over many decades. Sue's extensive research has produced a well thought out work that can offer a roadmap to those desiring to 'connect' with a wide variety of animals, always coming from the heart first. Achieving a fertile learning environment is the goal and once the animal's trust is gained, amazing positives follow. Congratulations Sue on this accomplishment!"

~Frank Bell, www.HorseWhisperer.com

"Dr. Chan has captured what many of us animal lovers feel. We have a deep passion for and deep desire to understand how animals think and FEEL...We as Humans must constantly evolve in our understanding of how animals communicate and make every effort to emulate what THEY do, not try to make them understand what WE do! It is obvious that Dr Chan has dedicated her life journey to a deeper understanding on how animals think and she has put it to paper for the rest of us to delve into!"

~ Gerry Cox, Mountain House Stables

The
WHISPERERS' WAY

The Essential Elements

For
Teaching And Healing
Children And Animals
With Knowledge, Wisdom And Heart

Susan Chan DVM, MPVM

GOLD MOUNTAIN PRESS
VACAVILLE CALIFORNIA

LIBRARY OF CONGRESS CARD NUMBER: 2023902651

Paperback ISBN: 978-1-960637-02-4

eBook ISBN: 978-1-960637-01-7

Cover design by 100Covers
Proofreading by Jarred Conrey and Brian Lam
Formatting assistance from Shahbaz Awan

CONTENTS

DEDICATION

These books are dedicated to those who supported CETA Foundation & Phoenix Ranch through the years. Our programs have included animal rescue, animal-assisted therapy, low-cost spay neuter, humane livestock raising, petting zoos & pony rides, an annual sheep-shearing/open house and ranch visits. Through these activities, I learned what makes people and animals tick and how to influence health and behavior in a positive way. I owe this all to you and the animals that passed through our ranch. Here are some that went the extra mile:

T.S. Glide Foundation	Andrew & Adam Buderi
VIP Petcare	Barbara Reiley
Natural Pet Tooth Fairy	Delia & Jon Irving
Tractor Supply Dixon	Tony Helm
Higby's Feed, Dixon	Barbara Clark
Pure Grain Bakery Vacaville	Dr. Richard Yamagata
Nugget Market Vacaville	Barbara & Ken Mark
UC Davis Circle K Club	Golden State Accordion Club
Rev. Katie Wong	Judd Redden
Robin Ormiston	Joel & Linda Jang
Mrs. Jean Weber	Dr. John Menke
Dr. Mariana Lotersztain	Dr. Katie Patterson- Wolf
Dr. Karen Krstich	Beverly Chan
The Ignacio Martinez family	Jim Hamano
Dee and Eric Leger-Garcia	Countless UC Davis interns
Hsuan and Van Ly	

"In Memory of Ed and Helen Chan who raised me the way I should go and my "Po-po" Mew Yit Chew who taught me the power of a grateful heart."

SPECIAL THANKS to the "horse-whisperers"
who shared their wisdoms for these books:

Gerry Cox   Joe Fernandez   Paul Williamson
Frank Bell   Ahmad Alhuqayl   Perry Wood
Paul Dufresne

And to Dr. Stephen Porges for his patient
explanations of technical concepts.

INTRODUCTION

WHAT IS THE WHISPERERS' WAY?

M any professionals are good at working with most situations. The ones I refer to as "Whisperers" are masters at taking on even the hardest ones—those who act out, those who are fearful, some that are dangerous. "Hardcore" is a term that seems fitting. Some whisperers even heal physical issues as well. They quietly work in many professions: Animal trainers, veterinarians, teachers, therapists, doctors, nurses, care providers, that wonderful neighbor… It should be noted that whisperers I refer to in this book generally don't self-identify as whisperers, they just humbly get things done.

But it's not just a job, it's a way of life. Their commitment to a life of "service to others" gives them the extra drive to seek answers and willingness to be innovative and take risks. Their quiet confidence allows them to build trusting relationships, which makes for efficient teaching or therapy efforts. Their ability to keep negative emotions like fear, anger, insecurity and resentment out of their teaching and training encounters is critical and supported by scientific research. They are practical people being more concerned about doing what works than why it works because they need to get a job done. They aren't going to quibble about nomenclature.

This book looks into what they know and how they apply their knowledge.

THE THREE COMPONENTS OF "WHISPERING"

KNOWLEDGE—information about psychology, behavior and biology that affects behavior. This information is processed by the Right Brain with logic and in a linear fashion. It is processed by the Left Brain with creativity by linking information to produce new ideas.

WISDOM—the ability to apply that knowledge appropriately and the ability to develop new knowledge effectively

HEART—the inner sense that allows you to build good relationships, keep calm in the face of chaos and discern appropriate responses. The lower/primitive/subcortical brain processes information into emotional responses. The physical Heart also has a role in processing information and producing responses.

You will see how concepts that are called "spiritual," religious or touchy feely actually have a scientifically-supported positive impact on you and the individuals you are trying to help. I hope that this connection will allow people to be less self-conscious and hesitant about incorporating these ideas because it's not just silly stuff.

I will also discuss what I call "Metaphysical Laws" because this is an area that is not well understood but is the basis for practices called "alternative," "spiritual" and "woo-woo." I know through experience that these practices are effective and very helpful. I hope that through discussion of scientific discoveries about quantum mechanics more people will be open to trying them.

I have given much thought to what it takes to work in this way and how to put it in writing so that you can read it and understand. I focus on the practical ideas that are useful and easy to apply in real life situations. I provide you the information you need to execute them with more consistent success.

This book is the culmination of my knowledge as founder/ director of CETA Foundation. The core concepts of the mission were Respect, Compassion, Empowerment—Respect for our fellow human beings and animals, Compassion to take action to make their lives better, Empowerment with the sharing of Knowledge and building of confidence to take action.

Decades ago, the book *The Joy of Cooking* came out. It contains not only recipes from many cultures but explains the techniques and principles so that you could venture off on your own. Think of the Whisperers' Way series as that kind of cookbook: The authors of the *Joy of Cooking* give information on all the different ingredients used in cooking. They give you information on all the different ways to prepare foods (baking/broiling/braising…cutting up pieces, etc.) They give you more recipes that you could ever imagine making or want to make. It would be way more information that you can remember so you scan through it the first time, read the sections you need at the moment, know where to look things up when you need an idea for a problem later. You will find ideas that don't resonate with you like recipes for things you can't stand. Just skip over those. But buried in there are ones that give you that "Aha!" moment for an issue you've been struggling with. This information will give you more confidence to try things on your own.

I ascribe to the "If it doesn't cost a bunch and works for someone else, it's worth a try!" philosophy. Some call this "Open-mindedness." Some call this not being afraid to try something new and "Nothing ventured, nothing gained."

I am not a human health professional and I do not compete or show animals (I don't even ride my horses), so will leave the technical aspects of training to experts in those specific disciplines. These books will provide that deeper understanding of behavior so you can more effectively apply what you learn from those other experts.

These books are written with the assumption that you have a basic knowledge of training through your own experience or reading books on the topic. If you don't already have basic skills, seek out one of the many excellent resources available. Good people out there are happy to help you learn.

WHAT THIS BOOK OFFERS:

Doing this work proficiently requires an incredible amount of knowledge. **The Essential Elements** provides you with a unique understanding of behavior, and how to apply the knowledge you acquire from other sources as well as providing a unique understanding of behavioral concepts

The Whisperers' Way helps you use all that basic information but apply it more successfully. I have added what I independently discovered and combined information from many disciplines to connect many heretofore unconnected dots. Thus, my books have much deeper information and insights than you will find in most other venues. And much more to wade through.

I introduce the Threshold Concept and thinking of every situation (or body with a health issue) as having lots of moving parts. This is crucial to incorporate into your problem-solving strategy especially with difficult cases.

You will find that I repeat some ideas several times in the book. I did this because I assume that readers may not be reading the whole book cover to cover. Or if like me, they might not remember everything they read by the time they got to the related topic. Many will look up a section that interests them or that they need at the moment and won't have an index in the back to look up terminology. To reduce the chance of confusion over complex and interconnected ideas and avoid points being missed or taken out of context, I decided to just say things again, like a series of articles on related topics.

Just reading my books is not adequate to "work like a Whisperer." Like a video game that requires you to learn the rules and players, the more you know and practice what you know, the higher the level you can go. Each player will develop their own knowledge and skills differently. Like hiking trails on a mountain, there are many paths to the top. You alone should determine which path is right for you. And when you get to the top of the mountain, you will likely see more valleys and ridges to explore in the distance. Learning never needs to stop.

Even if you don't have the wherewithal to do this work, these books will help you recognize people out there who do work along these lines. Please remember that "professional" just means somebody takes money in return for the hope of a desired result. "Certified" and "licensed" just means a person took a particular course or passed a test. It does not mean they will necessarily know how to help your child or pet. They may not even take them down a path that you like. You need to know enough to recognize what they do not know so you can stop things before too much damage is done.

"Scientifically-based recommendations" also have their limitations because research is based on what the human being who put together an experiment or is interpreting the data actually knows.

I have researched and simplified technical information so that you will be better equipped to understand what "scientifically based recommendations" may not be totally sound.

Your children and animals rely on you to be their advocate. You can and should call the shots for the ones you love. Your knowledge will empower you to do this. And don't forget to take care of yourself because you deserve love, too.[1]

---

[1] **graphic by Michelle Barrett, Solano County Mama Bear Defense**

I hope to expand awareness of different ideas with this book. Due to constraints on my time, I have not been able to provide many citations in this edition, for which I apologize. However, you can likely find the sources using keywords in internet search engines.

RELATIONSHIPS WHERE WHISPERER SKILLS ARE USEFUL

Teacher/student	Therapist/client
Supervisor/employee	Doctor/patient
Troop leader/scout	Pet owner/pet
Rider/horse	Farrier/horse
Dog groomer/dogs	Rancher/livestock

Parent or caregiver/child
Business owner/customer
Law enforcement/community member
Veterinarian/animal patient (and their "parents")

OTHER BOOKS PLANNED FOR THE SERIES

The Essential Elements covers the main topics with enough depth that you should be able to use it if you have background knowledge in training. I hope that life will allow me to produce a series of related books to include everything I can offer. The introduction and a version of The Big Picture Overview will be repeated in every book of this series to provide context for readers of those installments. The other books will expand the discussion with more details and stories to illustrate points relevant to the species of concern. If you run into difficulties, you can always refer back to **The Essential Elements** for **The Deep Dives** to get more information on nuances that aren't covered in the Big Picture Overview

If I don't have these books done, I will have information on my website on how to best contact me with questions or ideas.

The Whisperers' Way: Notes on Dog Training and Handling
(With an expanded discussion on "drive" and aggression.)

The Whisperer's Way: Notes on Horse Training and Handling
(With an expanded discussion on communication and working with physically large animals)

The Whisperers' Way: Animal Handling Ideas for Veterinarians, Ranchers, Groomers and Other Animal Professionals
(With an expanded discussion on restraint techniques)

The Whisperers Way: Animal Assisted Therapy

The Science behind The Whisperers Way
(With an expanded discussion on research pertaining to behavior and health)

WHISPERING IS AN ART

You can use instructional manuals and cookbooks to do a lot of things on a basic level. Then you can work like an artist. Sculpting is an art. Healing is an art.

It came to me that an artist takes thorough knowledge of materials to come up with creative ways to get to the next level. In street language: You have to know your stuff and how to stick it together to create something of beauty.

In Whispering, your knowledge of facts is your materials. You develop understanding (wisdom) of how to play with those facts to get the desired results. To take the finesse up an extra notch, add heart and soul to give you the eyes to see and create something beautifully.

These books are just illustrations of my way of working. I by no means claim to have the definitive definition of "Whisperer." You may find other methods that work better for you, but at least you might glean some information and ideas in these pages to help you in your endeavors. The important thing is that you end up with a happy healthy individual at the end.

> *"He who works with his hands is a laborer.*
> *He who works with his hands and his head is a craftsman.*
> *He who works with his hand and his head and his heart is an artist."*
>
> ~St. Francis of Assisi

MAKING ART INTO
SCIENCE

While it appears that an artist creates out of thin air, there are specific rules that make the composition of a piece "beautiful." I make a humble attempt to explain the rules of Whispering. I recently learned a new big word for what I'm trying to do:

CONSILIENCE: The linking together of principles from different disciplines especially when forming a comprehensive theory

~Merriam Webster

There are many excellent instructional books and videos out there utilizing different methods on how to get something done. In medicine, we call these step-by-step instructions "Protocols". This is also called "the Cookbook method" by those who have experience on the front lines and recognize the limitations of strictly adhering to the instruction manual. In real life, you have factors that can vary from the controlled setting in which the protocols were created. Following written directions to the letter will not take into consideration all these variations and allows room for failures to occur. Too many people will blame the protocol when in fact they were at fault by not recognizing what needed to be changed.

My mom's childhood friend in Fort Bragg, CA taught me how to make flaky pie crusts. She gave me a recipe but then said, "Always see how it looks when you're done adding the ingredients together. The humidity changes, so you might need to add a few drops of water or a sprinkle of flour to get it just right."

Moral of the story: Don't be afraid to make changes to what's written in the recipe if the situation calls for it.

If you have a failure, you don't throw away that cookbook! Just figure out what caused it to fail THIS time and add it all together in your toolbox of knowledge.

The Whisperers' Way teaches you how to deal with those differences in factors. With much more information at hand and deeper understanding, you can develop your own way of dealing with problems and become really good at what you're trying to accomplish.

Understanding how all pieces of information fit together gives you the context in which the information should be considered. Thus, when you need to make decisions, you will know how to prioritize all the information at hand. If you keep these relationships in perspective, you will be able to develop your own problem-solving algorithms (i.e., "If you get A, do B; if you don't get A, do C.")

For these books, I gathered together the information I found important over my decades of working with people and animals and organized the information in a way that would be easier to understand and remember.

It helps me stay oriented and utilize information in the appropriate context if I have a quick look at a whole program before diving into details. So in this book, I introduce the concepts in a summary section (The Big Picture Overview), and then I repeat the information with an expansion of the topics from the first time around. Think of it as information being presented in layers.

> *"Ogres are like onions... Onions have layers. Ogres have layers. Onions have layers. You get it? We both have layers."*
>
> ~Shrek

Instead of having an index, I have made the Table of Contents more detailed than normal. Scanning it will help you find what concepts you want. It will also help you understand how these ideas fit together so you can keep everything in the appropriate perspective.

Experienced trainers may find the Big Picture Overview enough to achieve breakthroughs. **The Deep Dive** discussions will be useful if more details and background information are needed to understand the nuances and exceptions to the typical responses in challenging cases.

Nothing drives me crazier than jargon, which is terminology that is only understood by people who have been trained in specific disciplines. While it's great when you have been taught the definitions and associated concepts, jargon stifles communication and learning for everyone else who isn't in the club. At the risk of being called unsophisticated, I will intentionally use words that are understandable to more people and try to explain complicated terms so more people can apply this knowledge. I will also use multiple words in sentences to convey concepts, which some may find obnoxious. Please understand that words have depth and different meanings for different circles. When I use a certain word, it may not mean much to one person but to a person who understands it differently, they see a whole wad of ideas associated with this one simple word.

I came across this cute diagram on a Facebook post. This sketch has been posted widely on many social media accounts. I couldn't find a source that named an artist so I want it to be known that I cannot take credit for this clever idea and will be happy to acknowledge this person if they come forth. But I wanted to share it because it so aptly depicts how I hope you will be able to process and apply the information you glean from my writings.

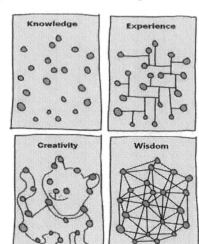

WARNING/DISCLAIMER

Whispering can be risky business. Whispering involves working just below the point of potentially triggering fear, anger or panic, which I discuss in detail in the section on Thresholds. When working with animals, the bigger they are the more potential they have for causing physical harm and injury to you. We, who are determined to increase our skill, will push the limit and take the risk. Many of us have scars to show it. Some have even lost their lives.

I discuss ways to minimize the risk but there is never any way to eliminate it completely. For legal reasons, anything you try after reading this book, you are doing completely warned and agree to accept any risks.

BENEFITS OF READING THIS BOOK

Not all excellent trainers work the same way I do. Some will even criticize my books. But I take the position that there is no such thing as "The Ultimate" anything—one style that is better than another—only a style that fits you. Just consider the Whisperers' Way one of many options. People who like a slower, thoughtful approach and are more willing to develop patience should find *The Whisperers' Way* rewarding.

Even if my style doesn't work for you, the universal nature of **The Knowledge** section will be useful with other styles of training.

I was always taught in the traditional Chinese way that Knowledge is Power. Knowledge gives you power over your own life because you do not need to rely on others. You alone know what's in your best interest. If you have adequate knowledge, you cannot be led astray by those who would take advantage of you.

There are people who will withhold knowledge because they want to control you. They want to keep secrets so you will need to use the services of an "expert." Then again, some are also afraid of liability because people will use pieces of information inappropriately and sue the source of that information when they get hurt. Take for instance when television's Dr. Oz offered the idea of heating "ice packs" in the microwave to lay on sore muscles (which

I do all the time). Someone (likely intentionally) overheated a pack and burned himself, then sued Dr. Oz. Now many are hesitant to offer these ideas to those who could benefit and these packs now carry warnings not to use them for this purpose.

I offer this information because I want to help people despite the risk of someone misinterpreting what I write or doing something intentionally so they can sue me. Therefore, I am relying on you to be honest, responsible and take ownership of your own mistakes. Please use this information to do good for others and yourself. And above all, stay safe!

HOW IS THIS BOOK DIFFERENT THAN OTHERS?

Drawing from experience with so many different species I describe patterns of responses not discussed in other books. For example, I describe the concepts of Threshold and Spasticity as applied to teaching, managing aggression, herding and the healing arts.

- I use concepts from human psychology, such as impulse control, to explain and change animal behavior.

- I explain how to use the autonomic nervous system to enhance calming, learning and bonding.

- I explain techniques that reverse the effects of emotional trauma (PTSD) from abuse or events through rewiring the circuits in the brain.

By having this wide range of information in the pages of one book, I hope to make it easier for you to see how this is all interconnected. You can then develop your own skills in a more profound way.

A BRIEF HISTORY

HOW THE WHISPERERS' WAY CAME TO BE

We all are born with gifts. Those gifts are just a start. It takes hard work to make those gifts into something that's useful. My gift is loving to be around animals. With hard work, I became good at working with them, too.

Over the past 40 years I have worked with countless personalities in equally countless scenarios. I worked as a veterinarian in pet hospitals, animal shelters and high-volume vaccination clinics. I developed Phoenix Ranch to house many species in a semi-free-range environment and founded CETA (California Education Through Animals) Foundation to provide educational, therapy and animal rescue programs. These animals provide volunteers, visitors and children in need opportunities for close encounters with friendly animals. I rehabilitated rescued animals so they could be placed into new homes or integrate with our ranch family. As one who raised dogs, livestock, horses, poultry and parrots, I was able to see how behavior and responses change from birth to old age.

To develop my skills, I voraciously read books on animal training and human psychology and practiced daily with the animals at Phoenix Ranch. I realized that the strategies I used with animals worked with my own children and the special needs visitors that came to the CETA Foundation programs. I learned and developed some techniques that calmed agitated animals down and made them easier to tame. These "tricks" worked on kids, too. Over time, I learned how to mellow out dangerous dogs and horses, and heal psychotic parrots. Special needs and foster children thrived when visiting my ranch. One foster child felt so comfortable here he even asked if I would adopt him. I used these skills to "doctor" ranch animals without an assistant to hold them still and brought about healing in animals other veterinarians would have put down. I never thought what I did was that special but occasionally someone would call me "A Whisperer." [2]

I learned much of this from other trainers and teachers who are also called "Whisperers"—Whisperers of horses (Tom Dorrance; Frank Bell; Linda Tellington-Jones; Gincy Self Bucklin; Allen Pogue, Gerry Cox),Whisperers of dogs (Barbara Woodhouse, Monks of New Skete, Carol Lea Benjamin, Cesar Milan)

---

[2] **Some Phoenix Ranch family members**

and Whisperers of livestock (Bud Williams, Dr. Temple Grandin.) While there are many others who bring to the table excellent and valuable knowledge, these all are people whose working style resonated with me and helped me accomplish what I needed to do. Theirs is a slower, more analytical and observational way of going that takes a bit of patience and understanding of nuance. Tom Dorrance called this "working by feel." All of these people use Trust as the basis for their work.

In subtle ways, I pass on what I do to the student interns at Phoenix Ranch and help those who come for the CETA events. Then came a county decision that I could not continue the ranch visits and annual open house without expensive and labor-intensive compliance measures. My insurance company forced me to take any mention of our programs off our website. We temporarily scaled back looking for ways to reopen. I knew how many people and animals could be helped if only more had my knowledge and could develop these skills. I was too shy and technologically-challenged to do videos so books seemed like the most efficient way to accomplish this.

Whisperers are more doers than talkers. Many never really talk about what they do; you just see them do it. Horseman Tom Dorrance and livestock expert Bud Williams held clinics but it was clear from participant comments that one must study their actions because their words often left people puzzled. I set out to act as a translator and write books to help people do what we do.

I re-read all the books on my shelf. I researched the writings of "people Whisperers" like Dr. Karyn Purvis, Tracy Hogg, and Perry Woods (who is also a horse whisperer.) The combining of medical and veterinary knowledge is a concept called "One Health" pioneered by my graduate advisor, Dr. Calvin Schwabe of the University Of California School Of Veterinary Medicine. Articles on human psychology helped me put into words concepts that animal trainers and handlers see in the field. The works of Jennifer Giustra-Kozek and Dr. Daniel Amen gave me insights into the physiology of behavior. The research of Dr. Jon Kabat-Zinn on the neurological effects of mindfulness exercises connected esoteric religious and spirituality concepts with mental well-being. Dr. Joe Dispenza's work connects how and what we think with our physical health. Hypnotherapists Mark Tyrell and Marisa Peer provide a different but complementary perspective on how to heal emotional damage. Robert Quinn's work on "Highly Effective Teachers" gives insights into teaching. Dr. Gabor Mate delved into the effects of emotional trauma on brain structure and how to reverse the damage. This is all helpful information to apply when trying to help others who are in distress or whose behavior is causing problems.

I analyzed what I saw in herd/flock/pack dynamics; responses to training techniques, human-animal interactions and interactions between animal species. Many problems required solutions—like how to keep dogs from killing the other animals on the ranch. I considered how the social interactions within groups affected behavior and how my own mindset and approach affected the effectiveness of my training efforts.

There are several different strategies for altering an existing behavior into one that is desired: **The Behavioral Model** of interventions uses deterrence (punishment). **The Medical Model** focuses on diagnosis of a condition and drug therapy. The Whisperers' approach seeks out and tackles the root of every problem in the context of the individual's physical and emotional status and relationship to others. I recently learned that Dr. Gabor Mate, a speaker on parenting and addiction therapy, calls this approach the **Bio-Psycho-Social Model** using "compassionate inquiry."

I mulled over what it takes and how to explain it to others. I struggled to understand and explain the neurophysiology behind behavior and the "tricks" we use. And I had to learn the art of book production. Over a six year process, I compiled shelves full of articles and books. I keep finding exciting information that I want to include. Every day I learn more from my animals, too. The project evolved into *The Whisperers' Way* book series.

The whole point of this massive endeavor is to make this information accessible to anyone who wants to learn. There is nothing more uplifting than sharing a skill that gives such joy. To be able to connect and communicate a lesson, to fix broken relationships, to heal emotional scars—all these skills for helping people and animals can be accomplished with the Whisperers' Way. For those who are already skilled at training or healing, you may find new information and ideas to add to your repertoire.

The learning never ends, but there comes a point where the information needs to get out to do anyone any good! There will be less citation of sources in this book than I would like and probably things I wish I would have included or written better. However, I am doing this while single-handedly keeping a ranch and non-profit going (and have discarded the dream of winning a Good Housekeeping award.) This is my best humble effort. I have been blessed with this understanding. This is my gift to you so you too can help others.

PART I

THE BIG PICTURE OVERVIEW

THE BIG PICTURE

This section is a relatively quick overview of what will be covered in the rest of this book. Each topic will be discussed with more details in subsequent chapters. I have done this because it is important to understand how all of this fits together as a cohesive plan and not hyper focus on any one aspect. It's like when you cite a single sentence out of a report without context, it might lead to a different conclusion than reading the whole report. Too often practitioners forget where they are in a forest because they are inspecting the leaves of a tree and end up going down the wrong path.

As mentioned before, I believe many experienced trainers will benefit by just reading this Big Picture Overview to find concepts to add to their repertoire.

In each of the other books in the series, The Big Picture Overview will be repeated, and then information for the different species is expanded. (e.g., dog owners will read about "drive" and aggression, horse owners will read about more horse-related topics) If readers of those books need more explanation of the concepts, they can refer back to a copy of **The Essential Elements** for **Deep Dive** discussions.

Remember, the sum is greater than the whole. In other words, you will get much better results if you keep all facets of Whispering presented here in mind and not just use certain parts alone.

THE THREE BASIC ELEMENTS OF THE WHISPERERS' WAY

Heart + Wisdom + Knowledge

THE HEART AND
PARADIGM OF
WHISPERERS

I am going to start with a discussion of "Heart" and "Paradigm" because unless you understand this element, you will never achieve your highest potential.

Some people seem to "put out good energy": They are easy to be around. They make you feel good about yourself. You feel like you can trust them. Whisperers do this without thinking about it. If it doesn't come naturally, you can learn to be this way, too!

THE HEART

In analyzing the writings of other Whisperers' and my own core beliefs, I found certain consistent themes: Whisperers all work by gaining Trust through their personalities and the way they present themselves This attribute comes from the Heart. The heart also reflects the spirit (philosophy) in which you approach your work. The Heart keeps you oriented in the right direction and making the right choices. That is, if you have your Heart in the right place. St. Francis of Assisi was a model for every Whisperer I looked at.

While you can "Fake it 'til you make it," learning to BE this way is ideal because a fraud will eventually be found out and called out.

While this might all seem "touchy-feely," I will explain to you the scientific reasons these strategies actually affect the physiology of both you and the individuals you work with. Through these mechanisms, you can promote a good relationship and increase their rate of learning so your teaching efforts will be more fruitful.

THE HARD DRIVE

The life choice to be of "Service to Others," a term used in the Light and Love communities, is an attribute evident in Whisperers. This predilection is like the hard drive operating system in a computer. It's the essence of the person. This gives them the drive to help others regardless of risk to themselves, the willingness to think outside the box and to put the well-being of those they are helping as a top priority. It keeps you grounded in the right frame of mind to never give up and do no harm. It is the moral compass.

Some people seem to be born this way. It can also be a conscious choice.

It may sound complicated but in reality it is very simple: Follow the Golden Rule and practice Unconditional Love. The details and nuances of these concepts are discussed further in the next chapter. A person wanting to work like a Whisperer should consider installing this operating system.

THE PERSPECTIVE

The paradigm is the perspective from (or lens through) which you see the world around you. This affects how you interpret and respond to the actions of others. Whisperers "see things in pictures," a phrase Dr. Temple Grandin uses, and is a predominantly Right Brain activity. Other terms that apply are "holistic approach," "Gestalt thinking," and my personal favorite, "Spectrum Thinking." These all involve seeing how multiple factors can have an impact on a given situation, thus leading to better finding solutions to a problem

The personality traits and core values of Whisperers involve terms that seem fairly self-explanatory. Each term, however, can have many interpretations and nuances. I have listed these concepts here briefly. To get a deeper understanding of how each of these fits into Whispering, please read the **Deep Dive** discussions of each in "The Heart and Paradigm of Whisperers".

PERSONALITY TRAITS SEEN IN WHISPERERS:

A sense of service and stewardship
A sense of humility
A sense of humor, joy in creativity
A Seeker of knowledge
A Risk-taker
A "Spectrum thinker"

WHISPERERS' CORE VALUES

Trust
Respect
Unconditional Love
The Golden Rule
Positive Aspects of Duality
Compassion

> ## WHAT'S THIS THING CALLED "UNCONDITIONAL LOVE?"
>
> Unconditional Love is not judgmental
> Unconditional Love does not take things personally
> Unconditional love is not punitive
> Unconditional Love embraces empathy
> Unconditional Love sets boundaries
> Unconditional Love never stops caring

THE STYLE

The martial art of Aikido is the style in which Whisperers operate: They take as a strategy the flexibility of the bamboo as opposed to rigidity of the oak branch. They understand the need to balance Trust, Respect and Love in what I call the Holy Trinity of Trust-based Training. They understand nuances and select methods that are appropriate for a given situation. They can alternate between the persuasive "Way-shower" style of leadership to the more confrontational, domineering "Drill sergeant" leadership style when appropriate and necessary.

There are a lot of books that mention these concepts in vague terms. It is assumed that we all define and apply them in the same way. As Felix Unger in the 1970's sitcom "The Odd Couple" liked to say, "When you assume, you make an ass of you and me." As a result of vagaries, people are often not talking about the same concepts though they are using the same words. This creates room for arguments and inconsistent success using their techniques. I try to avoid these pitfalls by filling in the blanks with specific wording and examples to illustrate ideas and their practical applications. I try to show how concepts from different fields of study can be talking about the same thing using different words. All these ideas are discussed in more detail in the Deep Dive chapter on the Heart and Paradigm of Whispering.

WHISPERERS AS HEALERS

Whisperers are, in essence, healers. They "fix things" so that the other person or animal can function in a normal healthy way. Some people are healers of the body, some are healers of the heart, and some are healers of the soul. The principles in this book apply to therapy for physical health, mental health and emotional health.

Those that excel understand that you cannot heal any of those without understanding how the other two aspects of an individual must be healthy as well. This is the concept of Coherence or Alignment or Unity. Those who want to heal must know how to bring themselves into a state of Coherence so that they can draw (entrain) those they want to help into Coherence as well. In other words, make sure you have your own act together before you try to fix anyone else.

WISDOM

WHAT IT IS AND HOW TO GET IT

You can have knowledge but lack understanding. Understanding how pieces of knowledge fit together gives you the ability to know when to apply that knowledge to get the desired outcome. Understanding requires practicing the application of that knowledge in multiple real-life situations. Experience gives your knowledge depth. Deep understanding leads to Wisdom.

A rephrasing of these ideas: Wisdom allows you to create layers of understanding with the pieces of information you acquire over time. It is crucial to understand how they are related to be able to prioritize their importance. I use outlines to visually see how information fits together. I've designed these books to present the information in layers so that you will not get too bogged down in details and lose sight of the big picture.

4 CONCEPTS FOR DEEPER UNDERSTANDING

SPECTRUM THINKING Holistic approach, Gestalt thinking, Ecological approach

LUMPING BEFORE SPLITTING Seeing how things are similar before seeing how they are different

DESIGN THINKING Understanding the needs in order to achieve the goal

DISCERNMENT The ability to determine the relative importance of information in front of you

These concepts will be discussed further in the chapter on Wisdom.

"Wisdom is knowing how little you know."
~Socrates

"It's what you learn after you know it all that really counts."
~Tom Dorrance

KNOWLEDGE

THE SCIENCE OF BEHAVIOR AND OTHER IMPORTANT INFORMATION

To effectively change behavior requires knowledge of all the factors that create behavior. To accurately interpret their behavior, you must look at all aspects of a person or animal. This requires knowledge of psychology, biology and what I call the Body/Mind/Spirit connections—how the state of the body affects thinking and emotions.

You must look at how you as the trainer/parent/teacher present yourself and interact. You must also look at the dynamics of your relationship and if there are any issues in your own history that must be corrected. This is the "social" part of "bio-psycho-social."

You can learn this from others or learn through personal experience. Don't just memorize and regurgitate facts, ALWAYS LOOK FOR THE WHY. When you learn through books, videos or watching someone, it is important to try out a technique yourself because all the factors that come into play may work differently for you in subtle ways.

Don't just settle for someone's interpretation or critique of a method—read the original. I have found that there are a lot of misinterpretations of vintage horse and dog trainers' techniques by contemporary "experts" who delight in finding great faults in them. Reading the original works of John Rarey and Barbara Woodhouse in their totality brought me an appreciation of their brilliance.

When you find out what didn't work, you learn most when you think about **The Why**. Mentally file everything away because this knowledge becomes your tool box. The more tools you have, the more versatile you become. Knowing the Why leads you to Wisdom.

Through observation and analysis, I developed the Threshold and Spasticity concepts as mental tools that can be applied to teaching, managing aggression, herding and the healing arts. I also cover Whisperers' Tricks, techniques which enhance calming, learning and bonding.

Having deeper Knowledge makes controversial techniques like "dominance theory," "shock collars" and "laying horses down" effective and safer to use. There have been smear campaigns against people who use these techniques and even calls to ban "shock collars" or file charges of "criminal abuse." I couldn't understand this since I have used or seen these used so effectively. Then I realized gaps in knowledge create a potential for misuse or abuse. My goal became to put as much information into one body of work to reduce those holes in understanding.

The first half of the chapter on Knowledge covers what I call the "soft sciences" of psychology and animal behavior. The second half of the chapter of Knowledge is a discussion of the hard sciences of brain structure, autonomic nervous system (including Dr. Steven Porges' Polyvagal Theory), the effects of hormones, neurotransmitters, nutrients, disease states (allergies, imbalances), etc. These are the mechanics underpinning behavioral expressions. Knowing this information allows you to understand how to manipulate physical factors to change behavior.

Some will ask "Why should I bother to learn about this stuff?" Well, it's like learning the basics about how a car works. Sometimes you can fix simple things yourself. Sometimes you will need to go to a mechanic but at least you have an idea if the mechanic is lying to you about needing a new engine when it just needs a belt replaced. I've tried to explain everything in a way even my artist friends can understand.

"The One Health" approach—a combining of medical and veterinary knowledge—was pioneered by my graduate advisor Dr. Calvin Schwabe of University of California Davis School of Veterinary Medicine in the 1980's.

My peek into human psychology provided many insights and words to use to describe exactly what I see in animal responses. It's not "anthropomorphizing" to recognize the similarities. In fact, Dr. Barbara Horowitz currently teaches the similarities between people and animals at Harvard and UCLA and writes about them in her books. *Zoobiquity* and *Wildhood*.

I have made outlines of the topics covered in the Deep Dive. These are things you should understand when working on behaviors and consider if you have difficulties.

**Soft Sciences: Psychology and Behavior—
expressions of what's happening inside them**

The 4 Main Components That Impact Behavior:
Student/trainee/client
Teacher/mentor/facilitator/therapist
The relationship
The environment

IMPORTANT BEHAVIOR CONCEPTS: These are topics that I found are very important but not adequately discussed in other books. Applying the One Health Concept, many ideas used with horses would work nicely with dogs and people, and the other way around

INTRINSIC INFLUENCES (come from within the individual)

Coherence—mental, physical and emotional systems working in harmony and in sync.

Maslow's Hierarchy—how needs are prioritized from basic survival to spiritual longings

Threshold Concept—the invisible line between calm and excited; how you can move it around to stay more in the calm zone; also the line between confusion and light bulb moments

Spasticity factor—the genetic element affecting that Threshold that causes some individuals to get over excited more easily

The Interplay of the Pressure, Thresholds, Spasticity Factor

Impulse control—why some can't help "misbehaving"; how to help them control their behavior

Self-regulation—keeping oneself in a calm, collected state

Aggression—the many forms and causes

Stress

EXTRINSIC INFLUENCES

(external things that enhance learning and healing)
The Importance of Face Time
The Value of Play Time
Observational Learning—letting the student watch the process makes it easier to learn the process.

TEACHING/BEHAVIOR MODIFICATION CONCEPTS

Principles of Highly Effective Teaching
Two Styles of Leadership
Pressure & Communication
Appropriate Correction—how to avoid crossing the line into counterproductive or even abuse
Use of "Pain" in Training
Use of "Fear" in Training
Counter conditioning—replacing an undesired behavior with one that isn't so bad
Desensitization—training to not react to triggering events
Imprinting, Bonding and Taming
Healing Trauma (my personal strategy)—healing PTSD an over-reaction to triggering events
Animal Assisted Therapy
Safe Practices

Hard Sciences: Neurology, physiology, other -ologies—the Body/Mind connection, the mechanics behind the expressed behavior

THE BRAIN: The anatomy and function
    The two major different parts
    The "Upstairs"/Cortical brain/Conscious thoughts
    The "Downstairs Brain/Subcortical/Limbic system/
    Subconscious reactions/ emotions and feelings
    Neuroplasticity—how the brain can change with experience and training
    Brain waves and associated states—how you can alter them
    How nutrition and body processes affect brain function

THE AUTONOMIC NERVOUS SYSTEM
    Sympathetic=Fight/Flight/Excite/Delight=Adrenaline
    Parasympathetic=Rest/Digest/Think/Create/Love
    =Oxytocin, Serotonin, et al
    The Polyvagal Theory—how these two systems work together

THE HEART
    Electromagnetic influence
    Hormonal release
    Coherence measured by HRV

BODY CHEMISTRY AND BALANCE
    Nutrition
    Hormones
    Neurotransmitters
    Glucose
    Hydration (Body water content)

METAPHYSICAL STUFF

I struggled with the decision on including this topic because it is
so foreign to the scientific world that bases information on what
is visually observable and measurable. I am well aware that the
inclusion of this topic will raise the eyebrows of my colleagues and
set me up for attacks. After long consideration and soul-searching,
I came to the conclusion that I could not in good conscience withhold information that could help many heal themselves and others.

I have a confession to make: I learned how to use Christian
Science healing techniques and Qigong when I became frustrated
when the things I learned in vet school failed. As crazy as it sounds,
the stuff works! In addition, I had an animal communicator tell
me over the phone what a parrot had for breakfast and an astrol-
oger tell me my life history just by knowing my place and time
of birth. I have felt the energy emanating from the hands of a
Qigong master and seen other things happen that are hard to
explain with Science.

What's even crazier is how you have to throw away all you
learned about "the real world" and think in terms that are very
foreign and honestly weird. But it all really works! I have learned
that using these concepts can resolve behavioral problems as well,
which is what Whispering is all about. And now there is information on Quantum Physics developed by very smart people in the

academic world to back it up. Hence, I needed to include this in my book for you.

> *"The story of quantum physics starts at the beginning of the 20th century with scientists trying to better understand how light bulbs work. This simple question soon led scientists deep into the hidden workings of matter, into the sub-atomic building blocks of the world around us. Here they discovered phenomena unlike any encountered before - a realm where things can be in many places at once, where chance and probability call the shots and where reality appears to only truly exist when we observe it."*
>
> ~From the intro to YouTube video

"The Mind Bending Story of Quantum Physics (Part 1/2)"
| Spark

As I researched the science, I realized the broad application of Metaphysics:

- Metaphysics explains about every other healing modality that mainstream medicine shuns.

- Metaphysics is how the Shaolin Temple martial artists perform amazing feats.

- Metaphysics is an integral aspect of every religious tradition and spiritual practice.

I am going out on a limb to present this information for these reasons:

- To open minds to the usefulness of "alternative" methods through scientific explanation of Metaphysical Law

- To give practitioners of "alternative" healing modalities higher success rates through understanding and application of Metaphysical Law

- To reduce the conflicts and fear-mongering between believers of different religious traditions through the understanding of their common link in Metaphysical Law

- To have an excuse to research and understand Metaphysical Law.

I'm introducing this topic a bit lightheartedly so that you won't take me as an evangelist wanting to convert anyone or presenting myself as an expert on this topic. I merely want to offer as Sergeant Joe Friday would have said, "Just the facts, ma'am." This section is rather lengthy because there isn't much common knowledge about metaphysical principles. I had to pull what I've learned from many different sources to build an introduction and foundation for understanding.

If I haven't lost you, please enter a different realm of understanding with me with deeper discussion!

WHY TALK ABOUT METAPHYSICAL LAW?

Metaphysical Law operates in religious traditions, spirituality and traditional healing arts. The nuts and bolts of metaphysics bring real results for those who practice these things, which is why belief in them persists. Understanding Metaphysical Law gives you an ability to use these practices in more powerful ways to help yourself and others.

I have tried many different "alternative modalities" and seen amazing things happen with my own eyes. It concerns me how the scientific and medical communities demean techniques that are really helping people and animals. Practitioners and believers in these practices are stigmatized by the media and academic community. Not wanting to become a target of regulatory action, I've kept quiet about techniques I use. Now that I do not rely on my veterinary license to survive, I can be more open about non-standard protocols that work in my hands. I recently realized that Metaphysical Law explains why they work. And SCIENCE now has given me ways of explaining it, too. If that intrigues you, keep reading!

Different circles use different words for the same concepts. To help you connect the dots, I may use words with similar meanings separated by slash marks. This might be obnoxious, but it's a way to communicate concepts more efficiently. For atheists who wince at the word "God," just substitute the word "Good" anywhere you see "God." They are synonymous.

> *"The day science begins to study non-physical phenomena,*
> *it will make more progress in one decade than in all the*
> *previous centuries of its existence."*
>
> ~Nikola Tesla

WHAT IS METAPHYSICS?

If you look up the term "Metaphysics", you will find wordy phrases and mind-numbing definitions. Merriam Webster's simple definition of Metaphysics, as "a study of what is outside objective experience," is the easiest to explain: "Outside objective study" looks at things you can't detect with your 5 senses—sight, hearing, taste, touch and smell—and therefore refers to "subjective study." By default, "subjective study" refers to topics that are considered outside modern mainstream science.

But SCIENCE has come to the rescue! Another way to explain it is that everything we observe with our 5 senses (i.e., Objective study) can be described with the natural laws pertaining to matter—Laws of Thermodynamics, Gravity, Motion, Electricity, Pressure, Chemistry's Periodic Table, etc.

Subjective study is covered by Quantum Physics. Quantum Physics explains the Natural Metaphysical Laws pertaining to energy and physical matter. This is the study of particles smaller than atoms (subatomic particles) PLUS the properties of energy (vibrational frequency.) Atoms are 99% energy and only 1% physical matter. These are the principles that describe phenomena which are not detectable and measurable by our 5 senses, and are the basis for taking "Deep Woo-woo" seriously. The Metaphysical Laws and Principles were described as far back as ancient Egypt by Hermes Trismegitus (described in detail in *The Kybalion*). They are utilized in what are considered Mystical aspects of every religious tradition.

Here is the basic take home message: Inanimate objects and living cells are made of energy. Thoughts and emotions generate energy in the form of electromagnetic waves. These electromagnetic waves affect the behavior of physical matter (at the level of subatomic particles) because physical matter also holds energy and responds to energy. Conversely, the energy held in inanimate objects affects living cells as well.

> *"Those who talk about life force are called victims of the "vitalist fallacy."*
>
> ~Robert Gilbert

Incredibly, your thoughts can have a real effect on the thoughts of others, on physical matter, on how your body functions and the outcomes of situations. (This is referred to as alchemy, transmutation, chemicalization, "Magic" without the rituals,) You can create with your thoughts! Some describe this as human beings carrying the potential power of the Creator God as part of their genetic heritage (actually co-creators, not gods in their own right). But I'm getting ahead of myself...

Metaphysics is the basis for religious beliefs, Mystery School teachings of secret societies (Rosicrucian, Freemasonry, Theosophical Society, etc.), "magic", esoteric knowledge, and everything that's referred to (sometimes disdainfully) as New Age.

Metaphysical principles explain psychic phenomenon, traditional healing modalities, extrasensory perception (ESP), telepathic communication, remote viewing, intuition, animal communication, chakras, souls, life-after-death, consciousness, astrology, Tarot, crystal therapy, Yoga and more.

Those who understand Metaphysical Law can recognize and appreciate the power behind these practices.

> *"Science and Religion are expressions of the same knowledge. To paraphrase Arthur C. Clarke: Any science sufficiently advanced is indistinguishable from magic."*
> ~Conny Mendez, *The Mystical Number 7*

There is more discussion in the Metaphysical Deep Dive. I hope you will join me there.

Metaphysical Stuff
Why Talk About Metaphysical Law?
What Is Metaphysics?
"Everything Is Energy"
Basic Metaphysical Principles
Human Bodies as Amazing Technology
Manipulation of Energy
Healing and Metaphysics
The Law of Karma
The Law of Manifestation/Attraction
Relative Frequency of Emotions
Duality/Polarity
A Few Words about "Faith"
Religious Traditions and Metaphysical Knowledge
Connecting With The Divine (And The Other Side)
Purpose in Life=Divine Mission
Miracles, Healing and The Law of Manifestation
The Controversy
Jose Silva
Conny Mendez
In Case You're Wondering

THE WHISPERERING
PROCESS

PULLING IT ALL TOGETHER

Knowing a lot of information is great. Knowing what to do with it is better. Knowing how to use it to do good things and help others is supreme.

The Whisperers' Way ties knowledge with the wisdom to apply it appropriately and be of service to others, which is good for your heart when it comes from the heart. Whisperers succeed where others fail by recognizing and not crossing the thresholds that trigger anger, fear or other negative emotions. They also know how to move the thresholds incrementally with what I call The Whispering Process in which you apply your knowledge of behavior in a certain sequence with prioritized goals.

THE 5 COMPONENTS OF THE WHISPERING PROCESS

1) Attunement—understanding their frame of mind

2) Build Trust—going both ways

3) Build Communication—understanding what they are saying and clearly sending your message back

4) Build Confidence—reduce the levels of fear in both you and the one you're working with

5) Build Respect—set your boundaries and learn theirs

A) **BUILDING THE RELATIONSHIP** Applying your **knowl**edge this way allows you to build the relationship foundation and work effectively. In other words, starting here allows you to build a solid foundation in your relationship on which to teach or heal. The more effort you put into building this foundation the more effective your efforts will be. In horse circles, this method of training is literally called "foundation training."

If you keep this order in mind, your foundation will be easier to build and be stronger in the long run.

One key concept: **Never reprimand or try to correct before you have developed a trusting relationship.** To step into a new situation and prematurely try to impose changes will create distrust and resentment. A similar phenomenon happens in work environments when new management comes in and implements changes without respecting the needs or input of the employees.

Where there is already a good relationship, you won't need to start from scratch. However, if you have any difficulties even with those established relationships, this is a good process to identify where a problem comes from. For example, when they are unco-operative, make sure you are not having a communication issue before assuming the problem lies in lack of respect.

For those working with traumatized individuals and more severe issues (i.e., Rescued animals, children in foster care, people with addictions), it is important to start at the top and patiently work your way through all the steps.

B) **BUILD YOUR OWN KNOWLEDGE THROUGH EXPERIENCE AND PRACTICE.** This process also gives you opportunity to practice what you've learned from others, as well as the experience to build your knowledge base and deepen your understanding. There is much you will learn when you do something and watch closely what happens. If you take the time to process what just happened and why it happened, you will gain an understanding that brings you Wisdom. You will develop discernment for the best approach to accomplish your training goals while maintaining a solid trust-based relationship for each individual case.

> TWO GOALS OF THE WHISPERING PROCESS:
>
> Build the Relationship
> Build your knowledge and skill

In the 1998 movie *The Horse Whisperer*, Robert Redford is asked to work with a horse that had been traumatized in an accident and became dangerous for its young owner to ride. In one session, he makes the horse lay down on the ground. After it gets back up, it has magically recovered and is back to its old, trusty self.

This is not magic. It's a technique that has been described in horse training manuals by John Rarey, Dennis Magner and Jesse Beery. I watched a horse trainer do this with five of my own horses before he took them on busy city streets pulling carts driven by a novice handler (me.) While they were on their side, the trainer created all kinds of commotion around them with leaf blowers, tarps and finally with his little kids standing on their sides. The trance state the horses entered during this process really intrigued me so I started asking questions of whoever I could ask.

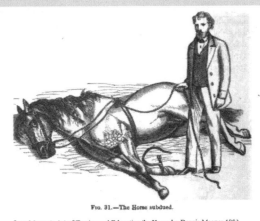

FIG. 31.—The Horse subdued.

from Magner's Art of Taming and Educating the Horse by Dennis Magner 1883

An email from Linda Tellington-Jones suggested I look into Dr. Stephen Porges' Polyvagal Theory. This opened up a whole new world to me. In my research, I learned that the main mechanisms by which this "trick" works is the "vagal response" (parasympathetic nervous system) that releases hormones like Oxytocin and/or Dopamine and controls the "adrenaline response" (sympathetic nervous system). This was the light bulb moment that compelled me to research more and write these books.

WHISPERERS' TRICKS

I t's all fine and good to expound on lofty concepts. It's quite another thing to get in the ring and wrangle. Knowing tricks (or as they say now "hacks") will get you there faster.

Whisperers utilize a number of techniques to achieve their goals to make combative subjects cooperate (calming, sedation, non-chemical restraint) or heal from trauma. One class of techniques mainly utilizes the autonomic nervous system (primarily the Vagal/Parasympathetic systems). Other mechanisms for training and healing mainly involve rewiring the limbic system in the "downstairs" or "emotional brain." Some Whisperers' Tricks work on the energetic level using metaphysics as well. These techniques affect multiple systems in the body—the organs, the brain and nervous system, the body chemistry down to the cellular responses—in what Dr. Tony Buffington terms "The Central Threat Response System." HeartMath Institute describes the goal of "achieving coherence" at the Heart-Brain level, which is a fancy way of describing "wellness" and "healing" on physical, mental and emotional levels. It is this Coherent state that allows optimal learning and building of relationships.

THERE ARE NO MAGIC BULLETS. These all work on the principle that they incrementally shift the body into a more coherent state. A technique will seem like a failure if you are relying only on this technique to get the job done.

Once the body is calm and the mind is mentally balanced, you will be better able to reach the subject with normal interactions. When you get to this point, you will see what looks like a miraculous breakthrough. It seems like a miracle because people have been frustrated for so long. This is simply what I refer to as reaching the "Threshold," which is discussed in depth as a Knowledge Deep Dive subject.

I've compiled a list of "hacks" that with modifications can be used on different species. I call it my list of Tools for Your Tool Box. You will need to do further research on their execution. The internet is a godsend because it gives you access to knowledgeable people all around the world. Most are very happy to share their wisdom through articles, books, videos and even personal communications. For ones that involve physical risks to you or the ones you are working on, it is advised to watch an experienced person in action and have them supervise you as you try them yourself.

> *"If it doesn't cost much, isn't hard to do and might help if done right, then might as well try it and see what happens!"*
>
> ~Dr. Sue

WHAT WHISPERERS' TRICKS DO

1) Increase relaxation
2) Increase feelings of bonding and affection resulting in prosocial behavior
3) Increased feeling of well-being & coherence
4) Accelerate the learning process
5) Help heal emotional scars by rewiring the brain
6) Allow medical procedures and desensitization efforts to go more smoothly

THE TRIGGERS FOR THESE MECHANISMS

1) Putting pressure on certain receptors (like acupuncture points) by direct pressure or by positioning the body certain ways.
2) Electromagnetic impulses exuded from the heart
3) Visual, sound or tactile stimulation
4) Vibrational energetics (Metaphysics/Quantum physics)

Here are the techniques utilizing these principles that are discussed in the Deep Dive chapter on Whisperers' Tricks:

Sensory Input/Control
    Electroconvulsive Therapy (ECT)
    Sensory Overload
    Hypnosis
    Covering the Eyes/Working in Darkness

Deep Pressure Stimulation
    Swaddling Babies
    Burrito-Wrapping Small Animals
    Bengkung Belly Binding Of Postpartum Women
    Temple Grandin's Hug Machine
    Weighted Blankets for People
    Wheat Pressure Box for Horses
    Newborn Animal Squeeze Sedation
    "Thundershirts" For Dogs
    Straitjackets
    T-Touch Body Wraps

Positional Triggers
    The Hamilton Hold For Babies (Human)
    Laying Horses on Their Sides
    Sheep Tipping (sitting them on their rumps)
    Flipping Sharks, Rabbits, Chickens On Their Back
    Neck Flexing/Bending Exercises

Skin Pressure & "Body Work"
    Massage
    T-Touch by Linda Tellington Jones
    Working the Happy Spots
    Pole-Taming For Wild Mustangs

Deep Breathing
  Pranayama Yoga exercises
  Running/Physical Exercise

Meridian/Acupuncture Points
  Tapping/Emotional Freedom Technique (EFT)
  Endotapping for horses
  Sucking On Lollipops to Stimulate Labor Contractions
  Tongue Pressure on Roof of Mouth During Breathing
  Exercises
  Ocular Compression
  Rolling the Eyes Upward
  Horse Twitching Lip Twitch/ Shoulder Twitch/Ear Twitch
  Mouth T-Touch or "Working the Tongue"
  Massaging the Gums
  Paul Williamson's TAP
  Massaging Points On and Behind the Ears
  Cat Scruffing ("Clipnosis")
  A Rope Around the Left Front Leg of a Horse

Other Methods
  Occupational Therapy Tools
  Mindfulness
  Vagal Maneuvers
    Carotid Sinus Massage
    Mammalian Diving
    Valsalva Maneuver
    Hang the Child Upside Down
    Do a Handstand for 30 Seconds
  Acts of Kindness / Service to Others
  Reflex Integration
  Sound Frequency
  Rhythm
  The Magic of Music

Dancing
Animal Assisted Therapy
Jose Silva's Ultramind and Everyday ESP Systems

Once you understand the mechanisms behind these concepts, you will see how they work in many other things we do. You can get creative! Just be sure you are careful and check with experienced people before you try things on your own.

DISCLAIMER: These techniques are not without risks so make sure the way you do things is not going to get you or your "victim" (just a joke!) hurt in any way. I WILL NOT TAKE RESPONSIBILITY FOR INJURIES INCURRED DURING THE EXECUTION OF ANY OF THESE PROCEDURES.

IN SUMMARY

W e have just gone through all the things I consider important for executing The Whisperers' Way. The pages that follow contain more information about each of these topics which will help especially if you are having difficulties with a case. As they say, "The Devil's in the details." Let's get down to details!

PART II

THE WHISPERERS HEART
Deep Dive

THE CULTURE OF
WHISPERERS

There are certain people whose words resonate with me either in conversation or on paper. In our conversations about behavior, we see the same things, approach situations in the same manner. It didn't matter if we were talking about people or animals, we just clicked. We understood each others' words, each others' intentions, and shared the same values. This is known as coming from the same Culture.

Beyond Words: It is important to recognize that words can elicit different mental pictures depending on what culture you come from. I believe this simple fact (plus differences in expectations and standards) explains why there is so much controversy over training and parenting techniques. Whisperers don't get too stuck on terminology; they just want to know what works. They subsequently figure out how to make things work.

Just as Americans have a hard time understanding the Chinese or Mexican cultures even if we're all speaking English, the Whisperers' culture is a little different than what the average person understands. In looking even closer, there are even personality traits that are shared.

Emotions Matter: Sentience is defined as being able to feel emotions. The concept of sentience has many implications and nuances. We all know how people make decisions that don't seem to make sense, even when they have information indicating that it is not a good choice. This is because ultimately, decisions are made on an emotional level. It has been shown that people who cannot feel emotions due to a brain injury also struggle to make decisions when offered options. [3]

Emotions actually produce energy that has an impact on the thoughts and actions of others and even inanimate objects as explained by Quantum Physics and Metaphysics. Jose Silva's research links brain waves and activity in the Right Brain to amplifying this effect. The physical heart is considered a center for emotions and communication of emotions in the spiritual circles (The Heart Chakra) and Heartmath Institute has done much research on the communication through the heart's electromagnetic rhythms. Emotions are as impactful whether they are generated by thoughts or as reaction to a current situation. Therefore, training yourself and your subject to control both what they think about and their emotions are elements to consider when dealing with behavioral problems like Whisperers are called to do.

---

[3] https://www.ninds.nih.gov/health-information/clinical-trials/
neural-basis-decision-making-deficits-traumatic-brain-injury

THE HEART AND HEART-CENTERED CONCEPTS

Heart-centered is a term that has emerged in recent years in reference to leadership style, healing, counseling, business, branding and other endeavors that involve creativity and intuition. This kind of thinking is associated with the right side of the brain. This is in contrast with Mind-centered, left brain analytical thinking. Authors and websites have a variety of ways to define "heart-centered" using words associated with compassion, humanity and generally positive vibes. You might also see reference to "The Divine Feminine" in contrast to "The Divine Masculine." Please note that these are both important to make a healthy and whole person.

The Whisperers I know are often gruff-mannered (don't ever suggest they are softies!) but ultimately inject a good dose of heart-centeredness into their decisions-making process. They are a practical bunch with a focus on working efficiently, but the well-being of the individual they are working with is paramount. In the discussion of psychology and neurophysiology, you will see how this approach has a lot to do with the Whisperers' success rate.

THE GOLDEN RULE: **TREAT OTHERS LIKE YOU WOULD WANT TO BE TREATED**

If you ever have any questions about a choice you need to make, just remember this simple principle: Right Action is based on the Universal Law of The Golden Rule. You can't go wrong if you stick with this. While some think this is a Christian doctrine, it is actually a principle taught in about every religious faith.

The Golden Rule is basic empathy and in turn leads to compassion. Take care that you aren't projecting your wants onto others. They might not necessarily have the same perspective or needs as you. However, the Golden Rule is easy to remember and a good starting point that stops you from doing harm.

For those who are familiar with the term "Karma" can easily see how following the Golden Rule benefits yourself: If you cause suffering, you will in turn go through suffering. Who needs more of that?

Christianity: In everything, do unto others what you would have them do to you. Matthew 7:12

Buddhism: Do not offend others as you would not want to be offended. Udanavarga 5:18

Islam: Islam teaches that Muslims must treat others well no matter how they treat the Muslims: "Verily, Allah enjoins justice, and the doing of good to others; and giving like kindred". Qur'an 16:90. "None of you are true believers until you love for your brother what you love for yourself". Prophet Muhammad.

Judaism: What is hateful to you, do not do to your neighbor. Hillel, Talmud, Shabbat 31a

Confucianism: Tzu-kung asked, "Is there one word which can serve as the guiding principle for conduct throughout life?" Confucius said, "It is the word altruism (shu). Do not do to others what you do not want them to do to you." Analects 15:23

Sikhism: I am a stranger to no one; and no one is a stranger to me. Indeed, I am a friend to all. Guru Granth Sahib, pg. 1299

Taoism: Regard your neighbor's gain as your own gain and your neighbor's loss as your own loss. T'ai Shang Kan Ying P'ien, 213–218

Jainism: One should treat all creatures in the world as one would like to be treated. Mahavira, Sutrakritanga

UNCONDITIONAL LOVE

WHAT IT IS AND HOW TO EXPRESS IT

I don't know many Whisperers who would be caught dead talking about "Love." It's just not their style to use mushy language. But if you understand the many facets of Unconditional Love and watch Whisperers in action, you will see how they do apply it and are thus able to reach individuals labeled by others as "unreachable."

Unconditional Love is what drives all the other facets of Whispering. While this term is most often used to describe the good relationship between a mother and child or a dog to its owner, all Whisperers have deep love and affection for the animals and/or people they work with. This concept encompasses compassion and empathy, wanting the best for them without regard for self and a high level of attunement.

Applying the tenets of Unconditional Love gives a person the best chance of reaching others the way Whisperers strive to do. This term is thrown around a lot in vague ways but never really defined very often. In looking at how spiritual types talk about it, I've found several ways that it can be applied to "Whispering." I will try to summarize how spiritual leaders explain this nebulous phrase and what I have gleaned from the works of those I consider "Whisperers":

UNCONDITIONAL LOVE IS NOT JUDGMENTAL

This does not mean you shouldn't make observations or have an opinion about the actions of an individual. Certainly, one should have "good judgment" about actions, but that is different than judging a person. "Passing Judgment" on a person involves labeling an individual and assigning a value to them based on their actions. Whisperers recognize that an action does not define the character or value of an individual. This does not mean the behavior is allowed to continue, but by avoiding labeling, Whisperers will look at potential (see the good in the person, the diamond in the rough) and work for change. In other words, labels are not used. A bossy, aggressive child is not a "bully." It is understood that the child is expressing what he/she is feeling due to past experiences, learned behavior or physical status. While a behavior may be inappropriate or undesirable, the behavior does not reduce the value of that individual who still deserves caring and compassion. It is also understood that the situation is never hopeless.

UNCONDITIONAL LOVE DOES NOT TAKE THINGS PERSONALLY

When you are treated a certain way by a person or animal, or get a certain reaction, step back and look at the scenario like an uninvolved bystander or something unfolding on a television screen. This allows you to not react in anger or fear, which destroys the progress you've made. This allows you to forgive more easily, too.

In this book I mention how a trainer laid down my horses in preparation for being taken on the city streets. One of the fascinating aspects of his technique was his total impassivity and lack of emotion while the horse fought against the restraints. In fact, I never saw him get angry with any of the horses. I actually wouldn't call this particular trainer a "whisperer" but he did use this strategy well.

Those that have been traumatized by inappropriate training methods or therapy will challenge you. They will test you to see if you honestly love and care about them. They will attack you or do things you ask them not to do. They will make you wonder why you are going to all this trouble to help them. They will watch for your response. If you react in anger and punish them, you have proven to them that you do not love them. If you react with calmness and understanding, you pass the test. It is only after you pass this test that you will gain their Trust and be able to turn them around. This is why it is imperative that you DO NOT attempt to train or correct behavior before gaining trust, especially with these individuals. On this note, it is best not to put them in a situation where you might need to make a correction until you get that trust.

> *"It's not what happens to you but how you react that matters."*
>
> ~Epictetus, Greek philosopher

UNCONDITIONAL LOVE IS NOT PUNITIVE

Transgressions are stopped effectively but punishment is not meted out. In other words, once a behavior is stopped, the corrective pressures are released. Seeking Justice is a popular concept in American society but is not a strategy used by Whisperers.

UNCONDITIONAL LOVE EMBRACES EMPATHY

Empathy is the ability to feel what others feel. When you feel the pain of another, you are moved to stop that pain. Fear and anger are expressions of pain. Healing is required to stop pain.

UNCONDITIONAL LOVE DOES NOT MEAN "BE A DOOR MAT."

You must be able to distinguish lip service of attempts to change from sincere attempts to change for the better. You must love yourself enough to step away from abuse while simultaneously being able to let go of (forgive) past hurts. This is what is called "setting boundaries."

UNCONDITIONAL LOVE NEVER STOPS CARING

Even if someone acts like a jerk, you don't stop caring about their well-being and will never want to do anything to hurt them. This provides the moral compass/brake that allows you to use riskier techniques and keeps the relationship on track. This Unconditional Love is the impetus and tenacity to stick through the challenges brought on by difficult individuals.

It is important that you utilize all these concepts authentically—no "fake it 'til you make it" especially with those who are in need of healing. If you really don't embrace it, those that you work with will figure that out at some point and resent you for the fraud.

BENEFITS OF INCORPORATING UNCONDITIONAL LOVE INTO YOUR WORK

It allows you to persist with tenacity when the odds seem insurmountable

It allows you to not react in anger or fear, which destroys the progress you've made

It allows you to connect through layers of distrust, fear and anger

---

It should be noted that Unconditional Love is considered the most powerful force in the Universe by Christian mystics. Those utilizing it are capable of transforming and alchemizing. There is more about this in "The Metaphysical Stuff."

AN ILLUSTRATION:

There is nothing quite like facing someone with addiction, mental illness or other reasons for rage. It can escalate to a very scary situation in which you have no control with the potential for physical violence. I came upon a podcast by Erin Michelle Galito conversing with a man and his wife distraught over their adult son with Tourette's Syndrome and bipolar who refused to seek help. The extent of their anguish and fear was evident in their disclosure that the police would not help them because of the laws. The takeaway messages with practical advice are below and I wish I had been able to use them when I went through my own "lessons":

There are two Minds: The Right Mind (Holy Spirit) is the mind of peace and love. The Wrong Mind is the ego mind that will choose the path of conflict and judgment.

When you are faced with a person causing problems through anger and desperation, the Right Mind will see it as a call for love. Your reaction will be out of kindness, acceptance and gentleness.

If you react with anger or upset in any form, you are using your Wrong Mind/Ego Mind. This is a sign you are judging. Your decision at that point will create more conflict and never lead to healing of the situation.

In every situation, you choose which path to take. If you are reacting in anger or upset or feeling overwhelmed, you must step back and ask yourself why you are upset. Upset is a sign that you have given your power over to your ego mind. Is there another way you can interpret the situation so that you will not be triggered into anger? Can you let go of your need to control the situation and "fix" the situation?

When you get yourself into a centered, calm state of mind and are able to feel love and compassion for the person you are dealing with, you will make decisions on the actions to take through your Right Mind.

COMPASSION

Being compassionate is helpful to more than the recipient of a compassionate act. One of the core elements of putting yourself into a Coherent state is thinking a compassionate thought. Gregg Braden presents an interesting definition of Compassion as described by the Tibetan Buddhist monks and nuns that he worked with. I will try to present it here as best as I can:

Compassion is the end of a sequence. Sympathy is when you acknowledge someone's pain though you don't feel or experience it. Empathy is when you can actually feel their pain. Compassion is where you feel the pain and accept the suffering without judgment—there is no right or wrong, good or bad in the suffering. With compassion, you have no attachment to the outcome but you have made room for the possibility of a greater outcome.

Braden states that the monks who are meditating and embracing the feeling of Compassion put their brain into Gamma wave production. Gamma waves unify both hemispheres of the brain, and he contends that it allows you to "hack the matrix" and transcend the laws of physics, time and space.[4]

From my readings of other works, this ties into a discussion of quantum physics and healing that is done by those who practice metaphysical techniques.

It is good to understand why doctors who are compassionate might have a much better success rate than those who think of their patients as machinery that simply needs repair with drugs or surgery. It also gives you a reason to try incorporating thoughts of compassion as defined by these monks when working with people or animals.

---

[4] LondonRealTV. (2019, March 10). Gregg Braden - raising human consciousness - part 1/2 | London Real. YouTube. Retrieved October 13, 2021, from https://www.youtube.com/watch?v=4N3fGnP9v_8.

Further discussion of topics involving belief in God and spiritual concepts can be found in a chapter called "Metaphysical Stuff."

This is a beautiful piece for those working with adults and children with special needs or challenges:

"I know what you are thinking - you need a sign. What better one could I give than to make this little one whole and new? I could do it, but I will not. I am the Lord and not a conjurer. I gave this mite a gift I denied to all of you - eternal innocence. To you, he looks imperfect but to me he is flawless, like the bud that dies unopened or the fledgling that falls from the nest to be devoured by the ants. He will never offend me, as all of you have done. He will never pervert or destroy the work of my Father's hands. He is necessary to you. He will evoke the kindness that will keep you human. His infirmity will prompt you to be grateful for your own good fortune. More! He will remind you every day that I am who I am, that my ways are not yours, and that the smallest dust mite, while in the darkest space, does not fall out of my hand. I have chosen you. You have not chosen me. This little one is my sign to you. Treasure him!"

— Morris West, *The Clowns of God*

"*Faith, hope and love abide but the greatest of these is Love.*"

~New Testament 1 Corinthians 13

"*You can fool some of the people all of the time and a lot of the people some of the time but you can't fool all of the people all of the time.*"

~Abraham Lincoln

PARADIGMS

To understand the Whisperer's Heart, you need to understand what goes on in a Whisperers' head. The way we see and interpret the world around us is the Paradigm we use. In psychology lingo, it's the "cognitive" part of "cognitive therapy." Our sensory mechanisms, what we are taught and what we have experienced, all interact to create our Paradigm. Because we perceive and process information a certain way, we react in a certain way as well. For example, when one person comes across a snake in the road, they react in fear, while another person will try to catch it and find out what species it is.

Whisperers see and interpret things at face value. They do not read too much into it or place judgment until gathering a lot of information. They consider the individual they are working with to have intrinsic value which gives them the drive to go the distance to do whatever it takes to help them. They are open-minded enough to try things before dismissing an idea. This all ties into the personality traits of Whisperers, which is discussed in the next section.

PROJECTED ENERGY

The manner in which each person carries themselves gives others certain impressions about them. Some in New Age circles call this the Energy You Project. Some people put so much stock into an animal's ability to accurately sense this Energy that they will choose whether or not to go on a date based on their dogs' reaction to this person.

Whisperers project an energy that they can be trusted and are approachable. They are often told, "My dog isn't barking at you like he does every other stranger." They do subtle things that send out positive energy. Research done by Heartmath Institute shows that touchy-feely actions, like "sending thoughts of love and appreciation," actually have an impact on the neurophysiology of both the sender and the receiver. (www.Heartmath.org) Whisperers keep themselves and those they work with in a calm and happy mindset where learning and bonding happen more easily. This is explained more in the section on Hard Science.

THE JOURNEY

It should be recognized that Whisperers are not born with these skills. It takes many years for them to learn and develop themselves as well as their skills. Often they go through hardships that give them a deeper understanding and empathy for those they excel in helping.

It's the motif of Chiron the Wounded Healer. In fact, an acquaintance whose family was impacted heavily by drug abuse once told me, "Nobody who hasn't been through addiction has any place counseling those who are trying to recover." Going through an experience gives insights that textbooks or college curriculum cannot touch. This involves both the emotional knowledge and cognitive (factual) knowledge levels.

Those who go through difficulties understand the best way to climb out of the pit. My father exhibited classic indications of Aspergers' Syndrome. As a child, I exhibited classic indications of ADHD and admit I was pretty obnoxious to live with. The two of us drove my mother crazy. Our three-way clashes were epic. While all this made for a difficult growing up, it did give me a profound understanding of these "spectrum conditions," of parent/child dynamics, of depression and of the struggle for wholeness. You may curse the headaches your people or animals give you, but know that these challenges can make you into a better human being if you choose the right way of moving through them.

SAINT FRANCIS OF ASSISI

Saint Francis of Assisi is the quintessential Whisperer. The story of him stopping a wolf from terrorizing an Italian village by just talking to it is legendary. He is called the patron saint of animals for his compassion and empathy toward them. His writings are inspirational. Anyone who cares about animals or people would do well if they tried to emulate him.

I've always loved a poem attributed to him. You don't need to be religious to take these ideas of doing good into your thoughts. The message of fulfillment through service to others is timeless and universal.

THE PRAYER OF ST. FRANCIS

Lord, make me an instrument of your peace:
where there is hatred, let me sow love;
where there is injury, pardon;
where there is doubt, faith;
where there is despair, hope;
where there is darkness, light;
where there is sadness, joy.
O divine Master, grant that I may not so much seek
to be consoled as to console,
to be understood as to understand,
to be loved as to love.
For it is in giving that we receive,
it is in pardoning that we are pardoned,
and it is in dying that we are born to eternal life.
Amen.

PERSONALITY TRAITS THAT WHISPERERS SHARE:

H ere are a few things you will notice about Whisperers when you read between the lines of their work. These are things that we can nurture in ourselves even if they don't come naturally.

SEEKER OF KNOWLEDGE

Whisperers have an open mind, the drive to learn and find solutions.

PATIENCE & TENACITY

Whisperers do not give up easily. There is a stubbornness in them that makes them overlook the concept of failure. They will continue to search for solutions long after others have given up.

RISK TAKERS

Whisperers are willing to take calculated risks to try new things. Whisperers are innovators. This requires an honest assessment of your skills so that you don't get hurt or hurt whoever you are working with. Mistakes can happen, which is part of the learning process. But if you proceed with caution, the damage will not be irreparable. (More about this in discussion of the Threshold Concept and Safe Practices.)

> *"There are no mistakes, only lessons"*
> *"Patience and tenacity of purpose are worth more than twice their weight of cleverness."*
>   ~Thomas Henry Huxley

> *"Do not fear to wonder, Grasshopper. He who asks is only a fool for a moment. He who does not ask remains a fool forever."*
>   ~Master Po, "Kung Fu" TV Series

SPECTRUM THINKERS

Spectrum thinkers use a Holistic/holographic/integrative/gestalt approach, meaning they understand that a number of factors are involved in the final output. They have the ability to see how all these factors work together. You must recognize that this is a dynamic system, whereby a change in one factor can affect the response associated with other factors. To approach behavior and training with the linear "cause and effect" scientific approach is to set you up for failure. This is also why research conclusions on behavior and training have little value in real life situations.

Interestingly, people with brains wired "on the spectrum" (autism, ADD/ADHD, Aspergers') do this type of global thinking really well which is why they excel at engineering, medical/healing arts, creative arts and home repairs quite naturally.

I will discuss this concept of Spectrum Thinking in the next chapter on Building Wisdom.

A SENSE OF SERVICE AND STEWARDSHIP

Some people have a drive to help others. Some take this to stewardship where they accept the role of caretakers as well. They do not see this as work but as fulfilling a mission that brings them great joy. The end result makes the hard work easier to bear.

HUMILITY

It has been my observation that arrogance is one of the biggest obstacles to learning. If you know everything, you can't learn anything. Humility confers a willingness to learn from others. It also provides a willingness to recognize and admit mistakes, which allows you to learn from those mistakes. It should be noted that mistakes are a means by which we are humbled as well. For some, humility ties into recognition of a Higher Power/Consciousness and the concept of submission, which leads to a discussion of metaphysics.

All the friends I consider "Whisperers" are humble sorts who are open to new ideas. We get into some really fun discussions of our observations and discoveries.

While we take our work seriously, we don't take ourselves too seriously either. Along with Humility is the ability to laugh at one's own shortcomings and mistakes. A decent sense of humor helps a person overcome some of the toughest times. One of my favorite horse whisperers jokingly describes himself as "just an old guy who likes to help people with their horses."

> "The razor blade is sharp but can't cut the tree. The axe is strong but can't cut the hair. Everyone is important according to their unique purpose. Never look down on anyone unless you are admiring their shoes."
>
> ~Bishop Mutendi

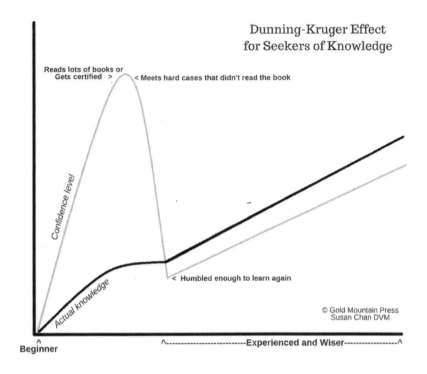

"*It is one of the essential features of such incompetence that the person so afflicted is incapable of knowing that he is incompetent. To have such knowledge would already be to remedy a good portion of the offense.*"
~ W I Miller in *Humiliation: And Other Essays on Honor, Social Discomfort, and Violence*

THE DUNNING KRUGER EFFECT [5] Everyone comes out of training programs thinking they know more than they really do. Then they meet real life. Some people get stuck at that peak where they think they know everything, but don't. These people just plow ahead and are prone to creating damage without even realizing it. Some people will realize they don't know everything but won't admit it. They just hide their insecurities, pretend they know what they're doing and create damage in their wake. In contrast, Whisperers operate with the concepts of HUMILITY and SELF-REFLECTION. They will take that fall, dust themselves off, then seek out more knowledge through research, finding mentors, and testing new ideas. A Whisperer never stops learning.

I first heard of the Dunning Kruger effect a couple years back at a symposium for farriers and veterinarians.[6] In short, it describes how people get full of themselves because they don't know what they don't know. Then reality hits and knocks them off their "expert" pedestal. The speaker excitedly showed us a graph depicting this concept. I couldn't find the copyright holders to reprint them here but just do a search on Google images to see what people came up with. Some are pretty cute and amusing. There are graphs for Wall Street traders, aviators, medical students... seems it applies to just about everyone trying to become an expert in something. I had fun creating this one

---

[5] Kruger, J., & Dunning, D. (1999). Unskilled and unaware of it: How difficulties in recognizing one's own incompetence lead to inflated self-assessments. Journal of Personality and Social Psychology, 77(6), 1121-1134. doi:10.1037//0022-3514.77.6.1121

[6] Karpen, S. C. (2018). The Social Psychology of Biased Self-Assessment. American Journal of Pharmaceutical Education, 82(5), 6299. http://doi.org/10.5688/ajpe6299

I have been knocked off the pedestal many times: Decades ago my babysitter had an unruly Springer Spaniel with no training whatsoever. Having read tons of books on dog training techniques and not many dogs to train, I offered my help. After all, my dogs were great off leash and understood every word I said. Well, it didn't go well with this dog and I came off as too bossy. My friends were not impressed and I wasn't asked back.

A similar situation happened after graduating from vet school and getting my license. After all, I just passed the National and State Boards and completed the grueling curriculum of the best vet school in the country. I got a job as a relief veterinarian in a single doctor clinic. Big mistake. Vet school gives you just enough information to get yourself into trouble. Thankfully this hospital was associated with the multi-vet practice up the road. The vets there taught me things like "the first thing you do with a vomiting puppy is to test for Parvo," not x-rays and expensive blood panels like I learned to do in school.

A SENSE OF HUMOR AND JOY IN CREATIVITY

The Whisperers I know are not stodgy and all business but are generally fun people to be around who don't take themselves too seriously. It helps to be able to laugh at oneself when you blow it. This gives you the ability to avoid feeling shame for your "mistakes" and try again. It gives you the courage to get creative and try things others haven't done before. This applies to Whispering, artistic endeavors and home improvement projects.

If you read the chapter on Metaphysics, you will see that Joy is the emotion with the highest vibrational frequency. Feeling joy in accomplishing your goal is the payoff for all the hard work and gives you the impetus to slog away at a problem until you conquer it. It also keeps you on the positive side of Duality and in the Vagal Zone. Feeling Joy daily is one key to good health and longevity.

> *"You don't have to stop having fun when you get old*
> *but you get old when you stop having fun…"*
> ~a bumper sticker

The work that Whisperers do is far from fun and games. It can be dangerous, downright grueling and require infinite patience. But the joy of getting those breakthroughs and being able to make things right is what floats their boat and lights their fire.

The moral of the story: Find joy in doing what you're doing. It won't seem like work, will give you the boost to accomplish more and can also be good for your health.

THE AIKIDO APPROACH

If you watch practitioners in action, you can see how "Whispering" is similar in execution to the Martial Art of Aikido. They work with a calm, Zen-like quality with no emotional outbursts. Movements flow gracefully without force. Some compare it to a dance between partners. Both take years of disciplined study and practice to master. Both have similar philosophies and flow. Notably, horse trainer Mark Rashid is an Aikido master as well and there is community that blends Aikido with horse riding and training

With Aikido, you use the opponent's own energy against you to take them down. This is in contrast to a martial art like Karate where direct force and strength is used to accomplish the same goal. However, Aikido is not a powder-puff martial art. The power is derived from mental and energetic focus rather than physical force. I just mentioned this for those who might be intrigued like me by this concept and wish to research Aikido on their own.

Aikido *(☐☐☐) is a modern Japanese martial art developed by Morihei Ueshiba, as a synthesis of his martial studies, philosophy and religious beliefs. Ueshiba's goal was to create an art that practitioners could use to defend themselves* while also protecting their attackers from injury.*[Ueshiba envisioned aikido not only as the synthesis of his martial training, but as an expression of his personal philosophy of universal peace and reconciliation"*

~ Wikipedia

YODA: Unflappable in the face of chaos
Focused when necessary
Lovable
Good sense of humor
Connected to his inner knowing
BE LIKE YODA

EMBRACE AND BALANCE
TRUST + RESPECT + LOVE

All Whisperers start with the foundation of Trust and balance it with Respect and Love in what I refer to as **the Holy Trinity of Trust-based Training.** These three themes run through the works of every Whisperer I studied. If you have Trust without one of the other two, or Love without Respect, or any other combination missing one of these elements, you will run into difficulties somewhere along the way.

The light bulb moment of the Trinity's significance came while studying the videos of Ahmad Alhuqayl, a trainer of Arabian horses in the United Arab Emirates. As he explains, the Arabian horse was bred to go into battle. They needed to react quickly to commands, to be alert for threats. To protect themselves and their rider, they rear up and strike out with their front feet. You can really get hurt if something you do makes them upset. To control an animal like this takes a special level of understanding and skill. (NOTE: The term "Control" raises the hackles of some people because it is associated with Domination. However, if applied in the context of Love and concern for their well-being, control is not a negative thing. With animals as powerful as horses, control is a vital safety necessity.) Here are his words:

> ## TRUST IS THE BEST AND ONLY WAY
> ## FOR TOTAL CONTROL IN HORSEMANSHIP
>
> **Total control** cannot be had without Love, Trust and Respect. The better way to gain control is by trust: With horses it is the ONLY way. With trust you automatically achieve control and love. Any horse that trusts you loves you. Trust, Love and Control all go together. Control gained by strength does not achieve Love. If I control a horse, he loves me and knows I will protect him. When horses TRUST you they will always treat you like they treat other horses. They will try their best to be close to you because they know that their safety is with you, so the more they fear things the more they want to be close to you.
>
> ~Ahmad Alhuqayl

There are no visible ways to gauge the levels you have of each element. You can only know by watching and interpreting actions/ reactions in various situations. For example, a horse will trust you enough to let you lead it almost anywhere—except into a trailer. A duck will trust you enough to take food from your hand but act afraid for its life when you try to touch it. In fancy terms: These are dynamic and not static. The Whispering Process provides ideas for building that crucial Trust.

Here are some important points to remember:

- As experiences with each other increases, the relationship develops these levels in one direction or another.

- Every interaction between you two can move the levels one way or another.

- You can damage the relationship but you can also fix damage.

These three elements affect what I call the Reaction Threshold. As Alhuqayl puts it, a horse will be afraid going into battle but, if it trusts you enough, you can override that fear. My dogs might freak out when they hear fireworks but are much better when they can huddle by my side.

IN SUMMARY

Developing these traits in yourself can take time. Don't beat yourself up if you miss the mark. Just remember that trying to think in these ways will help you work better with problems in relationships or individuals who need help.

A SUNDAY SCHOOL LESSON

A lesson by Koren Chin, my Sunday school teacher at First Chinese Baptist Church in San Francisco, stuck with me all these years: She read us 1 Corinthians 13, a popular passage you see on gift store plaques:

"Love is patient and kind. Love is not jealous or boastful or proud or rude. It does not demand its own way. It is not irritable, and it keeps no record of being wronged. It does not celebrate the pain of others but rejoices whenever the truth wins out. Love never gives up, never loses faith, is always hopeful, and endures through every circumstance"

She then said, "Can you put your name in wherever you see Love?"

That's a tall order! I just mentioned this because it's actually what you need to do—and be—when you are working with a tough person or animal. You might not have this book handy but you might remember 1 Corinthians 13.

PART III

WISDOM
Deep Dive

Spectrum Thinking Thinking in pictures

"Lumping before splitting" Information Analysis

Experiential Learning

Design Thinking

Discernment

WHAT IS WISDOM?

The following is a review of what was presented in the Big Picture Overview:

WISDOM = Knowledge understood: Knowledge alone is not enough. You can have knowledge but lack understanding. Understanding how pieces of knowledge fit together gives you the ability to know when to apply that knowledge to get the desired outcome. Understanding requires practicing the application of that knowledge in multiple real life situations. Experience gives your knowledge depth. Deep understanding leads to Wisdom. This allows you to build a solid foundation in your relationship on which to teach or heal. It helps develop discernment for the best approach to take to accomplish your training goals while maintaining a solid relationship.

Wisdom allows you to create layers of understanding with the pieces of information you acquire over time. It is crucial to understand how they are related to be able to prioritize their importance. I use outlines to do this. I've designed these books to present the information in layers so that you will not get too bogged down in details and lose sight of the big picture.

"Wisdom is not just intelligence. It is something deeper. Wisdom sees the totality of things. It does not attack one problem and create 3 more problems. Wisdom sees the totality then takes action on the basis of that."

~Eckhart Tolle

"Wisdom is knowing the right path to take. Integrity is taking it."

~M.H. McKee

SPECTRUM THINKING

S pectrum thinking is also called the "holistic approach," "holographic thinking", "gestalt thinking," ecological approach and other monikers. This approach has vast advantages in problem solving in the real world (or as veterinarians say "in the field"). In the trenches, you can't control variables. If you are really observant, you can develop and use a bigger knowledge base.

Spectrum Thinking casts a wide net simultaneously looking at many factors in play, not just one thing at a time, seeing a given situation as a "Dynamic System." Dynamic refers to how a change in one place affects how everything else works. As my wise friend Dr. Dennis Wilson puts it, in biology there are feedback loops so that changing one thing can change how something else in the system responds. Think of a biological soap opera with interweaving plot lines and characters that exist independently most of the time but create drama when they cross paths.

Another way to look at this is comparing a flood light to a spotlight: A flood light allows you to see how all these factors work together at the same time as opposed to a spotlight that zeroes in on small areas. This gives you a better ability to find the root of a problem and figure out how to fix it. This is the approach of engineers, healers and all Whisperers.

In contrast, scientific research methodology takes a spotlight approach by attempting to tease out the effect of one factor on a situation by standardizing all other factors. It is also a "linear approach" whereby an action causes an expected reaction. For example, a study tests the effects of a certain dosage of a new drug on white mice from a cloned colony to eliminate the effects of different genetics. Or in epidemiological retrospective studies, researchers collect data from one district then account for variations due to age, sex and ethnic background. Some refer to this as "The Cook book Method:" If you follow these steps, you should expect a certain outcome.

Important recommendations and whole protocols ("code of correct conduct") are made based on findings of this focused research. The laboratory mice are easy to control, but how does this really apply to humans? If you control for the effects of age, sex and ethnicity, you are still not controlling the effects of smoking, obesity, diet, socioeconomics, and a myriad of other things. And what about the data from other geographical areas? An internet search for images of "Recipe fails" can be pretty entertaining.

In my humble observation, this incomplete picture leads to a high failure rate and eventually a dismissal of the original information, which is a loss of potentially useful knowledge.

Then there are those who design experiments inappropriately and come up with incorrect conclusions. For example, researchers who have no clue on the appropriate use of electronic ("shock") collars basically traumatized dogs with jolts of electricity then declared shock collars shouldn't be used at all. As you can see, these studies take a huge leap to application in the real world where there is no way to control or even anticipate all the other variables that come into play. The amplification of this mistake happens when people make decisions based on the results of these studies

Some people are born with the brain connections to easily use Spectrum Thinking. Many who excel at this kind of information processing are considered "on the autistic spectrum," (or would be if they were tested.) By the way, being "on the spectrum" should never be worn as a badge of shame.

Even if you don't have the wiring to naturally think this way, hard work and practice can get you there.

THINKING IN PICTURES ADDS DEPTH

Dr. Temple Grandin writes about how autism causes her to "think in pictures." She attributes her ability to troubleshoot problems with animal behavior to this way of processing information. I scratched my head for years over this phrase, "Thinking in pictures." It finally dawned on me that this was the basis for spectrum thinking and the holistic approach.

In a picture, there are many details—the setting, the cast of characters, the mood, the air, the time of day. Emotions are evoked and attached to those pictures. Good storytellers create mental pictures using words. It is said that Jesus chose to use parables to teach lessons effectively rather than just saying, "Thou shalt not..."

So take in the whole scene in front of you. Recreate those scenes in your memories. Appreciate how much information they hold.

"LUMPING BEFORE SPLITTING" INFORMATION ANALYSIS

To make sense of all these similarities and differences, I recommend using the "lumping before splitting" method of understanding—seeing how things are similar before seeing how they are different.

Using this process, you can more easily create a visual layering of the information like an outline or a family tree: For instance, "This group fits into this category but within this category we can break them down into smaller groups." This is how I survived vet school with the massive amounts of facts thrown at us the first two years.

In contrast, school teachers are taught a reverse concept called "differentiating then integrating."

I realized that I use this lumping-before-splitting process to sort out what worked, what didn't work, and then could subsequently analyze **The Why**. Those discoveries were mentally filed away for future reference. Eventually I was able to create mind maps or outlines that organized the information. Outlining information this way also helped me develop mental algorithms for fixing problems as well ("If A then do this but if B, then do that").

EXPERIENTIAL LEARNING FOR DEEPER UNDERSTANDING

While reading information helps increase your knowledge, experience in applying that information deepens and refines your understanding IF you take that experience and think about it.

> *"Insanity is doing the same thing but expecting different results."*
>
> ~Albert Einstein

Don't keep trying to do something with the exact same method if it doesn't seem to be working. That's just stubbornness. If you force a piece into an Ikea product you're assembling, you may end up breaking it and throwing the whole kit away.

Conversely, if a technique didn't work for you, only lazy learners will give up and declare it a worthless technique, "a piece of junk." In either situation, take a pause and look at why it's not working. Those who will look into why it didn't work will become wiser.

THREE THINGS TO DO WHILE YOU WORK

Watch what happens when you do something (action-reaction)
Notice subtle differences in responses
Analyze (ask yourself) what contributed to the differences
in responses.

DESIGN THINKING

DESIGN THINKING= Innovation is powered by a thorough understanding, through direct observation, of what people want and need.

A DESIGN THINKER'S PERSONALITY: Empathy. Integrative thinking. Optimism. Experimentalism. Collaboration.

From Tim Brown's article "Design Thinking." In the *Harvard Business Review*, (June 2008). The Spectrum

The Whisperers' Way can be compared to Design Thinking for Behavior. Design thinking is a concept defined by Tim Brown for designing products that fit the needs of people who use them. This goal-oriented creative thinking is important to develop in order to master high levels of skill in any field, including working with people and animals. This is a practical, no-nonsense approach for people who want to get things accomplished.

Keep your eye on your goal. Don't get caught up in the mechanics of the process or be too loyal to one method. The end result is all that matters. Some people won't try something that hasn't been proven in a study or they can't explain the mechanism. They will even accuse you of malpractice if you do use a method they don't understand. Good people on the front lines only care that something works.

In summary, Whisperers come up with innovative ideas because

- they always seek the Why,

- they are willing to be creative,

- they are willing to take risks

- they think outside the box.

- they know that even mistakes and "failures" provide important information.

This is what Wisdom is all about.

DISCERNMENT

Discernment is defined as "keenness of insight and judgment." It is the ability to take in information and decide if you should use it to make a decision. It is a kind of wisdom that comes from intuition (gut feeling) as much as from learned experience and knowledge.

Information comes from three types of sources:

1) One who knows accurate, complete information and shares it in good faith
2) Information from one who is acting in good faith but has incomplete information
3) Information from one who has a hidden agenda and intends to mislead.

With experience, we can all learn to discern what type of source your information comes from and whether or not to use it to make decisions. This does take effort and diligence but can save you a lot of grief and heartache.

IN SUMMARY

The concepts covered in this section are ways to develop your own Whispering skills. You can also use them in your every day lives and work place to make things go more smoothly.

It's a lot of information but don't let it overwhelm you. Just take a concept at a time and see how they work for you. It all takes practice. The more you do them, the more natural it becomes to you. It eventually becomes a part of you. Be patient with yourself, be brave enough to make mistakes. Even when we are told what is good for us or the right thing to do, we learn that words are cheap and executing them isn't as simple. Go easy on yourself. The only thing that matters is that you are better today than you were yesterday. And above all, enjoy the journey.

PART IV

KNOWLEDGE
Deep Dive

KNOWLEDGE—THE
SCIENCE OF BEHAVIOR

Why is my dog aggressive? Why is my horse so hard to catch up? Why does my child throw tantrums? Anyone who gives you a simple answer has just a simple understanding. If you choose to follow their advice, results will be hit and miss. Additionally, terminology used by people in various fields can make things confusing. I will try to explain things so that you will have an easier time understanding simple concepts and how they fit together in rather complex ways.

A behavior should never be evaluated in isolation. An action or reaction is only a snapshot at a particular point in time caused by a plethora of factors surrounding that situation. There are many factors that lead up to the expression of that particular behavior. It can take some work to dissect a situation and identify all those factors

You must look at all aspects of a person or animal to interpret their behavior and make desired changes. The emotional/thinking part falls under the "**soft science**" of psychology. The physical/neurological part falls under the **"hard science"** of neurology, physiology. The interactions of the soft and hard sciences produce what I call the Body/Mind/Spirit connections—how the state of the body affects thinking and emotions (and vice versa the Spirit/Mind/Body relationship). Bottom line, you can make less work if you work with Nature.

Then you must look at external factors that influence that behavior—the relationship with the individuals that triggered that behavior, the setting/environment, what or who triggered the behavior.

You must even look at how you as the trainer present yourself and interact. You must look at the dynamics of your relationship and correct any issues in your history together.

You don't need to go down the proverbial rabbit hole for every situation, but it's good to know there is a rabbit hole and what direction it goes when you come across difficulties.

You can go far in your training efforts just by understanding psychology and behavior. This is knowledge experienced trainers have intuitively or from experience. You can go even farther if you understand the physical underpinnings of behavior and responses.

Why did I get into the nitty gritty of all that physiology stuff? Well, I was looking at articles recommending supplements or actions to take if you have particular behavioral problems. The more I looked into these articles, it was clear many authors had no clue about the mechanics involved and were making recommendations that were potentially dangerous. My concerns were borne out when I dug into information that even I found difficult to understand. I felt it my civic duty to understand, extract and explain the important facts about complex physiological processes for you. Then if someone has offered you a recommendation involving one of these topics, you will at least have more information than most and be better able to evaluate what they are saying.

Deeper Knowledge also makes controversial techniques like "dominance theory," "shock collars," prong collars and laying horses down more effective and safer to use. There have been smear campaigns against people who use these techniques and even calls to ban "shock collars" or file charges of "criminal abuse" when trainers are seen using certain techniques. These campaigns cite academic papers declaring that techniques are detrimental. I realized these papers were written by researchers who cause harm because they don't know how to use these techniques correctly.

One needs to know how and why a technique works to execute

Griffon Ramsey, Power sculptor

it effectively and appropriately. A chain saw is great for cutting down trees. Chainsaws can star in horror movies. Then there are people who sculpt wood with chain saws. I hope my books will help people understand that we all need to know whether or not we have the ability to use tools and techniques correctly so we don't cause harm.

You can learn from others through direct teaching or videos and books they produce. You can also learn from experience. When I work, I learn what works, what doesn't work and think about **The Why**. Those discoveries are mentally filed away for future reference.

Don't just memorize facts, ALWAYS LOOK FOR THE WHY.

A COMMENT ABOUT CLINICAL TRIALS AND RESEARCH: The information I developed on my own has held true through many different scenarios. There are those who will dismiss much good information as "anecdotal" and not tested. Having studied research design, I know that studies vary greatly in the quality of their methodology and the conclusions they bear. Also, if a clinical trial shows a method "only" worked in 15% of the patients, it should not be dismissed out of hand. Your patient might be one of those 15% that it will help. In other words, be willing to try a novel, untested idea especially if the risks of harm are low. It might really work!

> *"Once is a fluke, twice is a coincidence,*
> *three times is a trend"*
>
> ~David Bautz, PhD.

THE SOFT SCIENCES PSYCHOLOGY, BEHAVIOR, ETC.

This section will cover all the issues I consider important in evaluating and changing behavior. I learned all this by both reading and coming up against hard cases.

THE FOUR MAIN COMPONENTS THAT IMPACT BEHAVIOR (or Your Checklist for Problem-solving)

Student Factors
Trainer Factors
Their Relationship
The Environment

These are all the things you will want to look at when you are working with animals or people. When things are going smoothly you won't need to consider everything mentioned in this section. But when things aren't going well—they aren't learning, they are acting up, either of you are getting frustrated or upset—go through this list so you can identify the root of the problem:

A. STUDENT FACTORS

(referring to the person or animal you are working with)

1) Their genetic makeup
2) Their age/maturity
3) Physical (health) status
4) Nutrition/Hormone / neurotransmitter levels
5) Body chemistry (glucose level, hydration, etc)
6) Vagal tone/ coherence
7) Past experience/training/trauma (neurophysiology)

You must understand how their behavior is an expression of who they are and what is going on inside their body and their head. It is an insight only on their state at that point in time. Remember—

1) **Don't label or judge.**
2) **Someone/something should not be defined by something they did at one point in time.**

Certain factors, like genetics, are fixed, but others can be changed. Therefore, you can change what/who you are working with to a certain extent and set reasonable goals so you face less frustration. This is referred to as "setting them up for success."

Let's go through each item with more detail:

GENETICS

Genetics provide your baseline. It affects both behavior at rest and responses to what happens to them in the course of life. It affects how the body processes food and chemicals. It affects how the brain is wired. This is why ADD, Aspergers' Syndrome and all those "spectrum conditions" run in family lines like it runs from my father through me to my son.

Genetics provides the wiring for reflexive behavior, which is like the default setting on your computer.

You can modify genetically predisposed behavior with training but keep in mind that if your student gets upset or excited past a certain point, their behavior can reset to Default. I learned the hard way that no amount of training can completely extinguish genetically implanted behaviors. (This is important to consider when deciding on a breed to be a family pet. Remember—Herding, hunting and protection breeds are selected for their propensity to bite!)

The good news is that you can still figure out ways to manage genetic predispositions to minimize risk. For instance, when you anticipate a guest coming into your home, which is a triggering event for many dogs, you can put the dog in a kennel run, crate or back room in the house. A leash while on walks is an important control measure for unexpected triggers. You can work on shifting the threshold for excitement by having people come to the door frequently so the dog gets used to it. But this all involves training work and vigilance. Don't forget that the bigger the dog, the more damage they can do if you aren't in control when they get triggered.

It is also important to recognize your own limitations in managing those risks. Sometimes it makes sense to rehome a dog. You do not need to put a dog to sleep because you weren't able to stop them from biting! They just need to go to a home that is prepared and able to handle them.

THE DISNEY DOG PHENOMENON

After a movie depicting an exceptional dog (101 Dalmatians, Lady and the Tramp, Balto, Homeward Bound), the market is flooded with puppies of that breed because they are marketable. Well-meaning parents buy them to make their children happy. These people generally have no clue what these breeds were created to do. Many of these new owners never had a dog before and have no clue about what it takes to train ANY dog, let alone a dog from working lines. About a year later, the animal shelters were sadly flooded with dogs that became too much for the family to handle.

Why am I mentioning these stories? Because I care about families which many readers will have. I want them to avoid heartbreak that I have seen too many times.

THE FURBABY PHENOMENON

Dogs have become increasingly popular as surrogate children. They are invited into our homes and even into our beds at night. Breeds become fashionable to have and some are chosen to convey an image the owners wish to project. Because I have seen some very sad stories stemming from the misconceptions about the human-dog relationship, I want to share my insights from 50 years of observations:

1. Dogs that were bred to do a specific job usually take a lot of training work to make them great family pets.
2. All dogs have teeth. Teeth are used in play, to defend themselves when they are afraid. These teeth are used as tools for herding and protecting. Dogs will use them when the dog thinks it's appropriate. You can train a dog when NOT to use their teeth but if you are not watching them, this training may become null and void, especially if the dog gets over excited as in play sessions or if they get loose into a place that is new, strange, scary or exciting. A dog that is reported to "authorities" for using its teeth in a scenario deemed by human beings as "inappropriate" is unfortunately labeled "a dangerous dog." The consequences of this are far-ranging.
3. The larger a dog is, the more physical impact they will have when their body is thrown against a person or they grab a person or animal with their teeth.
4. Dogs from herding, "varmint-killing," protection and other working lines naturally will use their teeth more than a lap pet. Owners of these breeds MUST learn how to train and control these dogs. Just sending them off to a professional trainer will do no good if the owners haven't learned these skills, too.

THE PIT BULL CONTROVERSY

This an ideal platform on which to discuss genetics. Some people insist all Pit Bull Terriers can be lovable goof balls if raised a certain way. Others think the breed needs to be banned because they were "bred to kill." Neither are completely wrong, nor completely accurate. It all boils down to blood lines.

I have met Pit Bulls who are nothing more than rolly polly couch potatoes that wouldn't harm a kitten. I have met litters of pit bull puppies that are trying to kill their own litter mates by the time they are weaned. The diversity within the breed is astonishing.

There is nothing cuter than a Pit Bull puppy and there are many available in rescues. However, I have met people at vaccination clinics who adopted pit bull puppies already showing the aggressive trait. This is definitely not a breed issue but due to genetic lineages. I've seen the same thing with Chihuahuas. These aggressive dogs can be great with the right people who are mentally and physically equipped to handle them.

There are several take home messages here:

1) With breeds that are going to be big and powerful, Be sure you are physically and emotionally able to handle a dog of this size and power.
2) If you are a newbie dog owner or not willing or able to be forceful with a dog, don't adopt a puppy from a shelter or the back of a van. It's important to know what the puppy's parents are like, especially with large breed dogs.
3) It needs to be recognized that potential for hurting people is in ANY large breed of dog, which is why bans on Pit Bulls is just political posturing that hurts good dogs and their human families.

GENETICS INGRAINED IN A HERDING DOG:

Years ago, I took in a year-old Australian Cattle Dog (aka Queensland Heeler) that had no training whatsoever. If we were walking on the sidewalk and a bicycle rode past us, she would reflexively run after it, yanking me and the baby stroller with the leash. When I had visitors, she would get excited, start pacing, and then bite them on the knee while we were talking. It took a lot of work to control this predisposition and I still had to watch her like a hawk when we had guests. But she was an incredible protection dog. I always put her in the car when I went into town at night because I knew nobody would get in the back seat and surprise me with her inside.

PHYSICAL STATUS: Physical status refers to how the individual presents to you at that immediate point in time. We should want our students to be happy campers when they come to class so they can learn and have a positive attitude about learning. Physical status has a great impact on their attitude/mood, ability to focus, and ability to mentally process a lesson (learn). This is the Body-Mind connection. You, as teacher, can plan ahead and control or alter much of these physical factors so that the animal/human student is in an optimal state for learning (i.e., not hungry, tired or thirsty, no inflammation, allergies, illness) I have a binder full of research papers that show each of these factors have a detrimental effect on learning and mood. More details about this aspect are discussed in the Hard Science section.

If training hits rough spots or behaviors become a problem that belie your best efforts, look for a physical cause. Sometimes it takes a bit of detective work, but this can be the key to your success.

The Importance of Burning off Energy: This is a topic that doesn't get enough attention. When certain individuals are not allowed to move around, such as children, puppies, horses in box stalls, they build up Energy. If that energy is not released, it impairs their ability to focus and can lead to foul moods. It can even lead to emotional depression, which I can personally attest to.

For example, in some stables, horses must be lunged (run in circles) before they are mounted for riding to cut down on problems under saddle. Some hunters or ranchers keep their dogs in kennel runs when not working and must let them run a while before they settle and are ready to go to work. When little boys from the group home came to my ranch, I knew that I had to let them run like maniacs for about 20 minutes before we could do any kind of learning activities. Parents, teachers and trainers who don't recognize this fact of life face an unnecessary uphill battle.

PAST EXPERIENCE: Past experience affects how they might react to certain things. If you know of and understand their past experience/trauma, you can work to heal it so that learning can take place. Working with dogs from an animal shelter, horses bought at auction and children in foster care present additional challenges because history is often not known.

THE IMPACT OF A LIFE EXPERIENCE ON THE BEHAVIOR OF A GROUP OF SHEEP

Someone bought sheep from me and commented how calm these ones were compared to the sheep he bought 2 years prior. The first group was "just wild" and never settled down. I had to think about that because these were from the same parents with no addition of new bloodlines.

I then realized the difference: The first group had been separated from their moms into a pasture across the road from "home." They were traumatized from the separation. It was also a bit of a rodeo catching them up to be put into the trailer.

The ones in the second group were kept with their moms until they were loaded into the trailer to go to their new home. We also caught them up while they were still busy eating (the guys just picked them up and put them straight into the trailer with little chasing involved.) This is an example of how profound an effect life experiences will have on behavior and reactions.

Temple Grandin's "Guide to Working with Farm Animals" is one of the best books I've ever seen that covers every aspect of what I am calling "student factors." She covers not only how animals think but why they think what they do, what to watch for so you can anticipate how they will react to you and how to be prepared for those reactions. Even those who work with people and non-livestock animals will see how relevant her insights are to their daily interactions.

"RESCUING DOGS"

While on the topic of Past Experience, I want to mention this: Adopting dogs from a shelter or rescue is in some circles the socially preferred way to acquire a new pet. It needs to be recognized that these animals are not a "clean slate." You will rarely know what they have gone through before you get them. Because of their past experiences, they can react in unexpected ways and exhibit behaviors that cause difficulties.

As a shelter vet and doing animal rescue through CETA Foundation, I saw too many wonderful dogs returned because inexperienced dog owners had no clue what to do with their aberrant behavior. (Biting, barking, hiding, leaving presents all over the house...)

These problems in a rehomed dog are more difficult to correct than with a dog that came from a loving home. Inexperienced new owners just give up and bring these dogs back to the shelter. Shelter personnel just accept the dogs back without counseling the owners on how to work with the behaviors.

Many of the returned shelter dogs became depressed. Because they wouldn't engage with visitors they no longer were considered "unadoptable" and ultimately met undesirable ends.

Shelter staff and animal rescuers should keep these things in mind when placing animals. People looking for new family members from the ranks of foster children also should keep this in mind. (Recall the situation with children adopted out of Romanian orphanages in the 1990's. Both the children and adopting families suffered greatly.)

"Rescuing" should only be done by those who are ready and committed to going the length needed for returning the "rescued individuals" to wholeness.

B. TEACHER FACTORS

(referring to you as the trainer, teacher or therapist.)

You must also understand how your own body and mindset affect the training/teaching process.

1) Your physical size/sex/ appearance and how you are perceived by the student/animal
2) Your skills and what you know
3) How you react emotionally

PHYSICAL APPEARANCE AND CAPABILITIES: Obviously, you can't change your physical size and sex (without major medical interventions) but it does help you put in perspective why an animal or person might be reacting to you. Some will associate you with a previous person in their life with the good or bad emotions attached.

A small person or woman tends to be less intimidating, which is helpful when working with a timid student. However, small people will need to project a bigger personality when working with "alpha" or aggressive students. I am less than 5 ft tall and hover around 110 lbs. I had to learn to be assertive and project a big persona with animals AND with building contractors who want to take advantage of me.

If you look like someone who scared this individual in the past, you will receive a similar response. If you look like someone this individual knows and loves, you will also receive this similar response.

> When my son was a baby, a neighbor came to watch him while I had to paint a room. Andrew snuggled up with her even though he never met her before. I realized it was likely because she was a Caucasian woman with short silver hair and wire-rimmed glasses just like his grandmother.

Your moods affect how you respond so it is important to recognize this when working with others. If I am stressed or distracted, I get different reactions from my animals because 1) I am less patient and 2) they sense the tension in me, which makes them wary. (The discussion on electromagnetic fields in the Coherence section ties into this latter reason.)

> Jed the bull will come in from the pasture fairly quickly when I call him in. When anyone else takes my place, he drags his feet and they practically have to beg him to come in. Sometimes it takes an excruciating 45 minutes. But when my daughter came to help one afternoon, he came in just fine. Even though she never works with him, she looks enough like me that he decided he'd better listen to her.

At one afternoon feeding, my Katahdin ram Blizzard came up behind my intern Jarred and gave him a head butt. It took us totally by surprise. Then I remembered that earlier that day, Blizzard watched me and a buyer catching up his babies to go to a new grazing home. Jarred looked close enough to the buyer— tall, blond hair, plaid shirt—that Blizzard was going to give him a piece of his mind. Thankfully Blizzard is one of the nicest rams I've had and didn't continue the attack.

Blizzard and his girls

A larger person can handle a large dog on a leash and make it comply. A small person like me can get dragged or knocked over by an exuberant 60 lb. Labrador retriever. Your physical size (including weight) and strength have a bearing on what you can accomplish on a physical level. What you can't do physically, you need to find alternative aids, like managing energy levels or extra restraint equipment.

YOUR SKILLS AND KNOWLEDGE: There is no replacement for studying and doing to increase your skills and knowledge. Soak in all you can through books, videos and talking to people who get good results.

Hands on experience are just as or even more valuable than "book learning." In fact, it's important to see how information works out in your particular situations. Your own makeup can be different enough from whoever wrote a particular book that your results can be completely different and the experience frustrating. I have tried following many different training methods. I always learned something, even if it was that they didn't work for me. That didn't mean they weren't valid techniques. Sometimes I could make it work with minor adjustments, other times I had to just get a different book.

Above all, SAFETY FIRST. The more you know the more risky things you can do without getting hurt. You need to know how to protect yourself. This means learning and seeing the danger signs (body language) and what kind of equipment to have in place. Recognize your personal limitations. You need to know how to balance working through a challenging situation with being careful. Don't be afraid but don't be stupid either. Remove yourself from the situation that becomes too risky, change strategies or put on protective gear. More on this in "The Whispering Process."

YOUR EMOTIONAL STATE AND RESPONSES: The "energy" you project is what you will get in return in any inter-action. Think of times you encountered someone who is in a foul mood who rudely asks you for something. You might comply, but it can ruin your day, right? Or you might be rude right back at them. (Here again, the discussion on Coherence ties into this.)

People who work with animals recognize that animals pick up on their moods and frame of mind. If you are distracted, grouchy, scared or nervous, you have a harder time getting them to work. I'm sure it's the same working with people.

The Whisperers' Paradigm chapter describes the mindset I find most effective especially with challenging cases. This mindset was developed through trial and error over the years. I believe this perspective makes me effective with just about anyone or anything and able to find solutions to situations I never before encountered. The concepts, I believe, make me a better person in general.

One key point is NEVER TAKE THEIR RESPONSE PERSONALLY. If you do, you may react in anger which only fuels the fire. Recall the scene in Star Wars where Emperor Palpa-tine tells Luke Skywalker to feel his anger which will allow the Dark Side to win. It works here, too. We all come to the stage with a history and experiences that affect us on a subconscious level. This may cause us to react to certain behaviors that would be seen by others as "over-reaction." Anger and fear are counterproductive.

We must be willing to recognize and heal trauma in our own lives if we want to effectively teach and heal others.

C. THE RELATIONSHIP

Dynamics Between Teacher and Student

As well as understanding yourself and your student as individuals, you need to understand how the dynamics between you impact the outcome.

If you are just meeting the individual you're working with, you can create a healthy relationship for optimal teaching/training. If there is a history between you and the student, you may need to work to change the dynamic. It is important, actually crucial, that the dynamic is a positive one.

You need to like, even love, each other for maximal cooperation and learning. This is mediated through the Polyvagal (fight/flight and rest/digest) interplay and cardiac (heart) system by affecting both your physiologies. There is also an energetic component which ties into Metaphysics.

Be sure to look at the discussion on Two Leadership Motifs later in this chapter. The style of leadership you use in a given situation shapes the relationship between you and the student. It is important to recognize the differences so that you can use each one when appropriate.

To summarize, relationships are the foundation on which you build your ability to train and teach. "Whispering" is building this foundation on the Holy Trinity of Trust, Respect and Love. This relationship keeps the student in the Zen (Vagal) Zone where learning and hearing are at the highest levels. If you keep these two concepts in mind, you will stay on the right path.

D. THE TRAINING ENVIRONMENT

I found that the environment in which you are working has an impact on your success. This is especially true when you are just starting out with a new animal or person. This factor is too often neglected in discussions about training.

Old familiar environments are more comfortable and less distracting. The individual you're working with won't be constantly looking around to figure out all the new sights and sounds.

New objects or environments increase emotional tension especially if you are working with a reactive, high-strung personality. (See discussion on Spasticity Factor.) This increased tension makes an emotional outburst more likely (pushes them toward the Threshold of Reactivity.)

Environment also provides context to what you are telling them. Having one area for training and a different one for playing communicates expectations for the interaction. In other words, where you are working adds to the communication aspect of an interaction. If you train in the same location every day, the student will expect to pay attention. If you are training where they always run and play, you will have a harder time teaching.

There is also a time-of-day (temporal) component For example, I find that my horses will respond to certain commands when they are given in a particular time of day and place. If I call Malibu the horse at 4 pm from a certain gate, she comes over to get let out into the pasture. If I call her from a different location at a different time of the day, she might just stand there wondering what I want her for.

In Summary:

Keep these factors as a mental checklist when you are working with an individual and hit snags in your progress. It will give you ideas on where to locate deficiencies causing these difficulties. Once you find the root cause, you are better equipped to fix the problem. It may take some time and effort but as horse whisperer Tom Dorrance said, "The long way is the short way."

IMPORTANT BEHAVIOR CONCEPTS

I have tried many different techniques in many different situations on many different species and I've figured out a lot of reasons why these great techniques might fail. This section covers aspects of behavior I found are not discussed enough in most books on training if addressed at all. These gaps in knowledge are what lead their readers to have failures and frustrations when they try to apply information presented in those books.

My peek into human psychology literature also brought a whole new level of understanding of how animals behave and ways to explain what experienced trainers know through experience. In other words, I was able to put labels on those ideas. My hope is that by providing this deeper layer of knowledge and understanding, you will be able to get over those hurdles.

I have sorted the topics out in this order:

A) **Intrinsic**—Coming from within the individual that affect learning and healing
B) **Extrinsic**—Coming from outside that enhance learning and healing
C) **Teaching/training and behavior modification techniques**

INTRINSIC INFLUENCES

COHERENCE

C oherence is a relatively new term that is circulating in the health and wellness circles referring to harmony and connectedness. It embraces many different fields of study though these fields of study don't realize it. Understanding the concepts of coherence is important because Whisperers intuitively bring themselves into a Coherent state and through entrainment are able to bring those they work with into coherence as well. This capability is a fundamental aspect of being able to heal others.

This section is a bit long because I realized how central this concept is to Whispering and how fragmented the information available seems to be. The use and definitions of terms vary between writers and researchers of different fields which can be confusing. What I write here is my humble stab at explaining this concept so you can use it when working with others: I will connect the ideas so you can see how they all fit together. This chapter will give you an introduction into these concepts that have a profound effect on behavior. A deeper discussion of the nuts and bolts is provided in the "Hard Science" chapter

---

ATTRIBUTES OF THE COHERENT STATE

You can think more clearly, intuitively and creatively.

You can learn new things more efficiently as well.

Your physical organs and systems function better so you stay healthier even under adverse conditions.

When you face upsetting or scary situations, you are able to get out of the flight/fight/excite state faster and find solutions instead of staying in a panicked state.

You will see Coherence applied to the Mind, Body and Spirit, or in other lingo, the brain, the physical body and the heart." Thus, you will hear references to mental coherence, physiological coherence and cardiac coherence.

COHERENCE IS THE FOUNDATION OF EFFECTIVE LEARNING AND HEALING

Coherence is a state where the system is working optimally. You might compare it to a car that has the timing of the cylinders adjusted right. If the timing is off, it runs roughly and uses more gas than it should. When a system is working coherently, it has more Resilience to challenges before breaking down. If a state of incoherence (like rough idling) goes on too long, other parts of the car can start breaking down from the excessive vibrations and rattling. When you hit coherently on all three cylinders of Mind, Body and Soul, everything functions in a person at maximum efficiency. It also makes you more resilient, i.e., able to weather upsetting health or emotional challenges and bounce back relatively quickly. Feeling stressed is a cardinal sign of being out of coherence, in other words "incoherent."

The word "Coherent" is most commonly used in association with clear thinking and speaking. Incoherent is used most commonly describing someone who had one too many shots of whiskey. This refers to **Mental Coherence** that comes from conscious thinking in the brain.

Emotional coherence involves the subconscious/limbic/Subcortical /emotional systems of the brain as well as the Heart. Both the Heart and the physical body are involved in "visceral" emotional reactions.

The heart has been discovered to produce hormones like oxytocin, a major component of emotional response as well, which illustrates the complexity of all these relationships.

Physical or Physiological coherence refers to the body parts and systems.

The Vagal/Parasympathetic Autonomic Nervous system impacts both emotional and physical coherence. **Dr. Stephen Porges' Polyvagal Theory** will give you the best understanding of how the brain, organs, nervous systems, receptors, hormones and cells work together to affect behavioral and physical responses to the environment and interactions with others.

When you are working with an individual who is "acting badly," you are working with one who is likely "incoherent" on one or more aspects. Thus, Whisperers often need to work on bringing these individuals back into Coherence as part of fixing whatever they are trying to fix.

I'll sprinkle a little "hard science" in here to get your feet wet: The Physiological Coherent state is related to having a predominance of vagal autonomic (aka parasympathetic system) influence on the body.

The heart and brain both emit electromagnetic signals in measurable patterns. These patterns can be characterized as "coherent" or "incoherent. Your pulse is also an indicator of the heart signal

Coherence can be measured through ingenious complex calculations developed by Dr. Porges' team of Heart Rate Variability (HRV) but now is easily done with Biofeedback technology that is readily available even through apps available on Smartphones. Measuring electric impulses from the brain tells you which of the 5 different types of brainwave you are in.

The heart signals convey emotional information. The brain signals convey information about thoughts. The signal from the heart has a 10x stronger effect than the brain. The electromagnetic field emanating from the heart is likely what some refer to as a person's "Energy field" or aura. This is perhaps how energy can be used by some practitioners (Reiki, Qigong) to bring about healing through their thoughts or moving their hands over parts of a patient's body.

Meditation or even slowing down through aspects of Quick Coherence exercises quiets the brain, which Buddhist refer to as "the monkey mind" or Egoic thinking so that you can let messages from the heart intelligence come through. These exercises also trigger those Vagal responses to achieve physiological coherence and all the good things that happen to your body.

Learning through lectures or reading provides intellectual learning through the Brain. Learning through practice or experience provides an emotional layer of information to that learning (i.e., "heart based information"). This is another reason why learning by doing provides much deeper understanding than just "book learning."

When you find yourself stressed, you can think your way into a coherent state because your thoughts, especially memories, trigger emotions and emotions trigger physiological changes in your body as if you were going through that experience in real time. Conversely, you can think your way out of agitation when you find yourself triggered by an event that touches old wounds. In a circular fashion, a thought from your brain helps bring your heart into coherence, which in turn brings your brain into coherence, which then allows you to think more clearly.

I have heard many variations of breathing exercises that "calm the nerves." One speaker described it as "yogic breathing" whereby slowing your breathing allows you to "enter a state of bliss in between breaths." Heartmath Institute describes a simple 2 step method mental exercise that embodies these principles. There are many variations of this in online videos for "coherence" with ideas to help you "feel" the effects more, but here is the basic concept:

Quick Coherence Technique I don't have the constitution or time to meditate and I don't consciously do this whole exercise very often, but I do incorporate these principles in my daily activities: When I'm feeling myself tightening up which is my sign of being stressed, I stop and take a few deep cleansing breaths (I learned "breathe in 4 counts, hold 4 counts, exhale 8 counts"). Just doing this triggers the vagal cascade and helps me relax and drops my blood pressure 10 points. I also take time throughout the day to stop to notice something that is a beautiful sight, some silly thing the animals do that make me laugh, and to reflect on neat things that make me happy. I do think these simple steps help me to brush off challenges that used to upset me.

The Quick coherence Technique: Basic Concept

1) Take slow, deep breaths and focus on the heart beating in your chest
2) Think about something that makes you feel good— something you appreciate and are grateful for, a happy memory, someone you love, etc. (Simple appreciation for something you see was found to be the most efficient thought form)
3) Hold this for at least three minutes to give your body time to shift into coherence and the Vagal State.

You can do physical exercises to get more coherent too, because movement triggers receptors in your body. You can do variations on these themes to help yourself or those you're working with to get "more coherent." It is easier to work with those who have high coherence than those that are spastic! When working with people or animals that are having difficulty controlling their emotions or are "acting out" you can use methods mentioned in Whisperers' Tricks to help them regain coherence as part of your therapeutic tool box.

I did this little introduction because I know a lot of readers are going to be intimidated by the technical discussions and might not even open up pages to that chapter. Because this is such a simple, easy to do trick, I repeat it several times throughout the book so readers won't miss it.

A WORD ABOUT TRIGGERING EVENTS: Many times we are triggered by an event that reminds us of something that hurt or frightened us when we were a child. This memory is held in our limbic system (the downstairs reflexive brain). We can get over these triggers by searching out these past memories. One therapist describes imagining the adult you talking to the child you in a loving, comforting way, reassuring that child self that those things that triggered us no longer can hurt us because we are now an adult that has the capability of dealing with that challenge. This ability to shift from reacting to an event in fear or anger reflexively to one as an impersonal less emotional bystander is part of the healing process. A similar phenomenon occurs with Mark Tyrell's hypnosis therapy where he has the client imagine the triggering event as an uninvolved third-party observer.

COHERENCE AND INTUITION

Dr. Joe Dispenza presents in one of his podcasts research on how masters of yoga elevate their intuitive abilities. I was surprised to hear the process was basically the Quick Coherence exercise with the addition of asking a question at the end. He explains how the deep breathing plus contraction of specific muscle groups generates a circular flow of electric current through the spinal column to the brain. This generates an electromagnetic field which communicates to the outside world. The electromagnetic pulses also activate the pineal gland, which is considered the intuitive antennae on the body. I present the nuts and bolts in the Hard Science section for those who are interested in the mechanical aspects.

The Jose Silva Method teaches the technique of relaxation and visualization to slow the brain into producing more Alpha brain waves and establishing more connections between the Left and Right Brain to heighten intuition.

METHODS OF SHIFTING COHERENCE AND VAGAL STATES

Because the brain, body and heart are all interconnected, you can try a lot of different ways to get you or your students to achieve a healthier frame of mind using one of the 5 senses, physical exercises or even changing what you're thinking about. You can hire a professional therapist to explore these things. There are specialists in psychology, occupational therapy and other fields who do therapy using music, drumming, art, dance, animal-assisted therapy. But you can easily just do these things on your own. It may take a while to find which method or modality works for a particular individual (or yourself) but don't stop until you find just the right one.

Below is a list of ideas. The chapter on Whisperers' Tricks also covers many specific techniques to trigger the Vagal Response

MODALITIES FOR TRIGGERING
COHERENCE & VAGAL RESPONSES

VISION—Looking at beautiful artwork, scenes etc. Using colors to induce excitement or calm. Painting your rooms certain colors to create a desired mood, surrounding yourself with things you consider "beautiful" to uplift your spirits.

HEARING—The frequency of sound waves affects different organs of the body The pace of music, the volume, and the memories they evoke. Listen to music or playing music

FEELING—Rhythm of music, drumming, riding a horse and feeling the cadence of its gait; touching another person or an animal; the vibration of Himalayan singing bowls or tuning forks placed on certain areas of the body, T-Touch; massage.

SMELL—Aromatherapy

MOVEMENT—Tai Chi, Yoga, Feldenkrais, T-Team, dance

THOUGHT—Training yourself to think pleasant thoughts; Appreciation for beautiful or good things; feeling love for something; giving thanks and gratitude for something good in your life.

THE COMPANY YOU KEEP—Being in the company of people or animals who transmit coherent electromagnetic energy will often shift your own energetic frequencies to a coherent state. It is easy to think of times an angry person walks into a room and shifts the whole atmosphere as well as a time a person exuding positivity lights up the room and puts people at ease. Horse owners often talk about needing to hang out with their horse after a bad day at work. I joke about needing to hug my pig on those kinds of days.

A FUN CONCEPT FROM THE WOO-WOO WORLD: THE POWER OF A COHERENT MIND/BODY/SOUL COMPLEX

Christian healers from the early 1900's, those who study traditional wisdoms and modern self-help gurus describe what is now referred to as the Law of Attraction or Law of Manifestation. They may use different words but when you read between the lines they are talking about the same thing.

The process is basically this: If you want something to happen, you think about it or imagine it as already happening (create "thought forms.") Then you feel in your body the positive emotions of what you would feel if you have already achieved that goal. The combination of the "mind complex" with the "body complex" is said to create an energy of a frequency and amplitude powerful enough to "shift timelines," especially if the thought is aligned with your Soul/Spirit and for your best interest. Some call this "alchemy" or "chemicalization" whereby thoughts are brought into reality on the physical plane. The chapter on "Metaphysical Stuff" goes into this more adeeply.

ENTRAINMENT

Entrainment is the ability of one individual to pull another into alignment and even synchronization with their own rhythm, pattern or thought patterns. This can be done through the electromagnetic communications from the heart and brain, through pheromones (smells like with the Bruce Effect), through rhythm or sound.

It's been shown that just "sending thoughts of love and appreciation" will synchronize heart rhythms and heart rate variability (HRV). Interestingly, "sending thoughts of love" is a technique taught by animal communicator instructors to establish a line of communication with the animal target.

MASLOW'S HIERARCHY

Maslow's Hierarchy is an old discussion that is too often omitted from current curriculum on teaching or training. [7] However, it is fundamental to understanding and explaining behavior. Generally, this is the order in which individuals will focus their energy. When the first need is filled, (they are not hungry, thirsty or tired), they can pay attention to the next on the list (seeking shelter and protection). When they feel safe, they can look at being part of a social group. In some species, this belonging is actually a need. Once they belong to a group, they can think about who is boss. Some have the additional need to be on top of the pecking order.

Of course, Maslow's hierarchy is a very general concept that fits better in some situations than others. I don't think many horses get into transcendent thought. But then, neither do some people.[8]

It does help to keep Maslow's concept of priorities in mind when you are working with people and animals. Take care of those needs above the one you want to work on so that they will be able to pay attention to you and what you want them to learn.

For example: Feeling safe is critical to being able to learn. This is highlighted by the discussion of the Autonomic Nervous System. Critical and creative thinking is enhanced by being in the calm Vagal State. Your student must feel safe from others as well as from any threat from you. It also helps if you put yourself in the role of "Protector" because you have the added quality of Trustfulness.

In short, meet their needs so they can bring their focus to you and the lesson at hand. In other words, if you want to make your teaching and training efforts have the most success with less angst and frustration, make sure your students are not hungry or

---

[7] Maslow, A.H. (1943). "A theory of human motivation". Psychological Review. 50 (4): 370–96. CiteSeerX 10.1.1.334.7586.

[8] Maslow, A. H. (1971). **The farther reaches of human nature**. Penguin Publishing Group. P. 269

thirsty, aren't afraid of anything and feel good about you and feel good about themselves.

MASLOW'S HIERARCHY

1. **Physiological needs:** Getting enough to eat (food), drink (water), and sleep for physiological and nutritional needs.
2. **Safety needs:** Having shelter from harsh elements, protection from predators, bullies or enemies.
3. **Social belonging:** Preserving relationships with a partner, family, or tribe.
4. **Self-esteem:** Having recognition, status, importance, and respect or the ability to feel confident about one's worth from within.
5. **Self-actualization:** The desire to accomplish everything that one can, to become the most that one can be and to be able to express oneself.
6. **Transcendent thought:** Pondering the "meaning of life" questions. Seeking psychological and spiritual growth, altruism. "Transcendence refers to the very highest and most inclusive or holistic levels of human consciousness, behaving and relating, as ends rather than means, to oneself, to significant others, to human beings in general, to other species, to nature, and to the cosmos."

THE THRESHOLD CONCEPT

A threshold is an invisible line that when crossed generates a response. It can be used to describe learning, emotional responses (especially fear, panic, anger), and physical health conditions. With learning, we can all relate to struggling over a concept in school (for me, it was vectors in physics) then finally "getting it" like a light bulb going on. For example, when you play around with numbers and finally get that "Aha" moment with math problems.

With emotional responses, we all can relate to someone pushing your buttons until you've exceeded a tolerance level. Sometimes this response is little, like when you're moved to calmly say that something is bothering you. Sometimes the response is dramatic, such as an emotional outburst, meltdown or panic. For example, you can take the kids running around the house screaming until you can't anymore. You might calmly ask them to go outside, or you might hold off until you find yourself ranting. Think of the straw that broke the camel's back or squeezing a balloon until it finally pops. (The balloon analogy is discussed in the section on pressure and low-stress herding.)

With physical health, your body can handle a certain level of germs but if there is a breakdown in your immune system you will get sick or an infected wound. You can drink a half glass of milk without effect, but a full glass gives you gas. You apply a salve for several days, then when the infection is under control the wound heals over. You take shots of whiskey then get sick after the 4th one. Those are all little examples of crossing that threshold.

The threshold is set by an infinite combination of factors. You must look at the WHOLE picture to get a handle on it (some refer to this as the holographic or holistic approach, or Gestalt thinking) All the factors mentioned in the previous section are part of the picture. There may be more, too! Every situation has a different combination of elements at play. Sometimes you will find that one element to kick everything over that threshold and have your miraculous breakthrough.

This is also why there are no Magic Bullets that are the answers to every situation. Veterinarians and doctors are constantly looking at "the right" antibiotic to use. They are so focused on pharmaceutical studies that they forget to look at the other systems required for healthy bodies. No infection is going to go away if the patient is living in a miserable situation, exposed to toxins or eating bad food.

Additionally, just because something only works 25% of the time; you should not dismiss it as not worth trying because your situation might be one of those 25% where it works.

In training or counseling scenarios, you don't want to cross the threshold into anger or a fear response because the Calm Zone (Zen Zone) is where learning and trust happen. In the Whispering Process chapter, I discuss how to do this. But it's not always bad to cross the line. Now you know where that line is!

If you inadvertently crossed the threshold and face a meltdown, there probably was a factor that you need to find and explore.

Using spectrum thinking, look at every situation as having a number of factors creating what you see in front of you. This is also called the Holistic/Holographic/Gestalt approach or Terrain theory of health. As you change any one of those various factors, you might not see anything different for a while. You keep nudging things along with no response. Then **suddenly** you get the response you want (horse moves the right direction), a light bulb goes on, a wound heals up, OR don't want (the horse bucks, the child has a meltdown.) This lets you know you crossed that Threshold.

The threshold can be moved one way or another by working with the different factors. For example, if you get more sleep, you can take the kids running around in the house longer. You can also take it longer if they're doing it outside the room where you're trying to work.

Certain types of training, like desensitization and stopping the dog from chasing the cat, involve moving that threshold. You can move that threshold by changing the level of trust, by changing their physiology, making an experience familiar and boring—any of the things on that list of "Behavior factors." If you want to avoid crossing that threshold, make little changes at a time and watch for body language indicating tension. This tells you that you're reaching that threshold and at risk of the horse getting ready to blow up. If you want to move that threshold, you want to avoid crossing it because crossing it sets you back in your progress.

SPASTICITY FACTOR—

EXCITEMENT can be characterized as an adrenaline rush caused by fear, anger, play or even hearing wonderful news. I coined the term "Spasticity Factor" for the ease in which an individual is triggered into a heightened overly excited state. A High Spasticity Factor means you have a Low Threshold for Excitement and are easily triggered. I found that having terms like this help us visualize and communicate concepts.

**Spaz edging
toward spasticity**

Spaz doing yoga

Most of us have known a cat that would sit contentedly for petting, and then suddenly jump around as if they were taken over by a wild spirit. My cat that exhibited this tendency was named "Spaz", short for "spastic."

I had for years seen other animals (and people) get easily over excited and seem to lose all sensibilities when they do. Dog trainer Chet Womack says "the mute button turns on" as when dogs won't stop chasing something because they can't seem to hear you calling them. Animals (and people) don't think clearly when in this state either. I used to think it was just "stupidity," but realized more recently that excitation was the real culprit. These individuals unintentionally will try your patience, but don't give up! You can actually change factors in the individual to reduce the effects and raise the Threshold for excitement.

Spasticity is not linked to intelligence. Before I fully understood this, I thought certain animals were just dumb and not easy to train. (I have had a number of dogs that fit this bill.) Then I realized that highly intelligent, trainable breeds like Border Collie and Arabian horses have a high spasticity factor.

High Spasticity means they have low Thresholds for excitement. In other words, they are easily triggered, highly reactive and excitable, and enter the Overexcited Adrenaline Zone more easily. Nervous, reactive and high strung are also words to describe these individuals. When that threshold is crossed, they temporarily forget their training (recall the Genetic Default setting).

We all know people who get upset over what seems to us as "nothing." This is the human expression of high spasticity.

I've provided several stories to illustrate this concept.

> I learned the difference between intelligence and spasticity when I got dogs with Border Collie genetics for the ranch. This is one of the smartest breeds that can be trained to do dance routines. But they got excited so easily when they played that they would cause trouble (attack the chickens) if I didn't make sure they were under wraps emotionally at all times. If I was busy on a different part of the ranch and not supervising them, bad things sometimes happened. Rather than keeping them tethered or in kennel runs most of the time, I found better homes for these dogs.

My Arabian horse, another highly trainable, "smart" animal, will bolt (startle and run) at things that other breeds I have (Icelandic, Quarter horse and miniatures) hardly notice. This is a well-known characteristic of Arabians, which makes them not-so-popular and not-so-safe with a lot of riders. This characteristic was desirable for a rider needing a horse with fast reactions in battle but not beneficial for people just learning to balance on a horse

I had an adorable American Eskimo dog named Poppy that I called my brainless wonder. I am pretty good at training my dogs to stick close by even without a leash. But with Poppy, until she hit 5 years old no matter what I tried, she couldn't "learn" not to run across the street when she saw another dog or wanted to visit the neighbor her excitement just overrode her training.

I once needed to teach my ducks to eat their food in a dog run so I could catch them more easily later on. When I first tried to herd them in, some became so over-excited that they would run past the wide open kennel door where the huge piles of food sat waiting for them. Not just once, but repeatedly. They acted like I was trying to kill them as I walked slowly behind them even though I had raised and fed them since they were babies. It took about 20 minutes to get the last one to realize this was where breakfast was. Me being stubborn, we went through this exercise every morning. Each day it got easier and faster because they became less and less excited about being herded. In other words, I was gradually shifting their excitability threshold by teaching them I really wasn't trying to kill them. It took about a week to get them to herd nicely. It should be noted that herding sheep is pretty much the same training curve, though they seem to learn faster than ducks.

When I am moving sheep, some will get so over excited that they will run straight into wire fencing repeatedly as if they don't see it at all. This is not unfamiliar new fencing; it's the same pen fencing they've been in for years. This is an illustration of what overexcitement does to the thinking brain.

There is individuality within breeds. I have one German Shepherd, Halle, who gets much more excited than her half-sister, Charli. Halle has a high Spasticity Factor. I cannot trust her around the sheep, though the chickens are no problem. The other shepherd, her half sister, has a moderate spasticity factor. She is easier to keep under control and doesn't need to be watched as carefully. However, when the two are together, they play and get each other excited. When this happens, all bets are off. Sometimes I have to break up fights. Another trigger is when a horse or sheep is loose on the driveway or somewhere they are not supposed to be. Since barking at the loose animals can lead to going into attack mode, I have to put both of them into separate kennel runs when I move animals from the pasture through the driveway. Halle the Nut goes into a frenzy and tears up the kennel fencing or her blankets—and another dog if they're together. If they are out when horses or sheep are on the driveway and I am not there to supervise, I might have bite wounds to treat or animals to bury.

I am sure I will face the question "why do you have these dogs?" Well, I did try multiple times to find other homes for them but couldn't. They are otherwise wonderful dogs who didn't show these traits until they were here long enough to become beloved family members. They are indeed good deterrents for would-be intruders and it's become less of a problem as they age and I develop preventive strategies.

A NOTE ABOUT DOG PARKS: Some dogs definitely need to run and play to stay physically and mentally healthy. If you live in a city, you may only have dog parks available to do this. In a dog park, you are likely to encounter other dogs that are running off leash as well. Dogs that play get excited. Some dogs get aggressive when they get excited. Unless you know the dogs you encounter, you cannot predict what will happen when play happens. If both dogs are off-leash, nobody has direct control of them. Sometimes dogs get attacked or into actual physical fights.

Moral of the story: If you live in an apartment, stick to little dogs or old couch potatoes who get enough exercise running up and down your hallway. It will reduce your risk of injuries at a dog park and incur less damage to your furnishings from a frustrated dog that isn't getting enough exercise.

If you have to use a dog park, go at times where there are few other dogs around. If an owner says their dog is "friendly," know that it doesn't mean your dog might not get hurt when they play together or that your dog might not hurt the other dog.

I see the requirement for cage/basket muzzles on all dogs at dog parks as a reasonable way to keep all dogs safe from injury and their owners safe from huge vet bills. If everyone has to wear it, like motorcycle helmets, there will be no stigma attached. Who knows—maybe clever people will develop lines of fashionable muzzles!

THE INTERPLAY OF PRESSURE, SPASTICITY AND THRESHOLDS

Think of a party balloon. It has a certain thickness and resiliency built into the materials. This is like the genetic/physical makeup of an individual animal or person. That resiliency/resistance to popping can be seen as The Spasticity Factor.

After you put air into it, it can be squeezed a bit without popping. The air you put into it is like the baseline mental state.

The act of squeezing the balloon is the pressure or stress you put onto that individual with your communications or interaction.

The point at which the balloon pops is the **Threshold level**.

For example, if you are working in a strange/new environment, changing the routine or otherwise adding a stress factor, you are elevating the body and mind toward the Threshold for excitement. It's like putting more air into a balloon so you don't have to squeeze as hard to make it pop. The closer you get to that Threshold, the more likely you will slip into what I call the "Adrenaline Zone" where thinking/learning are set aside and reflex takes over.

When you cross into the Adrenaline Zone, you will start seeing "bad behavior" and the inability to learn. This is how the Polyvagal Theory and the Threshold concept come into play. It can be subtle or it can be dramatic (spastic over-excitement), as when a horse "blows" and starts bucking. In children, they "go into meltdown" and throw a tantrum.

GENETIC CONSIDERATIONS REGARDING EXCITEMENT AND TRAINING

Many times we see a dog (or person) acting "badly" and a lot of tsk-tsking about the lack of training is heard in the background. I fell into that trap. It took the dogs on my ranch to open my eyes to the fallacy in this thinking.

Every individual is born with certain genetics that impact how they behave and respond. You can train them to alter this response and the training will hold while they are calm. However, their genetics has a big influence on their default setting for both their responses to excitability and the levels of natural excitability. If they become excited (mad, scared, too happy) the default setting takes over. Early development, even in the womb, plays a role as well, but we'll talk about that in the hard science discussion of neuroplasticity.

A real-world application of this is in the choosing of a dog breed to add to a family household. Dogs bred for guarding, herding and hunting rats or large game are bred to use their teeth in their line of work. This means they will have a genetic predisposition for biting when excited. Dog owners who have experience in controlling, training and supervising dogs like this are good placements. However, dogs like this are not good for your average home that doesn't have this skill, especially if they have small children.

Jack Russell Terriers are a prime example of working dogs that are adorable and became the rage because of TV shows like "Wishbone." Most people don't realize Jack Russell Terriers were bred to kill. I personally like them because they are tough little cookies and I know how to handle them. However, I sadly recall one that was adopted from the county shelter where I worked. She was totally adorable. The family returned it days later and it was euthanized because she tore up the face of the 3 year-old. Not only did this little dog have the genetics for being prone to attack, it was highly excitable because of the stress of being in the shelter PLUS the stress of going into a new, unfamiliar home. A tragic end because well-meaning shelter staff didn't understand what a bad placement this was. Even sadder, I know the shelter staff continued to blame the dog because they didn't learn anything from this event.

IMPULSE CONTROL

Impulse control is the mental brake that stops that behavior. This is a component of training though the term isn't often directly used in books. It's helpful to realize that training your dog not to jump on you or chase the cat involves impulse control. When excited, (it has slipped into the "Adrenaline Zone") that brake might not work. It can be difficult to anticipate what will trigger "over-excitation" in an individual. The higher their "spasticity factor, " the more problems you will likely have. The more triggers going off at once, the more likely you'll have "an event." Think of it as a combined effect of several triggers that alone would be under the threshold for triggering but combined pushes them over that line into reaction.

People will call a dog "unpredictable" when in fact the behavior is totally predictable. A dog that is bred to herd or protect is bred to bite. This response is hardwired as part of their breeding program. You can train them to refrain from biting, but when they get excited they will forget their training and reflexively bite. The Polyvagal Theory explains the mechanics. Thus, it should not be a surprise when they do bite. It is your ability to keep that brake on or anticipate what will trigger that makes the behavior unpredictable. I discuss this more in the dog training handbook under "prey drive" or "drive".

My dogs roam freely on my ranch and I train all my dogs not to chase the sheep, horses, chickens and ducks. Generally the German Shepherds ignore the sheep and horses, especially when I am with them. We can walk around the pens with the livestock and the dogs are well-behaved. However, they would get over excited if they saw a sheep or horse out of the pen where it was not supposed to be and go into Chase mode. It is very hard to stop them after they start running because they are so excited that they tune me out. (Dog trainer Chet Womack calls this "Pressing the Mute Button.") Sometimes the poor animal got injured or killed. If I see the loose animal BEFORE the dogs do, I can get the dogs' attention and put on a verbal leash by calling them in to me then tether them with a physical leash so I can safely put the loose animal away. Most days, I manage by tethering or kenneling the dogs during times I am busy working or know they will be triggered (like when I run the herd of horses out to pasture.) Thankfully after the German Shepherds reached about 5 years old, coming across loose sheep or horses stopped being a heart-stopping event.

Interestingly, the German Shepherd never triggers on poultry which would set off my Border Collie crosses. I just mention this to highlight the differences you will find between breeds on things you would never think of.

"Is this dog safe with cats?" This question comes up frequently in responses to ads for rehoming dogs. Some dogs never show an interest in chasing cats. Others will stop after a few training sessions. We learned the hard way that you cannot completely train a dog not to chase (and kill) if you are not around. Jethro, our old orange tabby had coexisted on the ranch with the German Shepherd and McNab for 2 years because I let him roam in the back side of the house while the dogs were usually kept on the front side. When they crossed paths, I would always admonish the dogs not to chase him. Then one day I left to do errands. Jethro had roamed into the front side. I had to bury him.

SELF-REGULATION

Self-regulation involves monitoring your energy states, emotions and thoughts in response to stress, and altering them to produce positive results such as well-being, loving relationships, and learning. We all know how external stress factors are deleterious to health. You can train yourself or another person or animal to relax so as to not be as easily triggered over the threshold into anger or fear. Whisperers Tricks like breathing exercises that work through the vagal system are great for this. (See also discussions by others on "Counter-conditioning.")

Dr. Joe Dispenza is one speaker who discusses how thoughts that create emotions cause your body to react physically as if you are experiencing an event or memory in real time. This is how even our thoughts affect our health and wellbeing. When we find ourselves thinking negative thoughts, stop and replace them with thoughts of appreciation for something good in our lives or even look for something good about the person who is causing you grief. Teach your students to do this. It's part of self-care.

DECISION-MAKING

"There are two different types of decisions that people make. *Value-based* decisions in which you are thinking about which choice is better are made in the orbito-frontal cortex (OFC). *Habit-based* decisions in which you make a choice because that's what you've always done in the past occur in the basal ganglia (deep in the brain near the amygdala.)[9] The latter is subconscious, like emotional responses. What's interesting is that if the OFC is quiet then the habit part of the brain takes over. This means that people are either making a goal-directed decision or a habit decision, but *not* both at the same time."[10]

I found this information in an article written by a sales expert. Her intention was to illustrate why you should understand why a potential buyer is making their decision. If they are going to do something out of habit, like buy the same thing they've always bought or renew a service then don't say too much to change their mind. If you want to persuade them, only give them a couple choices because too much information triggers uncertainty and fear. I came across this article by chance while playing around on the internet. It's a good example of the benefits of exploring and of looking more deeply at information from sources outside your normal circles of activity.

While we are not trying to sell a product or service, this bit of information helps us understand how the people and animals come to the decision to respond in a certain way to events or cues around them. The difference between a conscious response and an emotional or habitual response is hard to see without deeper examination. It explains why some people make what seem to be nonsensical (dumb) decisions. We can then approach changing an

---

[9] Soon, C. S., Brass, M., Heinze, H.-J., & Haynes, J.-D. (2008). Unconscious determinants of free decisions in the human brain. Nature Neuroscience, 11(5), 543–545. https://doi.org/10.1038/nn.2112

[10] Weinschenk, S., (2019, February 7). How people make decisions. SmashingMagazine https://www.smashingmagazine.com/2019/02/human-decision-making

undesirable behavior into what is more acceptable. If the behavior is one that involves conscious thinking we provide them information and reasons why this isn't a beneficial response to them. If it is a habit, or emotional response you need to work on a deeper level through the limbic system. This is where repetition (and a lot more Patience with a capital P) or hypnosis may be needed.

AGGRESSION

Aggression is a major source of problems for dog owners. It is also in other species but because so many people have dogs and dogs have teeth, we hear about this as a problem most in this species. (In people, you can have "passive aggression" but that is a different animal, so to speak.)

I will approach this discussion using the dog model because this is where I've had the most personal experience and can provide examples to illustrate ideas. You should be able to see the corollaries in other species and with people.

Aggression is the outward expression of many different states of mind. You need to accurately identify the type and cause of the aggression to stop it. Many consultants forget this crucial point. They give advice on how to stop the behavior without seeing the Why. Dr. Gabor Mate uses the "Compassionate Inquiry" approach with people. The same strategy can be used with animals but through different ways of communicating and a little more detective work.

If you miss this step and use the wrong approach and use the "consequences" strategy for too long without fixing the root cause, you can end up with a very dangerous dog or a very broken one. I have had to repair both types.

If you use the medical approach of diagnosis and medication, you just end up with a drugged version.

Once you understand this, you can recognize how people and other species end up with behavior problems. You also have a head start in how to undo it.

ROOTS OF AGGRESSION

A) Fear/Insecurity—This is seen most often in individuals who are timid or even just not "bossy." You must counter by building bond and trust

B) Pain—Pain can come from ill-fitting equipment (saddles and bits in horses,) or injuries. If you reach for a dog that is injured and in pain or pick it up in a way that causes pain, you might get bitten. The feet of dogs in the city can be burned by hot sidewalks. Discomfort includes grouch-iness because they aren't feeling well. Feeling ill can be from infection, food imbalances, food sensitivity, allergic reactions, toxicities, nutritional deficiencies, etc. counter by finding where pain or discomfort is coming. Diagnose and fix this problem before anything else.

C) Alpha/dominance challenge—this form of aggression is seen with individuals who want to be the leader and boss. There can be a genetic (breed) component to this trait with Rottweilers coming to mind for me. You must counter by standing your ground and facing down the challenge so that you retain Respect in the relationship. Be sure you have the ability to stay safe and can win before you take on this challenge.

The Tough Love intervention concept assumes that this is the most common reason for bad behavior and acting out aggressively. In my experience, this is the least common.

Often there will be a combination of these root sources. This is where you must apply patience and tease the information with finesse and persistence. Some dogs act tough because they are hiding the fear inside—just like people. More specifically, especially in certain breeds, you more often have a combination of both Fear and Alpha/Dominance Challenge. When you scare them, instead of running they will turn on you. You will see this more in dogs that are bred to "have heart," like guard dogs, herding breeds and terriers/hunters. This can even happen with timid animals who feel cornered. Nothing is more dangerous than an individual that feels cornered.

SAFETY MESSAGE: Working with aggressive animals comes with the risk of injury. Those who attempt this assume personal risk. You can reduce the risk by becoming experienced in reading body language and anticipating responses to handling. This is a Catch-22—you don't gain experience and skill without taking risks. Good trainers all have battle scars. All good trainers will tell you that the risks were worth the lessons learned.

DETERMINING AND ADDRESSING THE ROOT OF AGGRESSION:

This is the strategy I've developed working with dogs, horses, livestock and parrots. It even works with people.

Start by trying to address these in this particular order:

1) Try to make friends first.
2) If that doesn't stop the aggression, look for pain. Do a thorough check of gear. Do a thorough physical exam for injury or illness. Check for the possibility of dietary factors, toxic exposure. Make any necessary corrections. Try elimination of dietary components that may be causing problems.
3) If the aggression still continues after all other reasons are ruled out, you can more safely assume it is a dominance issue.

DO NOT ASSUME IT IS A DOMINANCE CHALLENGE UNTIL YOU HAVE ELIMINATED ALL OTHER POSSIBLE REASONS FOR THE AGGRESSION.

Because aggression is such a complex and important topic, I am including a few stories that might help illustrate important points and ways to address particular problems

MY SAD ROTTWEILER STORY

An owner brought a young male Rottweiler into a vaccination clinic for its Rabies shot. Actually, dragging it in is more appropriate. This dog required the restraint of three technicians, screamed at being touched and took about 20 minutes to do what usually takes me 10 seconds. Of course, everyone standing around was shaking their heads at what they assumed was a case of "poor training."

I took a minute to ask the owner about the dog's aberrant behavior. She told me that police have stopped them when they tried to walk the dog on the street because they had to drag it on the leash to get it to move. Now, people will say "what a horrible, ignorant owner. How could they be so abusive to this poor dog?" But then she told me that they had spent $800 to have this dog go through a month with a professional trainer. The light bulb went on: This is an example of where someone had used techniques that were too harsh for too long on an animal that did not trust them and created a situation of emotional trauma. Also, this is an example of "professionals" who don't necessarily know how to do what's appropriate. (See section on "Appropriate Correction.")

Thirdly, this also illustrates how we shouldn't assume anything or pass judgment until we dig a little deeper.

THE "BE NICE" EXERCISE

Years ago, I had the most adorable Terrier/Poodle cross that looked like a stuffed animal but hated little kids. Little kids had an uncontrollable urge to pet Katie even if I told them not to. After I had one close call too many, I discovered this approach: I would hold Katie tightly with her head secured so she couldn't bite anyone. I would ask a child to pet her from behind. If Katie tried to bite or even growled, I would give her a deep growling "No!" If she didn't growl while the child petted her, she would get lots of enthusiastic praise from me. We did this in short sessions (just a few minutes long) whenever I came across a child that wanted to pet her (this was before I had my own children.) Each time, Katie growled less and less. There came a point when she would go up to a child on her own, turn her back to them so they could pet her and look at me like "Look, I'm being good!" When I did have children, she was just fine as a family pet. Of course, I never let my children use the dogs as toys and we never had a problem with Katie snapping at them.

SANITY TIP FOR DOG OWNERS OF DOGS THAT WON'T STOP BARKING AT VISITORS

Because this is such a pervasive irritating problem and I have never seen this strategy presented by other behaviorists, I wanted to share this with you: My daughter and son-in-law have the smartest most adorable Pomsky (Pomeranian Husky) that barked incessantly at visitors. Even after elaborate introductions and the visitors had been there for hours, he'd bark again if they moved suddenly or stood up from the couch. After a couple years of watching Aida and Clem's frustration, I suggested they pick up Yoshi, calm him down, and then hand him over to the visitors to hold in their arms. (transference of trust) The visitors were to hold Yoshi for a few minutes thinking nice thoughts and talking in a happy voice until he calmed down and relaxed before they put him down.(entrainment into coherence) If he barked at them again, they were to repeat the process. SUCCESS! Of course, you must make sure the dog doesn't bite the visitor in the face. If this is a concern, put a muzzle on the dog before starting this process. For dogs too big and heavy to hold, bear hugs are an option, too. It is important that the visitors "send loving thoughts." The close physical contact is likely a factor in making this work through transference of energy aka energetic communication.). I will include more tips like this in my book for working with dogs.

Yoshi making friends and getting "debarked"

STRESS

Stress is an event or situation that makes an individual uncomfortable or unhappy. It can activate what Dr. Tony Buffington refers to as the "Central Threat Response System" (CTRS) in his article[11] "Stress and Feline Health." This is a term that involves the brain, the peripheral nervous system, the autonomic nervous system and about every organ of the body to put the body into "survival mode." I refer to this state as the Adrenaline Zone or the Flight/Fight/Excite mode.

The list of things that cause stress could fill a book. Perhaps the simplest way to describe them is looking at the Maslow hierarchy. If any of those needs are not met, there is stress on the physical level or the emotional level. What happens on the emotional level eventually manifests in the body. Medical intuitives like Carolyn Myss and Julia Cannon talk about how certain ways of thinking will manifest as specific diseases.

Stress is more than worrying about being able to pay your bills or dealing with difficult circumstances. Stress is also any change that causes a balanced system to become unbalanced. For instance, we can cruise along in life because we know a certain routine, like driving to work on autopilot. But then there is an accident on the highway, so now you have to think about the traffic, how late you will be to work, if you need to take alternative routes, if your boss will be mad. Stress is not "good" or "bad." It just is. We need to factor it into any evaluating we do of a given situation.

Another aspect of stress is the inability to control one's circumstances to change factors that are uncomfortable. For example, a dog that grows up hanging out in a kennel while owners are at work will not be stressed. However, a dog that isn't used to being in a kennel for extended periods of time will be stressed while kenneled and struggle to escape confinement.

---

[11] Buffington CAT, Bain M. Stress and Feline Health. Vet Clin North Am Small Anim Pract. 2020 Jul;50(4):653-662

With children and animals, any change in who is in their world, what time things happen, where they are, what they are given to eat or play with, or any other change in their lives causes STRESS. They can't go on autopilot and have to think about what is happening. If they don't have confidence, they can start worrying. Their body may not be able to handle the change and something might "break" leading to health issues. Emotional breakdown manifests in "bad behavior." Consider this whenever you see bad behavior. Consider this when putting children and animals into foster situations as well.

CHANGE IS STRESS

People and animals like routine because they don't need to think about things, they just do things on autopilot. When there is a change in the routine or any other factor in their life, there is uncertainty. Uncertainty means they need to think about things and try to figure out what it means. Uncertainty creates stress and anxiety. Until it's all worked out in their minds, they will have an unsettled feeling, which is the manifestation of stress. They also start doing things in trying to figure out what is and what isn't allowable. In other words, they are testing the boundaries of acceptable behavior. Change is hard on both the individuals that are required to adapt and to the caretakers who have to deal with the ensuing behaviors.

One overlooked stress factor is going from an environment of free-ranging to one of confinement. If a horse is raised spending most of their day in a stall or a dog in a kennel run or a bird in a cage, they seem to be okay with it because they don't know any difference. Those that have a lot of freedom at some point in their lives can have a difficult time adjusting to confinement with restricted movement. I've seen a number of animals that were neurotic (pacing, self-mutilating, dramatic emotional outbursts) likely because of confinement. Those raised in confinement will adjust fine when they find themselves with more freedom but not the other way around. Thus, the environment an animal comes from and what we can offer with our respective lifestyles should be a consideration when choosing an animal to bring into your home.

The same goes for changes in the diet. The body has adapted to what it's been eating. If the food they're used to requires more of certain enzymes to digest or is deficient in some element, the body somehow figures out how to function in alternative ways. When the diet is changed drastically, the body struggles to make up for what is now different. For example, someone who hasn't eaten meat for a long time loses the enzymes to digest it. If they get meat in their meals, they become physically ill.

If you look at all the elements that are involved in living, you can see the multitude of things that can be changed causing a stress factor. The more of these elements that are changed at the same time, the more problems in health or behavior you may see.

In summary, be aware of the impact every change you make that affects the individuals. Recognize that changes can cause problems in behavior and in health status. Make sure you are not asking them to adapt to too much too fast.

EXTRINSIC INFLUENCES

THE IMPORTANCE OF "FACE TIME"

Face time is the current term used for what was formerly called "Quality Time." This is one-on-one time in the presence of another with two-way communication and few interruptions.

Too often, trainers pull an animal out for a "training session" then put them back in their kennels or stalls when the session is done. The animal spends the rest of the day in a kennel run or stall until the next session. The trainers miss out on so much.

Do not shortchange "hanging out." It gives the two of you the exposure required to learn each others' body language or what utterances mean. Every interaction gives you an opportunity to see if you understand each other or if you need to work on communication skills. They watch you and see if you treat others nicely or if you are a grouch. They experience how you treat them, too.

EXAMPLES OF USING TIME TOGETHER FOR MANY PURPOSES:

When my kids were young (and even now that they're grown) I would have them help me with mundane chores. This was not because it makes them get done faster, because in reality I could probably do them faster alone. Rather, it gives us an opportunity to chat about things that are on our minds while I work. This serves many purposes: You teach them how to do things the way you like them done. You get to know each other better. They see you care about what is going on with them. You transmit information about life priorities and values. They associate otherwise mundane chores with pleasant social interactions and develop a decent work ethic. And as I get older, I do appreciate their help with the heavy lifting.

At Phoenix Ranch, most of the animals are loose in herds and flocks. The ones that don't cause too much trouble get free range of the ranch. The advantage to this is that I am not responsible for keeping them entertained and the low density set up makes for less cleaning. While they are going about their life hanging out with their buddies, eating or even just resting, I make time to just watch them. This is an opportunity to learn how they act when they are feeling okay and notice when something is off. I will see who is getting picked on and if there is a bully that needs to be put in its place by me. When you do this, you can stop bad situations early and prevent too much damage from occurring.

I often clean the horse pens while they are still in them. I work much of my "training" into these times we spend together. During the time I am in the pens working, they are given verbal commands or hand signals to move. Sometimes I break up tiffs between them. When I can, I pull out carrots and have them do a few tricks. Every interaction gives them a sense of what kind of person I am and if they should trust me.

THE VALUE OF PLAY TIME

Remember when you were in grade school and the teacher took you out for recess to play "Red Light/Green Light" or any of those other games? Little did we realize those were techniques that taught us how to pay attention to the teacher's words and body language, self-control/impulse control, motor function/ coordination, how to burn off excess energy so that we could sit still in class and not fidget.

Generally, this was a fun activity generating positive feelings. Positive feelings feed into the quality of the relationship. The quality of the relationship enhances the ability to learn. I'll bet you never thought we were accomplishing all those things just running around having fun!

Teaching animals tricks can accomplish the same things. Because we've spent time working on the tricks, my animals and I are dialed into each other on communications and it is not a struggle when it comes time to ask them to do something. I teach tricks to my dogs, horses and even a couple sheep. It breaks up the drudgery of ranch chores. Books on clicker training, trick training, liberty training (for horses) provide lots of ideas. You can use a clicker but if you're like me, I never can find mine. I use certain words, sounds and signals that let them know they did what I was asking for—plus LOTS of enthusiasm. In the beginning a food treat adds to the positive response. You don't need to make a big production of the teaching sessions, just a little effort in the begin- ning. If I pull out carrot pieces while I'm in the horse pens and start asking for tricks, the other horses will come running over to get their turns and we'll have some fun for a few minutes. I think this makes the animals want to engage with people because the horses associate being around people with fun stuff. When visitors come, my horses come to the fence to meet them. I get comments quite often on how happy and friendly my animals seem.

Along this line of thinking, I included an extensive discussion on The Magic of Music in the section called Whisperers' Tricks. The more I looked at ways to help people through therapy methods, the more I realized how unrecognized and valuable tool music is. It is not "just for fun," it holds a means of shifting an individual's moods, thinking and psyche in profound ways.

OBSERVATIONAL LEARNING

Animals and kids soak up everything they see, even when you don't intend them to. (Why you need to be careful what kind of language you use in front of the kids.) They see what the others get in trouble for doing and the "consequences." Conversely, they see what others can get away with and start doing it, too.

They see how others react to you. Because my own animals don't run from me, newly introduced ones warm up faster. When I have newborn horses, I handle them while mama is calmly eating her breakfast. If I worked with babies while the mama was not eating, mama often got upset and there would be no calming the babies down.

When my dogs hear fireworks, I do not react and do not try to soothe them. I just go about my work and sound cheerful. They subsequently calm down and relax as well. I think a lot of owners get upset that their neighbors are scaring their dogs and get visibly upset. Their dogs sense their owners' emotional upset and attribute it to the fireworks, like they do. Thus, the dogs never get over their fear of fireworks.

They learn lessons by watching the others being taught.

When possible, have training sessions in groups so that participants can see and hear others going through the lessons.

It has become really clear to me that animals learn from watching each other. My horses are loose in a big area with connecting pens, arenas and open barn stalls. When one horse learned they could open a gate to go raid the hay barn, others started trying, too, and I needed to find a new way to secure the gate. Cocoa the old pony has an annoying habit of pawing at the gate when it is time for food or to go out to the pasture. Little by little, others did it, too. It took a lot of work to reverse this trend.

Hrima, the Icelandic horse, was taught to bob her head dramatically if we asked her, "Are you a good girl?" This was always followed by a carrot treat. I now have a bunch of horses that bob their heads when they see a carrot I have in my hand... which is preferable to the gates being obnoxiously kicked. I also have several horses that will come "smile."

Sylvie photobombing with a smile, a trick she learned from Hrima. She does this when she thinks we might have a carrot for her.

My training pen is within the big arena that is connected to the barns. The horses can watch each other learning new skills. In fact, they would come to the round pen to watch the show. When it was time for their turn, they had a general idea of what was expected of them and didn't act so confused.

Phoenix Ranch horses watching Hrima get a lesson

TEACHING & BEHAVIOR MODIFICATION

PRINCIPLES OF HIGHLY EFFECTIVE TEACHING

"Whispering" incorporates many principles of "highly effective teachers." The book *The Best Teacher in You: How to Accelerate Learning and Change Lives* by Robert Quinn, Katherine Heynoski, Mike Thomas and Gretchen Spreitzer is an excellent resource for those who wish to get deeper into this aspect of Whispering.

Through research and interviews with "highly effective teachers," they analyzed what makes someone a "Highly Effective Teacher." They found the complex nature of excellent teaching were what they called four categories of human needs that had to be addressed simultaneously:

A. **Belonging**: relationships
B. **Growth**: adapting to and embracing change to encourage continuous improvement
C. **Accomplishment**: high expectations and maximizing every student' achievement
D. **Security:** a stable environment with structure and processes

Here is my paraphrasing of their requirements for Highly Effective Teachers

A. **Embracing connections**: seeing how different pieces of information are connected as well as connecting with those you are teaching.
B. **Open your mind** and be willing to grow
C. **Open your heart** to build a community of collective learning
D. **Empower yourself** by developing yourself
E. **Empower your students** by making them blossom in knowledge and confidence.
F. **Honest self-reflection**

These were all important. It requires dedication, skill and constant attention to juggle what is required to keep these elements as balanced as possible. If you don't, you are not reaching your potential as an effective teacher and your students will not rise to their full potential either.

TWO STYLES OF LEADERSHIP

We hear a lot about the importance of having Leadership qualities. This again is a term that means different things to different people. It helps to break them down into two basic styles. These shape the relationship dynamic in different ways:

The drill sergeant style embraces discipline. Rules are to be followed "or else." Lessons at times might involve force. Transgressions are met with punishment--consequences meted out by the leadership. It is a highly efficient style of training in a short amount of time. An example is The Koehler Method of Dog Training which was used to train police dogs and dogs used in Disney movies. It works well with individuals (dogs) who have decent self-esteem and mental fortitude. Used without temperance, however, the user can break the spirit and the relationship with those who are sensitive.

The way shower style sets rules that are guidelines in which there is free choice to follow or not follow. Transgressions are met by consequences that come from not following the rules. "Purely Positive," Clicker training, Liberty training all fit this model. It works well with individuals who are sensitive or timid and have respect for the leader. It does not work as well with individuals who want to dominate and challenge the authority figure (like some Rottweilers and stallions.)

A comparison: Someone caught driving fast and dangerously is generally thrown in jail as punishment. With the "way shower" style, they are allowed to crash their car and not have a car to drive.

The **way shower** style is more often associated with women who tend to be caretakers and have more patience. I emphasize the word TEND because there are definitely men who are gentle and women who are drill sergeants.

The **drill sergeant style** is associated more with men because genetically men are physically able to get things done with force more than women. Temperamentally, men tend to be bolder, want to work faster and place less importance on relationship quality.

This is not being "sexist," just observational: A trainer of scent dogs used in tracking told me male dogs work faster, while female dogs who work slower and with more finesse don't lose the scent as often. I watch men handle large animals in ways I would never consider because I would get seriously injured.

Both styles have their own merits but if used inappropriately, both styles can lead to bad outcomes.

Whisperers are associated with the **way shower** style because this is what is necessary for working with traumatized or wild individuals to build that necessary trust. These are the situations that attract the most attention. However, Whisperers also can shift into **drill sergeant** style when situations warrant, as in when they are being disrespected and challenged. They know when this is appropriate because they are well-attuned to the situation at hand. Whisperers are by no means marshmallows.

In any situation where an animal or person fights doing what you ask or acts aggressively, think "is it fear/lack of trust or is it disrespect?" This leads to the question: How do you know which approach to take? You can't tell by just looking. With animals that already have a good relationship with me, I patiently use the way shower method and try different ways of communicating. If after a good college try, they are still giving me trouble, I will switch to the more forceful drill sergeant style. Generally, that will work.

AN EXAMPLE OF DECIDING WHICH LEADERSHIP STYLE TO USE

I had several miniature horses that needed wounds treated. Sylvie kept running away and was extremely difficult to catch. When I did get a rope around her neck, she would run off dragging me behind her. Now this is not a horse that had never been handled or distrusted me. I had her since birth and she had been trained to pull carts. After almost being slammed into a fence for the umpteenth time, I let loose a flurry of bad words at her. She stopped dead in her tracks and let me put a rope on her. After that, all I had to do was growl and she'd let me take care of her wounds. While there still might have been a little fear of the treatments, her respect for me overrode that fear so we could get the job done.

PRESSURE AND COMMUNICATION Pressure generally refers to any communication or action to get an individual to respond in a desired way. The action is referred to as "A CUE." The term "pressure" is used a lot in herding and horse training but the concept works for all animals (and even people). I realized this term can be helpful in visualizing what happens in interactions. I use it in the discussion with Threshold and Spasticity Factor.

PRESSURE can be applied through any of the senses: It can be a visual cue, like waving a stick or moving toward them. It can be tactile, like touching them on a particular spot on the body for specific commands. Words, sounds, volume, and tone make up the hearing component. (Okay, I can't think of a smell or taste pressure other than maybe skunk spray.)

You can "increase the pressure" by making any aspect of the cue bigger or more dramatic (increasing the volume, exaggerating a gesture). Think of this like turning up the volume.

You can also increase the Pressure by combining multiple cues for the same desired action (i.e., telling a dog "Sit."+ Gesturing with your hands pushing its' bottom to the ground.) Think of this like turning on several radios tuned into the same station.

The idea is to keep increasing the pressure until you get the desired response. Then you "release" the pressure to indicate that this is the correct response. Some horse trainers refer to the release of pressure as "the reward." It is a more subtle communication than the click used in Clicker Training, verbal praise or offering a food treat.

Herding Pressure is a concept that works with animals that have a little fear and are more in the Prey mindset. With herding, the animals still need to understand what you want when you do certain things. The livestock needs to move away from the dogs, not challenge them. The dogs need to navigate the livestock, not just run at them and try to catch them. It takes more than a little training to control the dogs as nothing comes naturally.

MY FUNNY LITTLE STORY ABOUT HERDING

When I first got sheep, everyone told me I needed dogs to herd them. They didn't mention how much training it takes to "control the pressure" and how much training to get the sheep to go where the dogs and I wanted them to go. The cattle dogs and McNabs would just scatter the sheep or horses if they could get them to move at all. With the German Shepherds who were too enthusiastic, I sometimes would be treating bite wounds afterward. My Border Collie/Poodle was the most controlled but she'd just bark at the sheep once then look at me like "Is that enough?" I realized that using dogs would take lots more training than I could afford to invest. Ultimately, I gave up on using the dogs. Now when the sheep get out or I need to move them from pen to pen, I tie up the dogs, use the Bud Williams low-stress herding method or grab a flake of alfalfa and sheep happily follow me back where I want them to go.

Herding strategies focus on moving into an animal's flight zone at certain angles to get the animal to move. Livestock whisperer Bud Williams was the pioneer in "low stress herding technique." He emphasized "working the herd" just below the point where they bolt (see "Threshold"), then you can get them to calmly walk wherever you want. Both traditional herding and the Williams method work. I prefer the Bud Williams technique because although it takes a little more time to implement, it keeps them in the Zen Zone (which you'll read about later), so I can round up and move the flock without help (and I'm usually faced with situations when I'm by myself) and it's easier on my body to not get run over by a panicking animal.

Pressure in horse training is a different concept. It works when there is respect for the person giving the command or cue and doesn't necessarily involve Fear. It does, however, involve training.

Pressure even works with children. For example, you ask them to stop playing and wash their hands for dinner as the first level of pressure. You increase the pressure by telling them you're counting to 3, which has a built-in "or else" component in the message. The next level is actually counting to three. The final level is implementing the "or else" consequence. Whatever consequence you mention MUST be something you will actually follow through on for the pressure to be felt. You can also increase the pressure by instituting the consequence earlier in the sequence. If situations required quick response, as in time could not be wasted or it was a safety issue, I never hesitated in implementing that consequence early on.

If the final consequence is not used when appropriate, you will have negated any effectiveness of your command (deflated your Pressure.)

There are two strategies of using this in training

1) **Start soft then increase the pressure**: In other words, give one cue you ultimately want them to know as the command and add more elements/modalities (physical, sounds/words, visual) until they do what you want

2) **Start loud/hard, and then lower the pressure**: In other words, give a lot of cues (multiple modalities) to get them to do what you want, and then gradually eliminate one at a time until they do what you want with the single cue. In my horse book, I include essays of Frank Bell's V Training to compare with Bob Jeffrey's reverse style. I use both and both work fine. It's just a matter of personal preference.

When I first got horses, people told me to poke the horse on a certain point on its side to get it to move its hindquarters over. So I would poke and poke to no avail. Well, it turns out horses need to be taught what that poke means. After I shove them over while doing the poke, they get the idea of what that poke means and will do it quite willingly. With work, you can get horses to move over by just pointing or looking at that spot. Horse people refer to this as "being light." The higher your attunement gets, the "lighter" the communication can become. Riders who have a good connection with their horses speak of how their horses seem to read their thoughts and do something before they are asked. This could also be due to the high attunement to the electromagnetic fields emanating from the heart and brain between the horse and rider.

At Phoenix Ranch I have a golf cart to drive between the properties and feed animals. The dogs and interns ride with me, which can be challenging. I say "go for ride" which brings a huge flurry of excited action (from the dogs). I use the word "Up" to get my dogs to get onto the golf cart. I use the words "Up, up" to get the German Shepherds onto the seat so I can get on and drive the cart without one of them stepping on the accelerator or gear switch. I keep repeating the words, pound on the seat and wave my arms until the two massive dogs are properly situated. We don't go anywhere until this is accomplished. They are also not allowed to get off the cart until we are through the second gate. This way I don't worry about them running off into the road and possibly being hit by a passing car. When the dogs are really excited, it can take some time. (This brings in the "Threshold for Excitement" concept) But persistence has its reward. When my son didn't enforce the rules and let them jump off prematurely, it took a lot of work to get them retrained.

Phoenix Ranch dogs patiently waiting to get inside the gate.

APPROPRIATE CORRECTION

In any training situation, you sometimes need to tell the student that what they are doing is NOT what is desired. Some parenting and training methodologies advocate ignoring the undesired behavior with the thought that the student will tire of not getting attention and eventually stop that behavior.

This might work in some situations. However, I have limited time to work with each individual and sometimes a behavior can be outright dangerous, so I opt for direct communications that stop a behavior in its tracks.

I also think the direct approach is fairer than making someone guess what exactly they did wrong and making them frustrated. I compare the indirect approach to telling your spouse to "decide" where to go for dinner then getting mad because he chose "the wrong place."

The direct approach utilizes a "correction" which is a response that will stop the undesired behavior dead in its tracks. Once that behavior is stopped and the desired behavior replaces it, the pressure is released and profuse praise is the reward.

The late Dr. Karyn Purvis of TBRI (Trust-Based Relational Intervention®) created a table outlining "appropriate levels of response" that are matched in intensity to the level of risk or challenge. The idea is to be effective yet not causing resentment that breaks the connection with the child. While it is written for working with children, you can see how the concepts apply to working with animals as well

TBRI GUIDELINES FOR APPROPRIATE CORRECTION

Level One: Playful Engagement—A low-level challenge, for example, mouthiness or verbal disrespect, may be met with playful engagement. For example in response to a child who demands "Give me that crayon!" the caregiver may respond playfully, "Are you askin' or tellin'?" Then the caregiver guides the child to a behavioral re-do in which the child asks with respect for the crayon.

Level Two: Structured Engagement—With a slightly elevated challenge, such as when the child doesn't respond appropriately to playful engagement, the caregiver may offer choices. For example, a six-year-old on the playground who demanded that her teacher pick her up and carry her in, was asked at Level One, if she was "askin' or tellin'." The youngster replied forcefully that she was telling, to which the teacher responded, "You have two choices, you may ask with respect or you may simply walk into the building yourself." At that level, the young girl asked with respect, and the teacher then carried her playfully into the building.

Level Three: Calming Engagement—When there is a risk of full escalation, the caregiver must be carefully attuned to this danger. At this level, caregivers are encouraged to give the child or youth a chance to do "time-in" and think about what they need while the adult is nearby. An alternative we have used in RTCs and homes with adolescents is that in advance of difficult behaviors, the caregiver and youth may choose a "quiet place" to which the youth can ask to go when they need time to self-regulate. Typically after a few minutes, the adolescent is able to return to the conversation, knowing what they need to say or do.

Level Four: Protective Engagement—At Level Four there is a significant threat of violence or harm by the child, either to himself or to someone else. At this level, TBRI encourages caregivers to contain the violence while remaining calm and reassuring. Caregivers should seek formal training in an intervention accepted by laws in their state or regulations of their organization. When the violence passes, the caregiver remains with the child or youth until the connection is re-affirmed and the youngster feels safe and secure again.

TBRI staff takes the position that it is NEVER okay to scare a child. I realized this is because they work with children recovering from trauma. When I have a good trusting relationship with an animal or child, I may find it appropriate to scare" or "startle" them when they are doing something they shouldn't. This is useful when 1) you need to quickly stop the activity for safety reasons (like going into the street where they could get hit by a car) 2) when they are acting in defiance or with disrespect toward you (resetting your boundaries and role as leader). Just make sure how you do it is appropriate for the behavior you are trying to change.

Some people institute "consequences" for undesired behavior. What they really mean is "punishment." There is a different strategy, which can be called "restorative justice" or "fixing the mess you made." I prefer this form of consequence because it avoids shaming and creating resentment in the one getting the "consequence" while building confidence in them and maintaining a positive relationship between you two. You also get the damage repaired in the process. I mention this comparison in the Whisperers' Heart and Paradigm under Leadership models.

COUNTERCONDITIONING

Counter conditioning is training to replace an undesired (fearful or excited) behavior with one that is positive/desired and calm (i.e., Lack of fear.) It requires reprogramming of behavior (response) ingrained in the subconscious brain usually at a very young age. You will understand more about how this works if you look at it through the autonomic nervous system (Polyvagal Theory.)

With animals, this is commonly done by offering a treat when the triggering stimulus occurs. A classic example is giving a food treat when the animal is exposed to something that normally scares them, like getting their nails clipped or being medicated. Eventually they look forward to the experience, or at least don't freak out as much. At my ranch, the horses actually line up to get their hoof trims because they know they will get carrots after each foot.

Another version one trainer suggested is training the dog to go lie on his bed instead of barking when he hears the doorbell. (Of course, I wouldn't recommend this strategy if you want your dogs to alert you to strangers on the property.)

Cognitive Therapy is a corollary for people who can use words to change responses. You talk through the beliefs and change the feelings associated with certain triggers thereby identifying and changing unhelpful or inaccurate thinking, problematic behavior, and distressing emotional responses. This involves the individual working collaboratively with the therapist to develop skills for testing and modifying beliefs, identifying distorted thinking, relating to others in different ways, and changing behaviors.[12]

This actually highlights the importance of identifying the root cause of an unwanted behavior. (See the discussion on Neuroplasticity).

People can use aids to counter condition themselves. Snapping a rubber band on your wrist when you feel the urge to reach for a cigarette or snack to remind yourself of your goals and the positive aspects of reaching those goals.

Counter conditioning can be part of self-regulation training, too. When you feel stress coming on, you remind yourself to do deep breathing exercises or getting a mental image of something beautiful or feeling gratitude for something in your life.

Mindfulness exercises and meditation are likely useful as well. All these work through shifting the threshold for excitement as well as fixing the lessons as learned responses in longer term memory.

---

[12] Wikipedia

DESENSITIZATION

Desensitization is eliminating the fear response to a triggering stimulus. This is done two different ways:

A) By starting with a low exposure then gradually increasing it. For example, a dog is afraid of a noise, you can make that noise louder and louder but keeping it under the response threshold.

B) Just do what scares them but keep repeating until they don't react at all (AKA extinction of a fear response).

Regardless of which approach you take, make sure there is no pain or negative association with that trigger or you can make the situation worse. Keep in mind that noise at certain frequencies can cause pain and disorientation. This could be why a desensitization exercise isn't working.

The most efficient method keeps them from crossing the threshold into excitement while being exposed to whatever scares them. There are several ways to keep them under that excitation/startle threshold. You can use the Whisperers Tricks to keep them in the Zen Zone while doing this. Feeding them is an easy way to keep the parasympathetic system in gear. This is why giving treats during desensitization works so well. So does holding them tight with "bear hugs" and thunder shirts that also trigger the calming vagal response. Light sedation ("chemical restraint" in veterinary terms) or calming herbal supplements also helps facilitate desensitization.

Bill Richey of the National Mounted Police Training puts horses through "despooking" exercises so they will work safely in crowds. He told me that in the past he used Acepromazine, a mild sedative, on horses before their first experience working at Mardi Gras so they would not react to all the commotion around them. After that, they never needed the sedation again. My horses were "laid down" and then exposed to leaf blowers, plastic tarps and all kinds of scary things before their trainer took them into busy city streets with horse carts.

You, the trainer/teacher/therapist, must also convey calmness, no fear, no anger and not respond with either of those emotions during the course of desensitization sessions. If you get "excited," so will your student.

CHANGING THE RULES OF THE GAME (Or THE IMPORTANCE OF SETTING RULES FROM THE START)

I've seen problems where kids are not taught rules and boundaries and respect for parents until 5. The same happens with puppies where people think it's cute when they grab your hands and act feisty—until they start drawing blood. The children and puppies assume this is okay and is how the world works. Then when the parents or owners change those rules, there is confusion and rebellion.

> I've been told (and even thought to myself) that new pets should be introduced into the home when we have lots of time to spend with them, like during school breaks and vacation time. So, the owners flood their new dog with attention for that short period. Then the owners go back to their work routines or school and the dog is left at home alone for hours at a time. The rules have been changed. The dog starts destroying the house out of boredom and frustration. It doesn't understand why it's being scolded when the owners get home.

THE USE OF "PAIN" IN TRAINING

This is an incredibly complex topic that triggers lots of heated debate. Some people think that any use of "painful stimuli" amounts to cruelty. Others ascribe to the "Spare the rod, spoil the child" philosophy. These two factions will argue forever because they will not listen to the nuances of the information presented. I will try to explain what I see:

Researchers call pain "noxious stimuli." In real experiments, they create pain when an animal does a particular action to see what happens to their behavior. The behavior does change but so does the psyche of the animal if the pain is not stopped.

I honestly think some of these researchers have a sadistic core. I'm referring in particular to the experiments on "learned helplessness" where they shock little animals until they just give up and lie there then declare that one should never use anything painful for training. I don't think these researchers have a clue about training, nor anything I consider resembling a heart.

Trainers, especially horse trainers, like to use the word "discomfort". It's a physical sensation to communicate what you want them to do (non-verbal communication), like pulling on the collar to get a dog to come the direction that you want them to go, or pressure on a bit to turn a horse. If they fight it, there is indeed a little pain. If you do it correctly, it's like giving them a choice of complying and not feeling pain, or not complying and "feeling the consequences." Horse trainer Warwick Shilling has the saying, "Make the wrong thing hard and the right thing easy."

The pain stops immediately after they do what is asked of them, thus it is NOT punishment. When you use this technique, you must ALWAYS be aware of the potential of injury and watch that you are not going to inflict lasting damage. If they fight it a lot to the point of potentially hurting themselves, it's a sign that you need to evaluate your relationship and where the problem lies. (The Whispering Process is a good tool for this.)

When you incorporate anything that causes pain in a "correction" or command, you need to be aware that the pain can cause fear. Occasionally, I have needed to make contact with the skin of the horse if they are being stubborn but this only needs to be done once. After that, just the visual movement of the whip is enough to get compliance because they know you mean business.

In some animals, the fear response will cause them to bite or kick you. You can create discomfort without any physical pain by doing something that startles, which can give you a greater margin of safety. Horse trainers carry whips so they can wave it and make noise, not to hit a horse as some people think. Throwing buckets at the ground near their feet also startles and generally gets animals to stop doing something but keeps you far enough away so you don't get kicked. When I have dogs that do something absolutely unacceptable, like kill livestock or try to bite someone, I will resort to grabbing them by the collar, pushing them to the ground and going into an angry tirade. I don't resort to physically harming them but I scare them into compliance. This did break a 5 year-old German Shepherd who for some unexplained reason decided killing and eating other animals on the ranch was lots of fun. (Note: other factors like excitability may cause this strategy to fail to stop the behavior, which is discussed in another section.) You tread that fine line where they may get so scared they bite you, so this needs to be done with great care! You must intently watch their body language to make sure you don't get hurt in the process.

Too many people will resort to "discomfort" when they really need to be looking at their training skills. They buy gadgets like Halti collars at the pet store that people recommend for "stopping" annoying habits like pulling on a leash. This is the lazy way and not very effective in the long run. These gadgets should only be used IN CONJUNCTION with training, never as the answer on their own.

Only in dangerous aggressive cases where there is no element of Fear is it generally necessary to use techniques like shock collars or prong collars to assert control. The other situation is where an animal is so focused on something that you need to get their attention—as in when a dog sees a potential prey animal and tunes you out so you can't stop them from attacking. (More on this in the discussion on Respect and Impulse Control.)

THE USE OF "FEAR" IN TRAINING

For most cases, it is best to avoid scaring students. Fear impedes the building of Trust that is so crucial to the learning process. There is one exception: The individual who is rebellious and is challenging your authority. This is a Respect problem. There is the difficulty of determining which category a given situation fits and sometimes it takes a lot of work to find out.

I will generally err on the side of caution and stick to trust-building exercises to a certain point. When I've determined it is a Respect problem, I will do things to scare the individual into submission and compliance. But you have to go back to work on Trust after an event like this.

THE ROUND PEN TECHNIQUE OF ESTABLISHING RESPECT

My miniature horses are kept loose in their large enclosure and are friendly, so I know there are no trust issues. They are rarely haltered or led by ropes, but when I need to work on them I need them to stand still. There are times they will fight with me to be caught up and when I do manage, they will fight to break free. This is not fun and either one of us can get hurt. In cases like this, I use a strategy that Monty Roberts popularized. Marv Walker calls it "The Bonder." Some call it "free lunging" or "round-penning. It involves putting them in an enclosure that is big enough for them to run around but not so big you get tired of chasing after them. I will follow them with a rope if the enclosure is too big or make them run in circles (swing a rope or whip behind them) if you are in a round pen. Stepping in front of them makes them change directions, which gives them the idea that you are controlling their movements. Making them run tires them out. If they are being obstinate and I am getting tired, I will throw in threatening "I'm going to get you!" vocalizations to add a little more fear. Some trainers look for a licking of the horse's lips as a sign that they are "surrendering." I know they "surrender" when they stand still and let me put a rope around their neck.

Once I have the rope around the neck and they are walking with me nicely (or at least not fighting me) I will change to a gentle voice, rub them nicely and shift into a calm state. I do not want them to be afraid to follow me so we are now going to be "friends." At this point, they will follow nicely. Sometimes, they will make me repeat this process, but each time the chase portion will be shorter and shorter.

The moral of the story: Use Fear carefully but don't be afraid to use it when necessary. If you do use it, only dole out enough to get yourself established as the authority figure, then follow up with positive interactions to avoid damage to the trust you have built up.

This works with horses because generally they will not turn and attack you. I would not use this strategy with dogs or other animals that are aggressive unless you have in place muzzles, restraints or other protective measures.

IMPRINTING, BONDING, TAMING

This section actually covers all three categories of Intrinsic, Extrinsic and Teaching. I thought it would be more effective to keep it altogether as one unit since this topic is important with those working to make animals good pets.

Konrad Lorenz working with Greylag geese showed how babies hatched in an incubator would imprint on the first suitable moving thing they saw after hatching during a "critical period." Farmers (and researchers) have observed that when certain species are imprinted on people, they choose people over their own kind when it comes to procreating. It should also be recognized that male Llamas who are bottle raised become dangerous when sexually mature because they have lost their fear of people. This phenomenon is likely true with some other species as well.

Dr. Robert M. Miller introduced the concept of handling newborn foals right after birth so they would similarly "imprint" on people and be easier to work with when it came time to getting them under saddle.

These concepts have many layers and factors that I think should be mentioned. I will do so using my experiences to illustrate:

There is an age-related openness to interacting with people. There is a genetic component that is discussed in the next section.

Newborn foals and calves are very friendly and curious right after birth. Within a day or two, they will start running away from people. It's best to work with them while mama is calm because "if mama ain't happy, ain't nobody gonna be happy". If you don't try to handle them when they are small enough to restrain, they will be more difficult to get halter broken because they will fight you. The bigger they are, the harder it is to restrain them so they can't break away. This is related to Respect.

There is a size-related factor to developing trust and respect as well. If an animal can break loose from you while you have a rope on it, it will fight you harder in subsequent tries. This is why it's important to pick your battles and only try to restrain/control when you know you will win.

SAFETY TIP: When you're working with large animals, you can use fencing, ropes and walls to control their movement. The smaller the area, the less running around they can do. The less running, the less excitement and easier it is to get them back into the Vagal Zone. This, of course, should only be a tactic you use when you are confident they won't or can't injure you by over-reacting. When I don't have an animal's trust, and am concerned about being kicked, I will get them into a pen made of fencing panels and slowly close the area down by moving the fencing panels like a squeeze. This way I can keep a fence panel between me and their feet when I reach through the panel to touch them in any way. With smaller livestock like sheep, they can't get the momentum to break loose in a confined space.

Age and Desensitization: When you work with babies, it is easy to get them used to scary things. If you put puppies in a crate and go for car rides, they don't freak out when they get older and need to go to the vet. I have a baby African Grey that I want to involve in presentations and therapy work. I take Scooter out to do our ranch chores. I also hand him over to interns to hold so that I'm not the only person that ever picks him up.

Genetic factor in reversion to wild: You can raise a bunch of animals the exact same way. As they get older, their personalities might change related to their genetics.

I had a bunch of Red Sex Link chicks from the feed store, and added to the group a chick that couldn't find its mom. The feed store chicks grew up to be hens that didn't struggle when you picked them up. The little ranch chick grew up into a red hen that hated being held. This is the main way I could tell her apart from the others. She also had the urge to incubate the eggs that were in the nest boxes, in contrast to the other hens that would only be in the nest boxes when they were about to pop out an egg.

The period for age-related openness varies with species and changes as the individual ages. I raise African Grey parrots. I pull babies from the nest for hand feeding after the parents raise them for a few weeks. This gives them nurturing that humans can't offer plus they have feathers so I don't have to worry about heat lamps. I found that if I pull the babies while the tail feathers are still short (about 5-6 weeks) they may still be wild if not handled regularly and consistently but tame down more quickly and like being around people even as adults. If I pull at a later age, there is more likelihood that they will prefer being around birds and revert to acting "wild." One pair of Greys produced babies that were wonderful pets no matter what age I pulled. With another pair, if I pulled babies at 7 weeks, half would revert to not liking people. With a third pair, all the babies would revert to being people-averse.

PEOPLE-FRIENDLINESS—THE GENETIC COMPONENT

In my experience, some breeds of sheep (like the Barbados/American Blackbelly) seem to have a wilder nature and are not fond of being around people as my Katahdins, East Friesians and Jacobs. The same goes for breeds of chickens: The ones on my ranch that have Spanish Penendenseca, White Leghorn, and Wyandotte genetics are hard to catch and struggle a lot when held. In comparison the ones with Turken Naked Neck, Red Sex-linked, Barred Rock and Buff Orpingtons genetics don't mind being held and stop struggling as soon as you have them in your arms, making them much nicer pets.

I mentioned elsewhere in this book that I had a pair of African Grey Parrots that would consistently produce calm, easy to tame babies. A second pair would produce a clutch that would always have one baby that grew up to be harder to handle and would "go wild" (hate being picked up) if I didn't work with it every day as it grew older. A third pair would produce babies that would ALL be harder to tame and revert to not liking to be handled by people unless I pulled them from a nest at a very young age. In short, sometimes you can pick up a baby and it's just fine but you might need to keep doing this so the fear doesn't develop

Domestication generally selects for people-friendliness in animals because they are easier to handle. This is obviously going to be more valued when the breeds are managed by families than in production units.

This applies to people as well though it manifests a little differently: I use to think being quiet around new people was a learned cultural trait. I have always been shy about talking to strangers. I thought this was a natural thing because most of my Chinese-American circle was this way. Additionally, many of us are taught not to speak up until asked for our opinion or ask for things from people outside our close circles because it's impolite. Then my daughter's kindergarten teacher remarked how Aida hung back in new situations but once she figured out what was going on, she was fine. That she seemed to think this was a negative attribute seemed odd to me. Then an acquaintance met my young kids and remarked how the Asian kids all seem to be shyer around new people than others. When I went to social gatherings after that, I started noticing this difference between the races. Of course, this tendency is reinforced by cultural training but I do believe there is a genetic component.

ESTABLISHING RELATIVE STATUS IN YOUNGSTERS

It is important to teach animals that you are "the boss" while you are still physically able to restrain them.

When you handle an animal and it responds in fear, you must keep holding it until it calms down. You must not do anything to cause physical pain or show anger which generates more fear.

If you do this while they are young, they will generally retain this memory that you are the authority and can control them. People need to understand this about any large animal, especially dogs. Too many people allow powerful dogs to go untrained until they are dangerous to handle. No amount of positive reinforcement is going to change a dog who decides it is the boss. It doesn't take a huge leap to apply these concepts to children and people.

> My equine dentist Tony Basile (who happens to train Belgian Malinois dogs for bomb-sniffing) told me that his kids always had respect for him. "They don't remember that I swatted their diapers when they did something bad. I never had to spank them when they were older, just use that tone of voice." Establishing the hierarchy early makes life easier in the long run.

HEALING TRAUMA

Many cases of "bad behavior" are a consequence of long-term misunderstanding of the cause of a behavior and inappropriate corrections which create a downward spiral in both the relationships and the mental functioning of an individual. If it goes on long enough, it actually affects the chemistry of the body and anatomy of the brain. There then becomes a constant overreaction of fear or aggression, what I termed "having a high Spasticity Factor."

EXAMPLES OF EMOTIONAL TRAUMA

In a shelter situation, a dog may be fearful when put in a kennel run with lots of barking dogs all around. It may snap at people who reach out to put a leash on. The people react with sudden movements to evade or catch it, only generating more fear and biting attempts. The fear response becomes etched in the mind of the dog in the subconscious levels. A human hand reaching out becomes the trigger to bite.

A child with special needs or processing differences such as ADD or autism may react differently than other children to the same instructions. They may be reprimanded but don't understand why. They start acting out only to be "punished" further. The anger and lashing out becomes part of the cycle of these dysfunctional interactions.

Another example: A horse jumps around because a saddle hurts. The rider thinks it's just acting up so "the rider pulls on the bit, uses the riding crop or verbally scolds the horse. Some horses will submit even through the pain, others will not. The latter group may become difficult and dangerous.

All of these are examples of what I consider emotional trauma that creates responses that are dramatic and can lead eventually to a type of PTSD (post-traumatic stress disorder) in animals and people.

Dr. Gabor Mate adds that emotional trauma includes needs not being met: for example, a baby cries because it needs to be held or fed but is ignored or lacks connection with a parental figure. These are real needs for normal social development and even the brain structure. Dr. Mate lists the following as traumatic childhood events: parental depression, alcoholism or drug; addiction in the family; physical or emotional abuse; seeing parental fighting. Mate contends that this trauma is the root cause of addictions (drugs, alcohol, shopping, sex, eating), depression and even cancer, obesity and auto-immune diseases. He uses a technique that he calls "compassionate inquiry" to get at the root cause.

The trauma causes

1) a disconnection between the emotions and the body,
2) difficulty being in the present moment,
3) a negative view of the world and self, and
4) a defensive view of other people.

There are, of course, lesser degrees of manifestations. In moments of self-reflection, I believe many of us can recognize these elements in our own personality.

Mate says that understanding that a condition had its roots in an external event, not genetically programmed or "who they are," allows the patient to let go of the shame associated with their conditions. This gives the patient the knowledge they can work to reverse the damage. Bottom line, it gives them hope.

Individuals who have experienced trauma have reactions to triggers (events, sights, sounds) that are more dramatic than normal. Generally, it's categorized as "bad behavior." Most of the time it falls short of what you would call "mental illness" but I have indeed seen the latter in animals. Observers who are unaware or untrained at recognizing the signs or are unaware of the history will misinterpret these reactions and institute inappropriate corrective responses (usually "punishment.") Of course, this just adds trauma on top of trauma.

Every inappropriate correction creates a dynamic with a downward spiral that deepens the damage to the brain and the body chemistry. Constant stress causes overproduction of hormones and neurotransmitters, sometimes leading to depletion in them as well. The limbic system changes, especially in developing children. But these changes do not need to be permanent.

The key to healing these cases requires someone who will intervene and change the course. There is no magic bullet or drug to cure it. It takes time. It requires someone who is willing to look past the surface and for a deeper reason for the behavior and the patience to tease out the factors by testing every possible reason. Patience builds a trusting relationship so that the individual feels safe and has room to heal. It also requires the wisdom to see attempts to manipulate the therapist or trainer, too. It takes time to return the brain to more normal anatomy, the body to normal balance and reactions to normal as well.

The key I have found is work just under the Threshold and pushing it slowly in the right direction. If you can do this with encouragement and unconditional love, they will slowly gain trust and confidence. This means changing just one factor a tiny bit, testing for reaction, and then changing it a little more. This strategy is in contrast to "flooding," whereby the triggering stimulus is repeated until the individual just stops reacting.

Those who develop the traits and skills outlined in these books will be able to reverse the damage caused by trauma. These traits are actually those that are found in doctors and veterinarians who are able to turn around cases that others couldn't. These are traits of all healers. These are also traits of a good handyman and engineer. I learned this from my dad who was a mechanical engineer and holder of many patents.

The section on The Brain and Neuroplasticity goes more into the mechanisms of Trauma and Healing.

I have outlined a sequence of steps I use to reverse/heal trauma in The Whispering Process

SAFE PRACTICES

When working with animals, you need to be aware of the potential for getting injured. Everyone who works with animals has had close calls if not serious injuries. This includes me. The larger the animal, the harder they are to control and the more damage they can do. An aggressive animal may use its teeth, claws or feet to inflict injuries. Even if the animal isn't aggressive, just getting run over or dragged by ones that you have on leashes or ropes as they try to get away from you can do a lot of damage. Wild species, animals without much human handling or training, or those who have been traumatized increase the risks exponentially due to that "spasticity factor" and lower triggering threshold.

It takes experience to know how fast an animal can strike out; the distance at which they can "get you," how fast you can react to get out of the way, and what body language or expressions are clues that they are going to strike out.

There are ways to protect yourself from animals that lash out or bolt. Muzzles and "toweling down" dogs and cats are my favorites to keep teeth and claws from your body. Using towels and ropes takes a bit of practice. Squeeze cages, pens and chutes are also helpful. A benefit for working in a confined area is that the animal can't get worked up because you are chasing them around a lot. They also can't get a lot of speed and momentum if there's less room to run. Covering the eyes slows some animals down because they aren't triggered by visual cues and are less likely to flee if they can't see. (I catch my chickens out of the trees after dark.)

Your biggest means of protection is staying alert, knowing your equipment and techniques, being cognizant of your limitations, making sure you have enough help, and never taking anything for granted.

The more I handle difficult animals, the less likely I am to get injured because I know my limitations and how to stay safe.

When I want or need to pick up parrots and cats that are likely to bite, I will throw a towel over them so I can pick them up without getting a fang in my hand or raked by claws. (This takes practice so be prepared to get nailed in the beginning!) For large animals, I corner them with barricades so they can't strike out with their feet or bite. When I don't have to react to their attempt to hurt me, they eventually stop trying. I can also proceed with my calming and bonding "Whisperers' Tricks" while they thrash around.

I have presented this topic to highlight the fact that just being nice to an animal will not keep you from getting hurt. The same goes for working with people.

"Ask the animals, for they will teach you..."

~ Job 12:7

THE HARD SCIENCE
OF BEHAVIOR:

NEUROLOGY, PHYSIOLOGY AND
OTHER "-OLOGIES"

The second part of Knowledge is a discussion of the hard sciences of brain structure, autonomic nervous system (Polyvagal Theory), the effects of hormones, neurotransmitters, nutrients, disease states (allergies, imbalances), etc.—the mechanics underpinning behavioral expression. This section is for all you science geeks.

WHY SHOULD I CARE ABOUT THIS COMPLICATED STUFF? If you find this information too overwhelming, don't worry too much about it. It is here to help you understand behavior if you are interested.

Think of your body as a highly functioning, well designed machine. The functioning of every system affects and is affected by every other system. When everything is going well, you don't need to care. When it doesn't work right, you can have a big problem on your hands. Sometimes it's just a little thing that you can fix easily. There are many problems that fit in this category. Take for instance, a car that won't start—a wire comes loose, you run out of gas, the alternator goes out, the ignition needs to be replaced, the battery is dead. Some of these things are simple to fix without towing it to a mechanic and spending a lot of money. Knowing how things work gives you an idea of what you can look into and maybe fix yourself. Even if you can't fix it yourself, you will be better able to spot "an expert" who either doesn't know what they are talking about or are trying to deceive you in some way.

The information in this section will give you an awareness and understanding of how some of the physical things in the body can affect behavior. Then when something goes wrong, you can try things or at least do some research. This is just a start to get you interested in researching on your own. Do not rely on experts to know everything. A degree or license to practice does not automatically confer a status of "all-knowingness."

I use very simplistic explanations so that people who never took science courses can understand the terms and what they refer to. After all, what good is knowledge if it is hidden by words? I am by no means an expert in these topics, just offering what I know about them as I see how they can be important when dealing with how animals and people behave.

Just think of the body like a car: The brain is the computer, the nerves are the electrical system. The hormones and nutrients are the fuel components and fluids. The muscle, organs and glands are the parts you buy at AutoZone.

I found many articles that have some really fascinating and helpful information. I also found that these articles use terms that can be confusing because they don't explain how these terms are related to other terms. Sometimes the authors don't understand the technical aspects and make recommendations that are not quite valid. This applies to peer-reviewed papers as well. I have read many papers in the scientific literature and wondered how they came up with those conclusions, which are then touted as "science-based."

Many articles I read about health were lacking in understanding about the complexities of physiology and offered recommendations that could lead to serious health problems. I discuss topics in this book not only to offer deeper information but to illustrate the importance of researching past a magazine article or even a physician's recommendation before taking that advice.

For example, there are articles recommending taking GABA supplements for depression because low levels of GABA have been associated with depression in people. But the recommendation is short-sighted.

Gamma-aminobutyric acid (**GABA**) is an amino acid that stops nerve cells from firing by binding to GABA receptors (serves as the primary inhibitory neurotransmitter between nerve cells in the brain and spinal cord) This prevents the neurons from being overworked and presumably causing depression.

However, the levels of GABA are affected by the functioning of the GABA-Glutamate cycle and the levels of Glutamate in the body. GABA is converted to Glutamate, which excites the nerves. Glutamate can also be called "Glutamic Acid." Glutamate levels can be raised by eating glutamine-containing foods and MSG. The enzyme Glutamate Decarboxylase converts Glutamate to GABA. But first, Glutamine in your food needs to be converted to Glutamate Therefore the recommendation to take GABA supplements to treat depression is not seeing the whole scenario and runs a good chance of falling short of expectations.

As you can see, this whole cycle is pretty complicated to understand. To make it worse, the terminology between articles is not consistent (i.e., some use "Glutamate." Others use use "Glutamic acid.") I will confess that it took me many hours to figure all this out. It would be really difficult for lay people to negotiate this mental mine field.

Another take home message: While the information may be valid, take conclusions and recommendations with a grain of salt. The authors may be experts, but they don't necessarily know everything.

I tried to research these inter-relationships and explain them as best as I can. Details are not included in every book, but the understanding laid the framework on which the information is presented. You can also use the key words to do your own research online, which I highly encourage

THE BRAIN

The brain is the main processing center of thoughts and emotions. It takes input from our five senses and sends out orders to the rest of the body. Dr. Karyn Purvis of Trust-Based Relational Intervention (TBRI) developed a way of explaining the concepts of how the brain works to parents and caretakers of traumatized adopted children. I've borrowed from her approach.

The Cerebral Cortex AKA "The Upstairs Brain"—The cerebral cortex is sometimes referred to as "gray matter" or just "the cortex" which means "outer layer." This is the section of the brain where conscious thinking (cortical thinking) happens.

EXECUTIVE FUNCTIONING SKILLS / CORTICAL THINKING:

Emotional Control   Task Initiation
Task Completion   Working Memory
Planning   Prioritizing
Processing Speed   Organization
Attention   Self-Monitoring
Impulse Control   Cognitive Flexibility
Foresight   Hindsight
Self-Talk/Internal dialog   Problem Solving
Persistence   Going from one task to the next

"Executive Functioning Skills" is a fancy way of referring to the complex series of skills used during tasks. These require conscious cortical thinking so you can start a task, organize and prioritize all those steps, adjust to problems and negotiate obstacles,

It is crucial to recognize that Cortical Thinking cannot operate when the body is in an excited, fearful, or angry state. (This is what I termed "The Adrenaline State.") Your thinking brain works best when calm, secure, and happy in the Zen/Vagal/Parasympathetic State.

The ventro-medial prefrontal cortex (or 'vmPFC') is part of the prefrontal cortex, i.e., the front of your brain. It is important in regulating fear. Other parts of your brain (in particular the amygdala) tell you when you should be afraid and what you should be afraid of. The amygdala is where "conditioned" fear responses are born and perpetuated. The vmPFC, in contrast, has an opposite role. It mitigates conditioned fear. It stops you from continuing to be afraid in certain situations. When the vmPFC is active then you are able to let go of conditioned fears. As a result, you are then able to make a decision. Thus, when this section of the brain has been damaged by injury or tumor, a person will have a hard time making a decision.

When you recognize that you are getting upset from a challenging situation or person getting under your skin, you will notice that your breathing is faster and shallower. It is hard to think straight when you are in this condition. Take control of your emotions and put yourself into the Vagal Zone by consciously breathing slower and deeper. Think "DEEEP CLEANNNSING BREATHS..." When you are calm, you can think with more clarity and more easily find a solution (see "Quick Coherence exercise").

You can teach this to the people you work with as well. While you can't teach this trick to your dog, you can calm it while you are with it by speaking with slow, calm words and keeping calm yourself. This process of drawing another individual into your level of calm is called "entrainment."

The right side of the brain is associated with non-linear thinking processes, creativity, female/Yin/parasympathetic/Moon/ calming attributes and alpha brain wave activity. This side of the brain can be encouraged to work with pictures and mental imagery and breathing through only the left nostril (Ida yoga breathing).

The left side of the brain is associated with linear thinking, logic, male/Yang/sympathetic/Sun/energizing attributes and beta brain wave activity. This side of the brain can be encouraged to engage with reading written words or symbols and breathing through the right nostril (Pingala yoga breathing).

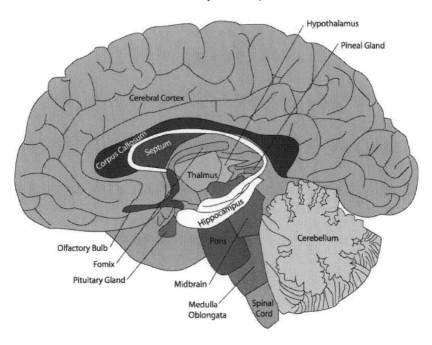

ACTIVITIES AND ATTRIBUTES
GENERALLY ASSOCIATED WITH:

LEFT BRAIN

RIGHT BRAIN

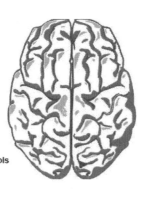

Hearing
Memory
Reading
Writing
Speaking
Understanding

Beta Brain Waves
Yang / Pingali
Moon
Divine Masculine
Action, Energy
Logical Thinking
Thinking in Words and Symbols
Sympathetic//Adrenaline
Trigger with
   Right Nostril Breathing

Movement
Vision
Hearing
Memory
Art
Music
Mathematics

Alpha Brain Waves
Yin / Ida
Moon
Divine Feminine
Calm, Nurturing
Creative
Non-linear thinking
Thinking in Pictures & Images
Vagal / Parasympathetic
Trigger with
   Left Nostril breathing
   or Looking Up

"Feelings are the language of the subconscious brain"

Subcortical Brain AKA The Downstairs Brain—The limbic system is where **subconscious processing and emotional life** reside (behavior, motivation, and sense of smell). It links memories with emotional reactions. Most of the function of this area is for survival—evasion of danger, seeking food, procreation.

Dr. Joe Dispenza talks at length about how our memories or thoughts generate emotional reactions that manifest in our bodies with physical reactions. This is likely how certain ways of thinking cause people to end up with certain disease conditions as described by medical intuitive Caroline Myss and quantum hypnotherapist Julia Cannon.

The limbic system is also referred to as the "Subcortical" region of the brain because it physically sits underneath the cerebral cortex. The amygdala, hippocampus, pituitary gland, hypothalamus, thalamus and other structures with long Latin names operate in this system.

It is important to recognize that your conscious thoughts are impacted by your subconscious feelings more than we generally recognize. Some compare the memory-driven subcortical reactions to a software program in our heads. Seeing, hearing or experiencing particular things trigger a feeling which then makes us think specific thoughts. In people, most of the programming is installed before the age of 7 by observing how things work in the world around them. This creates their rules for negotiating through life.

Thoughts of "gratitude" have been shown to change the amygdala (reduce its size and reactivity) so that the person regularly doing this will react with less stress to things they experience.[13] Interestingly, they also have less inflammation in their body which in turn leads to less pain and better overall physical health.

---

[13] Hazlett, L, Moieni M, et al, Exploring neural mechanisms of the health benefits of gratitude in women: A randomized controlled trial,Brain, Behavior, and Immunity,Volume 95,2021, Pages 444-453.

Conversely, we can use our conscious thoughts to change the subconscious feelings. This is where the concept of AWARENESS comes in. We need to recognize what the triggers are and why they exist so that we can work on reprogramming reactions to those triggers into healthier responses.

For instance, a person might be triggered by stress to reach for ice cream, a comfort food their mom always gave them. One stressor is the shame of being overweight, so when they are reminded of being overweight they reach for more ice cream. A parrot may freak out when a person wearing bright nail polish reaches to pick it up. One role of a Whisperer is to help others recognize triggers and reprogram that software.

NEUROPLASTICITY

The brain structure changes with age, hormonal influences, nutrition and with input, especially stress and traumatic experiences. This ability to change is referred to as "neuroplasticity." and "brain development." You can actually see changes in the structure of the brain caused by growing up in an abusive or otherwise scary environment. For example, with chronic, long-term stress, the amygdala in the downstairs brain gets physically bigger and more reactive while the prefrontal cortex, where thinking and decisions are processed, gets smaller. This explains why children or adults who grew up in stressful situations have a harder time learning and overreact to triggering events.

Pregnant mothers pass stress hormones through the placenta to affect the development of their babies' brains. This could be a reason that children born into families struggling with dysfunction or surviving poverty have more behavior problems. The writings of Dr. Karyn Purvis are good resources for understanding this.

ELEMENTS AFFECTING BRAIN FUNCTION

The functioning of the brain is affected by available nutrients (i.e., Blood sugar, water, minerals and vitamins, enzymes.) If enzymes aren't working correctly, the functioning of the brain is affected as well. More on this in the sections on nutrition, hormones and body balance.

Music, physical movement (kinesiology) and the feedback from every other body system have effects on how the brain takes in information, processes that information and what commands it sends out. These all have an effect on the brain waves as well.

The Whisperers' Tricks chapter and other sections of this book go into more details of how to change how the brain works from "Defensive" (too reactive and fearful) to more "Prosocial" (calmer, able to think clearly and bond with others).

BRAIN WAVES

Neurons in your brain use electrical signals to create thoughts, emotions, and behaviors. When neurons synchronize, this creates brain waves. Brain waves can be measured by a technique called electroencephalography (EEG). This technique involves electrodes put on the scalp to record electrical signals.

Brain waves can range from low frequency and high amplitude to high frequency with low amplitude. The brain waves create binaural beats. This leads to different mental states which affect the brain in different ways. Conversely, listening to binaural beats can shift your brain into different states through a concept called "entrainment."

This is an area of study in its infancy tying brain waves to mental states and function. I've provided descriptions of brainwaves from 3 different sources so you can see how slightly different the interpretations are. In fact, I heard in passing that Gamma waves are associated with transcendental states of Buddhist masters during deep meditation. So don't get too caught up in what someone might be saying about them as being the hard information.

THE FIVE DIFFERENT BRAIN WAVES:

Delta: 1-4 Hz. Delta is the lowest frequency state, and it's linked to:
- Deep sleep
- Healing and pain relief
- Meditation
- Anti-aging: cortisol reduction/DHEA increase
- Access to the unconscious mind

Theta: 4-8 Hz. Theta binaural beats benefits include:
- Meditation
- Deep relaxation
- Creativity

Alpha: 8-14 Hz. When you are in an alpha state of mind, your brain is focused and productive. Alpha brain waves help you to:
- Relax and focus
- Reduce Stress
- Maintain positive thinking
- Increase your learning capabilities
- Easily engage in activities and the environment because you are in a state of flow and creativity

Beta: 14-30 Hz. Beta is a higher frequency brainwave and helps in:
- Keeping your attention focused
- Analytical thinking and solving problems
- Stimulating energy and action
- High-level cognition

Gamma: 30-100 Hz. With a higher frequency than beta, these brain waves help in:
- Increased cognitive enhancement
- Attention to detail, helping in memory recall
- A different way of thinking, which helps problem solving

(source: https://www.webmd.com/balance/what-are-binaural-beats)

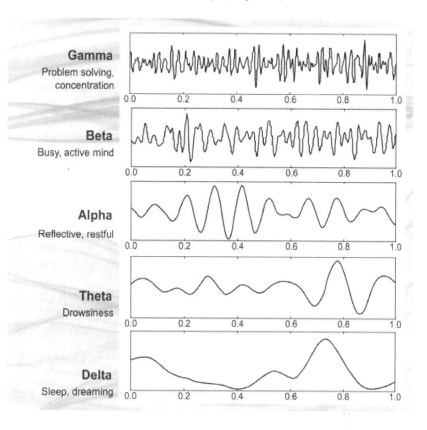

Image credit: Abhang, PA, Gawali, BW, Mehrotra, SC. Introduction to EEG- and Speech-Based Emotion Recognition, 2016.

BRAIN WAVES ACCORDING TO JOSE SILVA:

1) Brain waves can be classified through harmonics by frequency as "Octaves" with Theta/Delta the lowest frequencies) (0-7 Hz, then Alpha (7-14) then Beta (15-20 referred to as 20)
2) up to age 7, the brain uses mostly theta and delta and is programming the subconscious/subcortical mind as it gathers information through observation and experience.
3) from age 7-14 the brain starts using alpha as primary brain waves for conscious thinking.
4) after 14 years, in 90% of people the primary brainwave for conscious thinking is Beta and the left hemisphere is cut off from the right for conscious thinking.
5) After 14 years in 10% of people, they can utilize alpha waves to access the right brain during conscious thinking—and this is what Jose Silva refers to as the Alpha Dimension?
6) The Ultramind program designed by Silva trains the brain to open up the channels between the Right and Left Brain during conscious thinking through amplification of Alpha brain waves.

This total utilization of the brain
a) allows better performance in problem solving
b) allows better learning and memory/information retention
c) offers the ability to read information from the minds of others (telepathic communication) and matter (remote viewing)
d) allows the ability to communicate with the spiritual realm (The Kingdom of Heaven) at the Theta brain wave level.

Anna Wise developed the concept of The Awakened Mind whereby people use all 4 brainwave patterns simultaneously through the use of biofeedback technology. Like other methods such as those developed by Jose Silva, they are using the thinking Left Brain at the same time they used the Right Brain and expanded consciousness generally reserved for meditating and sleep.

Linda Tellington-Jones worked with Wise in 1984 to demonstrate that the system of touches and movement/exercises created an Awakened Mind state in the horses she worked with. This state provided a stronger connection and "a very special kind of communication" between the horse and person, which in turn affects the behavior, personality and performance of the horse.[14]

Notably, Jose Silva reports that those in what he calls "Alpha" and using the Right Brain can communicate telepathically. In this scenario, it's called Animal Communication or Interspecies Communication.

OTHER SILVA INSIGHTS: The Left Brain and Beta Wave activity is triggered when you take physical action. Beta Waves are also amplified when seeing with your physical eyes or even "thinking" about seeing with your physical eyes. Silva has participants close their eyes to reduce Beta Wave activity. He also has them mentally project the image past their eyelids onto an imaginary movie screen 20 degrees up from level. (The Mental Video technique) This helps suppress Beta waves and amplify Alpha wave activity.

More discussion of Jose Silva can be found in the chapters "Metaphysical Stuff" and "Whisperers' Tricks"

---

[14] https://www.slideshare.net/oxibond/anna-wise-and-linda-tellingtonjones-eeg-study-with-horses-and-humans-1984

THE AUTONOMIC NERVOUS SYSTEM (ANS)

The Autonomic Nervous system is composed of the sympathetic (adrenaline) and parasympathetic (Vagal) nervous systems. This is separate from the nervous system that moves muscles. It controls the production and release of all kinds of molecules that in turn switch on and off other functions throughout the body.

The ANS works with the conscious thoughts of the brain, subconscious brain activity and all body systems in very complex feedback systems. These systems co-regulate bodily functions and emotional responses

SYMPATHETIC	PARASYMPATHETIC
"Fight or flight"	"Rest and digest"
Increases heart rate	Decreases heart rate
Airways expand	Airways close down
Muscles contract	Muscles relax
Pupils dilate	Pupils constrict
Digestion decreases	Digestion increases
Dry mouth	Saliva production increases

THE SYMPATHETIC SYSTEM

Most people know of this as the "fight/flight" response. Another term I've heard is "Central Threat Response System" which includes all the parts of the brain, especially the limbic system, as well as the sympathetic nervous system. I have heard comments like "getting a horse into an adrenaline rush is bad because it makes it think it's going to die." Comments like this are generally followed with harsh criticisms of anyone who gets this response from a horse.

Actually, the sympathetic system should be referred to as "Fight/Flight/Excite/Delight" because it involves more than fear or anger. It can be triggered by happy events as well, like when you tell the kids you're taking them to Disneyland. When your dog is happy to see you, the sympathetic system kicks in and chaos ensues.

I like the term "Adrenaline State" when the sympathetic system is engaged because it operates through the release of **adrenaline** (aka epinephrine, norepinephrine) and related neurotransmitters. The release of these molecules in turn triggers a whole litany of physiological responses associated with survival. Also, most people understand the experience of "an adrenaline rush."

An adrenaline rush is not always a negative/detrimental state, and is actually helpful in certain situations. When you face the stress of a deadline or an exam, the sympathetic system imbeds learning, like memorizing information, into your brain circuitry. In an athletic competition, this adrenaline surge gives you an edge of focus and energy. Short term stress gives us the energy and focus to get out of and survive dangerous situations. Rational and creative cortical thinking does not take place. Physical and emotional reflexes or already learned behavior take over. You can think of this as going into Autopilot Mode

When the sympathetic system crosses into overexcited, uncontrollable states of panic or just plain overexcitement, I refer to this as Spastic moments. The ease in which a person or animal slips into this overexcited state is what I call the **Spasticity Factor.** That invisible line that is crossed I refer to as a **Threshold.** When that line is crossed, it's like a "mute button" gets pressed so they can't hear what you are saying. As I mentioned in the section on genetics, sometimes they will forget their training and revert to what they were hardwired to do. Teenage boys and dogs engage in pack mentality when overexcited and do the unexpected. These are the times you hear owners and parents talk about how their behavior is "just so not the person/dog I know!" That's because in that adrenaline fog, they temporarily lose their brain and forget all that training you so lovingly and painstakingly instilled in them.

THE PARASYMPATHETIC (VAGAL) SYSTEM

This is commonly called your "rest and digest" system. What's less commonly known is that there are two parts to the vagal system:

The Dorsal Vagal Complex (aka Primitive Vagal System) is found in reptiles and amphibians as well as mammals. When it is triggered, you will see what I will refer to as The Vagal Freeze. There are many different manifestations and names for this response but generally the individual is immobilized (can't move.) In some responses, the individual loses consciousness and will not remember what happened while in this state. In other responses, the individual will be fully aware but cannot move at all. Before the advent of Dr. Porges' Polyvagal Theory, these responses elicited by animal restraint equipment were attributed to the release of "endorphins." (Dr. P.L. Toutain in his 1978 paper "L Hypnose Animale" mentions the hypophysis as a source of these endorphins.)

Oxytocin and the other Vagal-associated compounds are released during this process, the benefits of this will be discussed later.

**DORSAL VAGAL/ "VAGAL FREEZE"
RESPONSES and their many names**

Animal magnetism   Hypnosis   Animal hypnosis
Trance   Suspended animation   Altered
consciousness   Emotional shut-down (human)
Clipnose/pinch-induced behavioral
inhibition (Cats, cattle, horse)
Induced immobility (Arkansas Line of Nervous Pointer Dogs)
(stiff body)
Tonic immobility   Catatonic state
"Deer in the headlight"
Fear-evoked freeze/attentive immobility (rodents)
(limp body)
Collapsed immobility   Fainting
Syncope with drop in blood pressure
Playing dead   Thanatosis (feigning death)
Prey response to capture   Apparent death

While the dorsal vagal complex plays a major role in these phenomena, other systems must explain why there are different expressions and triggers. A great discussion of these responses in both people and animals including the neurophysiologic aspects can be found in this article of the Harvard Review of Psychiatry[15] There is definitely more to be discovered by further scientific research.

The Ventral Vagal Complex is found only in mammals. It's associated with the suckling and bonding (social engagement) functions. (Birds have a similar structure but with a different name.)

When the Vagal Response is activated, you see the release of feel-good neurotransmitters and hormones like **oxytocin,**

---

[15] Kozlowska K, Walker P, McLean L, Carrive P. Fear and the Defense Cascade: Clinical Implications and Management. Harv Rev Psychiatry. 2015 Jul-Aug;23(4):263-87.)

serotonin dopamine, etc. I like to say it puts you in the Zen Zone, where you are relaxed, and feel great. In this state you can learn and think creatively and clearly. (And you also digest your food.) This is where teachers need their students to be to get the lessons through effectively and with less effort. This zone is where you need to be if you want to undo trauma/PTSD and heal emotionally. It is also the "Zone of Coherence" and good health. The more time you spend in this zone, the better your body functions. The more you are in this state, the "higher your vagal tone."

The Polyvagal Theory= How these three systems work together
   Dorsal Vagal (Parasympathetic) Complex (in reptiles AND mammals
   Sympathetic System (in all vertebrate species)
   Ventral Vagal (Parasympathetic) Complex
      This is only in mammals

WHAT IS THE POLYVAGAL THEORY?

Dr. Stephen Porges presented the Polyvagal Theory in 1995. He explained how the two vagal systems (hence the name "Polyvagal") plus the parasympathetic system developed and functioned together both evolutionarily and in early development of animals and people. He brought forth the idea that the ANS is more involved in the sense of safety an individual has at any given moment than we give it credit for.

> The Polyvagal Theory gave me insights into why I saw puzzling responses in animals and what I needed to do to correct them. I owe a great deal to Dr. Porges for his help in understanding details of the Polyvagal Theory and research technology. His patient explanations allowed me to explain these better to you and develop many of the ideas I put into this book.

Think of the Sympathetic System as the one controlling the survival systems of getting food, procreating or escaping or fighting danger. It has the gas pedal set at a certain speed in cruise control.

The Vagal System operates when you are safe and allows you to add knowledge (learn) and think creatively. It also puts a brake on the Sympathetic/Adrenaline System. Excitement takes that brake off. So, when your dog gets excited to see you, that brake is removed and the sympathetic system kicks into gear. And if they cross the Threshold into Overexcitement, there's the loss of cortical function (they forget all that training about not jumping on you.)" [16]

THE POLYVAGAL THEORY AND LEARNING

If you want your teaching efforts to be most effective, make sure the animal or human student feels comfortable, safe and not hungry. Just make sure they haven't had such a big meal that they get so deep into the "rest and digesting" that they nod off.

Another fascinating aspect of the Polyvagal Theory is that when an animal is triggered into "vagal freeze," they may or may not still be conscious, but oxytocin is released. These variations

---

[16] PORGES, S. W. (2009). The Polyvagal theory: New insights into adaptive reactions of the autonomic nervous system. Cleveland Clinic Journal of Medicine, 76(Suppl 2), S86–S90.

suggest that multiple mechanisms are involved that will require further research to understand.

I talk a lot about the controversial practice of laying down horses for training. Some have declared it as "inhumane" but in fact the mechanism triggers a calming and bonding effect on previously uncontrollable horses. Because the horse still absorbs what is going on around it while it is down and motionless, this state can also be used for the desensitization process (aka "bomb proofing.")

THE POLYVAGAL THEORY AND THREATS

The three different systems describe the three responses to perceived threats:

Ventral Vagal—try to make friends with the bully
Sympathetic—run from the bully
Dorsal Vagal—emotional shut down, faint or freeze

THE POLYVAGAL THEORY AND HEALING EMOTIONAL TRAUMA

Dr. Porges uses this knowledge with the National Institute of Clinical Application of Behavioral Medicine (www.nicabm.com) to teach therapists how to help trauma patients "help clients calm their bodies, manage their threat responses, and develop the capacity for self-regulation. The clients also learn that these are involuntary responses so they feel less guilt and shame over past events.

Taking a different approach, clinical psychologist Mark Terrell uses hypnosis to heal clients by having them relive a traumatic experience as a dispassionate observer. This way they experience the event without triggering the emotional response and can mentally process everything while in the vagal state.

"To effectively switch from defensive to social engagement strategies, the mammalian nervous system needs to perform two important adaptive tasks: (1) assess risk, and (2) if the environment is perceived as safe, inhibit the more primitive limbic structures that control fight, flight, or freeze behavior."

~Dr. Stephen Porges

THE POLYVAGAL THEORY IN A NUTSHELL

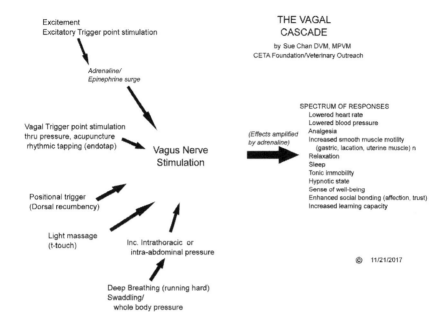

THE VAGAL
CASCADE

by Sue Chan DVM, MPVM
CETA Foundation/Veterinary Outreach

Excitement
Excitatory Trigger point stimulation

Adrenaline/
Epinephrine surge

Vagal Trigger point stimulation
thru pressure, acupuncture
rhythmic tapping (endotap)

Vagus Nerve
Stimulation

(Effects amplified
by adrenaline)

SPECTRUM OF RESPONSES
Lowered heart rate
Lowered blood pressure
Analgesia
Increased smooth muscle motility
    (gastric, lacation, uterine muscle) n
Relaxation
Sleep
Tonic immobility
Hypnotic state
Sense of well-being
Enhanced social bonding (affection, trust)
Increased learning capacity

Positional trigger
(Dorsal recumbency)

Light massage
(t-touch)

Inc. Intrathoracic or
intra-abdominal pressure

© 11/21/2017

Deep Breathing (running hard)
Swaddling/
    whole body pressure

WHAT DOES THE POLYVAGAL THEORY HAVE TO DO WITH WHISPERERS?

There are multiple ways the Polyvagal Theory explains how Whispering techniques are so effective:

1) To be in this Zen Zone, you need to feel safe, secure and stress-free. Whispering is so effective because it strives to keep a great, safe relationship built on Trust between the teacher and student.

Whisperers intuitively know to operate where the students stay calm and collected. Whisperers also know that they must keep their own emotions in check as well. This keeps everyone in the Zen State where learning and bonding can best occur. They avoid crossing the threshold for excitement, fear or anger, which impedes bonding and learning. If they inadvertently do cross that threshold, they work hard to calm things down (de-escalate). There is more discussion about this in the section on Threshold.

2) The Whisperers' Tricks all work by triggering and maintaining the Vagal response in their students and keeping them in the Vagal State.

> The methods of triggering the ventral vagal response include
>> Neurolinguistics/talking and interacting in a certain way
>> Sensory input from the environment
>> Activating trigger points (receptors) on the body (skin and internally)
>>> Pinch-induced behavioral inhibition (PIBI)
>>> Postures to trigger pressure receptors (baroreceptors)
>>> Stimulation of points associated with acupuncture meridians
>>> Squeezing the body
>> Working with "energy" on the metaphysical level through use of physical or non-physical tools.
>
> (The specifics are described in the Whisperers' Tricks chapter.

3) The dorsal vagal mechanisms can be triggered into putting an animal or person into an altered mental and/or physical state where they cannot move (are immobilized) without the need for drugs.

> There is a very practical side to understanding how to trigger and utilize this calming (ventral vagal) or altered state (dorsal vagal) to:

1) allow closer contact for bonding and trust-building exercises.
2) allow closer contact for desensitization exercises.
3) allow safer handling for grooming, examination, medical treatments and other needs.

These are especially helpful for working with large animals like livestock and horses and even big dogs where someone can get badly hurt when they don't want to cooperate.

The Polyvagal Theory describes the release of all kinds of hormones that affect emotional and physiological states. It's likely that oxytocin and other compounds released while in this tranquilized dorsal vagal state explain why when animals and people come out of it, (especially with electroshock therapy and laying down horses), they are calmer, more social and less distressed than when they entered it.

Here are some examples of techniques used to calm: Weighted blankets and Dr. Temple Grandin's "squeeze machine" are used to calm children with autism. Pediatrician Robert Hamilton has a unique baby-calming hold (the "Hamilton Hold") that he demonstrates in videos. Horses are restrained with equipment ("twitches") and postures that appear barbaric but trigger the Vagal response. These allow handlers and veterinarians to actually do medical procedures and other work on an otherwise uncooperative huge animal

Animal hypnosis is a class of techniques that utilizes the same mechanisms in the primitive Vagal response: Sharks and rabbits flipped on their backs go into a trance. A cat picked up by the scruff curls up and stops moving, like a kitten picked up by its mother (aka Dr. Buffington's Clipnosis). Horses laid on their sides can go into a trance/sleep state. Those are all reflexes that can be used to aid the trust building process as well as get a procedure accomplished safely. (Well, maybe not with sharks...)

The interplay of these three systems explains the behavioral responses and learning that mysteriously occur. The variation of mental states during this response points to even more complex interactions of the body systems.

IMPORTANT POINT: Some trainers claim that horses go into a trance state because they think they are dying and that it's horrible to do this to a horse. However, Adrenaline surges (sympathetic system) can kick the body into the Dorsal Vagal Response as with Paul Williamson's TAP technique and Clipnose in cattle. This is why overly excited horses will go into a trance faster with his technique than will calm horses. It is in this state that you can make fundamental changes in their brain wiring, like Robert Redford does in the movie "*The Horse Whisperer.*"

FOR THE SCIENCE NERDS: Because the responses are so varied and sometimes unpredictable, there must be multiple factors or mechanisms outside of the Vagal system involved in Whisperers' Tricks. Here are some salient points that bring up interesting questions:

1) People who are triggered by extreme emotional states from physical or sexual assault or in combat situations report a) fainting and not remembering anything or b) staying fully aware but unable to move. (Those who think this was evidence of cowardice and feel shame need to be made aware that this was an involuntary physiological response and nothing to be embarrassed about.) What factors and mechanisms created these different responses?

2) Cats who are clipped on the back of the neck ("clipnosis") respond by A) stiffening up and falling over OR B) purring, kneading ("making biscuits") and having a facial expression of a person high on marijuana. What are the factors that create these different reactions?

3) Horses laid down or are triggered by Paul Williamson's TAP respond by lying down sometimes with their eyes open or appearing to be asleep with their eyes closed. They will stay in that state for a while even after restraints are removed. We can't ask them if they are aware of what's going on around them, but you can desensitize ("bombproof") them by creating commotion around them while they are lying still on the ground. Horses that are fractious before they are laid down are easy to handle after they get up, pointing

to physiological changes. How "conscious" are they when their eyes are open? Are they in different mental states when their eyes are open or when they are shut? What factors contribute to these different responses?

4) Horses can be taught to lie on their sides to self-soothe (https://tomdorrance.com/memories-of-stick-by-julie-mattox/) Natural horsemanship trainers teach horses to lay down as part of a trust building exercise. How different are the physiological responses from those who are brought down with ropes or the TAP?

5) Cattle and horses who are agitated and have a resulting adrenaline surge go into a trance and down on their side (lateral recumbency/lateral decubitus) faster with the TAP and skin clips (this state makes it easier to perform medical procedures on them). Those that are tame or not easily upset will not go into this trance easily.

6) Clipnose, the Stabilizer and other devices that are used to calm and sedate work better when applied while the animal is calm and BEFORE the animal gets agitated. This points to a different set of mechanisms than #5. Both these products have fans and detractors who declare they don't work. I believe this is because there are subtle tricks that need to be known to use them well. So let's find out what those tips are!

As a veterinarian and ranch owner who has to work with uncooperative animals that greatly outweigh me, I become very excited to learn about techniques to get them to hold still without resorting to drugs that have lots of risks and logistical issues. I was stunned to find out that the French discussed "Clipnose" and the British knew about "foal flop response" for decades before they were ever mentioned in American veterinary circles. Even now, the only English language articles I can find on these phenomena were in research done fairly recently.

I sincerely hope more research can be done to understand how these techniques work. These are sedation techniques that do not require a licensed veterinarian to administer nor the use of drugs, which can have unpredictable, sometimes dangerous effects.

As things stand now, the success rates vary because we don't know enough details on how to execute them effectively. (Just look at the reviews on the cat clip product that's on the market and the remark about the horse twitch in the Whisperers' Tricks section.) So many animal owners rely on costly veterinary visits to get sedative drugs or procedures they could do at home if their animals cooperated if these techniques were better understood and taught. Even professional animal handlers would benefit from this knowledge.

REFLEXES

" Reflex" is a term commonly used to describe something your body automatically does without you thinking triggered by something you experience (hear, see, feel, smell).

Technically speaking, "reflex" refers to a reaction that travels through the spinal cord but doesn't involve any part of the brain. In strict terms, reflex refers to stimuli transmitted from the receptor to the spinal cord or brainstem that causes a muscle or other body reaction.

It turns out that most of us are using this word incorrectly and applying it to responses that require nerve transmissions through the lower limbic system, the Subcortical parts of the brain, which doesn't require conscious thinking. I decided it would be good to clarify what the word is supposed to mean.

So many people understand and use "Reflex" to refer to any automatic subconscious response that we won't bother arguing about it. However, it is important to know that there is indeed a difference in the mechanism if you need to troubleshoot a problem.

DIFFERENT CLASSES OF REFLEXES

Somatic reflexes are simple ones that cause a muscle to contract. Examples of these are the blink reflex, the knee jerk reflex, and the pupil constriction to bright lights.

Intrinsic reflex is when a muscle is stimulated to contract in response to its own stretching

Primitive reflexes are ones that people and animals are born with

Examples of primitive reflexes:

Mammals—suckling

Moro response—a baby throws its arms and legs out when it feels like it's falling

Palmar Grab Reflex—a baby closes its fingers around an object put in its hand

Foal Flop Reflex—a newborn falls asleep when squeezed around the chest. It's also seen in calves, alpacas. This phenomenon is used for treatment of "dummy foal syndrome" and similar conditions in calves and alpacas

Piglet sleep reflex—piglets also fall asleep in response to chest compression but don't always stay asleep

Cats, rats and other species curling up when "scruffed"

Postural reactions are reflexes that automatically maintain an animal in an upright position by slight changes in muscle tension in the body and supporting limbs. Postural reactions maintain the animal's center of gravity between or over the base of support (legs).

Righting reactions are reflexes that support, adjust, and readjust the position and alignment of an animal's head, body, and limbs. After movement or an impact from an outside stimulus, righting reflexes realign the head vertically, and align the vertebrae to create a straight line from the head through the end of the spine.

Equilibrium (balance) reactions are reflexes that support static (standing) equilibrium and those that support dynamic (moving) equilibrium.

Protective reactions are reflexes that enable an animal to maintain its balance against outside pressures. Jumping, ducking the head, withdrawing limbs, startle reflex, kicking, rearing, postural fixation reflex (bracing) and hopping, are spontaneous reflexes that engage to prevent loss of balance.

Escape reactions are reflexes in response to stimuli that causes pain, discomfort or fear of pain or discomfort and causes an animal to move away from dangerous stimuli such as when a horse gallops away from a perceived threat.

Some of these primitive reflexes normally disappear with age. This phasing out of the reflex is sometimes associated with a process called "integration", whereby the primitive reflex acts as a stepping stone in neurological development and becomes part of a more complex response that has a conscious thinking, voluntary component.

In animals, the phasing out process will vary between individuals. This is why some adult cats will curl up when "scruffed" and others won't. (more in Whisperers' Tricks chapter)

RETAINED PRIMITIVE REFLEX—When a child fails to integrate and develop properly, it's said to have "retained primitive reflexes."

Retained primitive reflexes can be found in children diagnosed with autism, developmental delays, and sensory processing disorder. They are also found in children who have experienced trauma. Retained primitive reflexes contribute to their aberrant behaviors and difficulties negotiating life. Many of these retained reflexes are associated with the Sympathetic/Adrenaline and physiological "survival" responses, leads to the child being in a constant state of physiological stress, leading to the emotional stress for caretakers. Anyone who interacts with children, like parents, teachers, pediatricians, and therapists should therefore be aware of this phenomenon.

In animals, there is the "dummy foal syndrome" whereby a newborn has difficulty standing and doesn't nurse well because it doesn't seek out the mother and lacks the normal suckling response. A similar condition is seen in calves and alpaca crias (babies). While intensive nursing care until they hopefully "grow out of it" is generally the standard treatment, thoracic compression (a bear hug or the Madigan Foal Squeeze) will snap these babies out of it. After falling asleep with the squeeze, a release of the pressure after about 10 minutes will allow many of them to wake up with normal function. This technique is discussed more in the chapter called "Whisperers' Tricks."

REFLEX INTEGRATION THERAPY—I don't think thoracic compression has been tried in children with autism and sensory processing disorder. However, many of the problems associated with the diagnoses are said to dramatically improve with Reflex Integration Therapy and Primitive Reflex Exercises. These involve triggering the reflex then manipulating the body into the voluntary action that the primitive reflex should develop into, which help the body and brain learn how to adapt their response to the stimulus rather than being "stuck" in the reflexive response. These exercises can be incorporated into play activities to make them fun. It's reported that coordination, whole brain learning, social interactions and emotional stability through stress relief greatly improve with these interventions. The positive interactions also help the child overcome the emotional trauma caused by the difficult social interactions caused by their conditions. Books, websites, occupational therapists and other professionals are available to help with this information.

INSTINCTS VS REFLEX

Instincts are complex behaviors that show up even when they are not taught. A classic example is a bird building a nest or a hen protecting her chicks, or a dog chasing and killing cats. Instincts can be bred into an individual so their natural level of aptitude excels what can easily be taught. For example, a baby border collie will show herding behavior while you are never going to teach a poodle to be a good herder of anything.

There are reflexes involved in this production of instinctive behavior, so some of the strategies for modifying instinctive behavior are similar to modifying reflexive behavior. Just recognize that instincts are more complex than simple reflexes.

The Threshold Concept explains why individuals will react despite training efforts when they get excited. Therefore, it is helpful to know other techniques to manipulate that threshold to a less reactive level, thereby keeping the individual from any over-excitement that will override training efforts. Always remember that reflex and instincts will always be part of the genetic wiring. Thus, it is important to make sure you keep that individual in an environment where someone can supervise at all times and have a handle on their excitement level.

TRIGGERED EMOTIONAL RESPONSES

This isn't technically a reflex but I wanted to mention it here because it represents an automatic dramatic emotional response that an individual has developed to a situation or even words being said. These can cause great upsets in the physical body as well as problems with social interactions. You see this on social media exchanges all the time. Because anger, fear or any negative emotion is not a good thing for clear thinking or stress-free living, or even getting along with others, it behooves us to sort out why we have these reactions. Once we identify the root cause, we can consciously modify our responses or help others modify theirs to ones that are better for health and social interactions.

THE HEART

The influences of the heart on behavior—also referred to as Cardiac or Heart Intelligence—are a newer topic of discussion in academia.

"The heart's electromagnetic impulses exert influences on others and convey information by their rhythmic patterns. The heart influences the brain and Autonomic Nervous System as well as the other way around. The power of the heart impulses is 10 times the strength of the Brain." Heartmath Institute (www.heartmath.org)

A lesser-known fact is that cells in the heart also produce hormones like Oxytocin and the catecholamines norepinephrine, epinephrine and dopamine.

The Heartmath Institute researches the heart/cardiac influences and the concept of Coherence for social, emotional and physiological well-being. Citations for these and many more fascinating concepts can be found in Science of the Heart which is available on the Heartmath Institute website www.heartmath.org. I will summarize some of their findings and incorporate their concepts with information on the other physiologic systems:

HRV and Vagal Tone: These are terms that are tossed about in articles like everyone should know what they mean. I suspect a lot of people pretend to know. Well, I'm not afraid to admit I couldn't figure it out so I asked Dr. Stephen Porges help me with this section. Here's how he helped me understand it:

Vagal Tone refers to how active your parasympathetic/vagal system is at this point in time. The higher your vagal tone, the more relaxed, calm and clear thinking you are. Your body is also affected by this level (rest and digest mode)

Heart rate variability (HRV) is the beat-to-beat variation in heart rate. In other words, the heart speeds up and slows down over time. Interestingly, the more it speeds up and slows down (higher HRV) the more resilient to stress you are. Young people have a higher HRV than older people. HRV is affected by RSA. You can now get apps for your cell phones and wrist watches that measure your HRV.

HRV = variation between beat to beat intervals

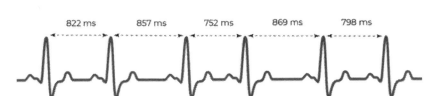

Heart Rate = beats per minute (on average)

Respiratory sinus arrhythmia (RSA) is an important component of HRV. Oscillation is the repetitive variation, typically in time, of some measure about a central value or between two or more different states. RSA is operationally defined as the oscillations in heart rate that occur at the rhythm of spontaneous breathing (the breathing you do when you're not thinking about it.)

When you exhale, your heart rate slows down because the vagus efference (impulses from the vagus nerve) to the heart's pacemaker increases. When you inhale, the heart speeds up because the vagus traffic decreases. The amplitude (magnitude/size of the differences between the variable's extreme values) of these oscillations is a valid indicator of cardiac **Vagal tone**.

In short, a high HRV is tied to a high RSA which is tied to a high Vagal tone.

More translation: In general, when you are calm, you have a greater Vagal tone. When you are "highly mobilized" (excited, mad or scared) the Vagal tone goes down, which allows the Sympathetic/Adrenaline system to kick in.

The higher your Vagal tone, the deeper you are into the Zen Zone (as my kids would say, "You're really chill.")

When you're really chill and have a high Vagal tone (i.e., high amplitude RSA), a little stress will change that measurement but your Vagal tone will return to "normal" after the stress goes away. In other words, you are more resilient.

If you are Resilient, your mind and body are less likely to break down.

Another term related to High Vagal Tone is **Coherence.**

Coherence The researchers at Heartmath Institute call this resiliency "having higher coherence."

Then there is the concept of coherence and heart rate patterns. The heart rate patterns also indicate what state you are in— Adrenaline vs. Zen. Stressed/excited vs. laid back and relaxed.

If you are feeling good, the heart beats will show a regular, even pattern, aka a "coherent" pattern. If you are feeling angry, scared, sad, or other negative emotions, the heart beats will have an erratic "incoherent" pattern

You can consciously alter your coherence and vagal tone. When you think good things, like how grateful you are, how beautiful the sunset looks, or how much you love someone/something, your heart rate variability goes up and so does your Vagal tone. Meditation, mindfulness exercises, and breathing exercises are all techniques that can be learned. Reliving memories that make you scared or angry lowers your Vagal tone, HRV and coherence. [17]

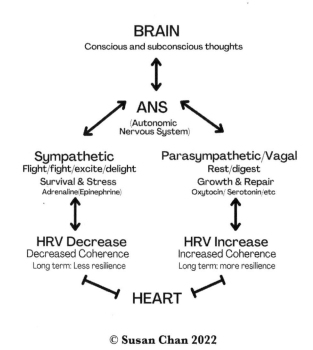

© **Susan Chan 2022**

TRANSMISSION OF HEART ELECTROMAGNETIC IMPULSES BETWEEN INDIVIDUALS

Light bulb alert! It's been shown in an experiment by Dr. McCarty that when you send these good vibes to someone, their heart rate variability patterns come in alignment with yours (entrainment) through electromagnetic communication. I found this so fascinating—your thoughts are reflected in your heart's electromagnetic patterns which in turn can have a physical effect on

---

[17] Edwards, Stephen. (2015). HeartMath - A positive psychology paradigm for promoting psychophysiological and global coherence (final revised jpa submission.

someone else's body! Interestingly, animal communicators instruct their students to "send love" to open communications with the animal they want to read. So don't think this is silly. Your thinking is part of your tool box in working with people and animals. And this is how Whisperers' work their magic.

"SENDING LOVE"

In one study, a boy entered a room where his dog was waiting for him. Without touching or speaking to the dog, he imagined how much he loved the dog and sent her those thoughts mentally. Not only did his heart rhythms become more "coherent," the dog's heart rhythms did, too! This phenomenon is called "entrainment."

In another experiment, a woman did the Heart Lock-in exercise with her horse. The same effect occurred in this pair as well.

https://www.heartmath.org/research/science-of-the-heart/energetic-communication/

Horses have big hearts physically (and sometimes in a different way, too.) Their electromagnetic impulses therefore have a fairly strong influence. When a calm horse with a high heart rate variability stands next to a person who is upset or depressed, the HRV of the person can come into alignment with that of the horse. This is probably why so many horse owners talk about going into the barn to hang out with their horses after a bad day at work and feeling so much better. This is also why horses are an effective tool for therapy work.

Con Su Permiso is an exercise by which people can connect emotionally with horses and experience the calming effect:

"CON SU PERMISO" (WITH YOUR PERMISSION)

One by one, participants entered the experimental arena in which their selected horse was located and were reminded to breathe more deeply and slowly than usual; slow breathing is correlated with improved cognition (Chandler et al., 2013). They slowly approached the horse (held by a handler on a loose lead line) in the presence of the facilitator, holding their hand out toward the horse's nose, palm down, said "Hello," and returned to the edge of the turn-out. Having rubbed their palms together to heighten sensation, they quietly approached the horse with palms open, under guidance from the facilitator. They moved closer when an invitation from the horse, such as looking or moving toward them, was perceived. Holding their palms 3 to 5 inches away from the horse's body, they scanned the shape of the horse's entire body with their palms, noting any sensations in their hands. Once the exercise was complete, they thanked the horse and returned to the starting point." Human heart and respiration rates as well as HRV (SDRR) increased significantly during interactions with horses and humans. Human self-esteem increased during interactions with horses and humans. During exit interviews participants used more positive and fewer negative gestures ($p < 0.05$) describing the equine experience compared to control; words and gestures were more consistent with each other. These findings mostly support our hypothesis and suggest that engaging with horses benefits humans, indicating an enlivened state without stress"

~Baldwin, Ann L.; Rector, Barbara K.; and Alden, Ann C. (2018) "Effects of a Form of Equine-Facilitated Learning on Heart Rate Variability, Immune Function, and Self-Esteem in Older Adults, "People and Animals: The International Journal of Research and Practice: Vol. 1: Iss. 1, Article 5.

"The heart is the bridge to the spirit world, the bridge to the soul."
~Suzanne Giesemann, Messenger of Hope

GETTING DEEPER INTO THE "WOO"

The Light and Love communities refer to the Heart Chakra or the "Heart Brain" that thinks in terms of emotions rather than words. Through this portal one can connect to Higher Wisdom or Realms, depending on which community's language you're using. Don't laugh! Despite what many think and say about this kind of talk, we already covered how Heartmath Institute has done a lot of research on the way the heart sends information and commands to the brain and the rest of the body as well as receiving information. In addition, vibrational frequency on an energetic level is a real phenomenon explained by quantum physics. This is discussed more in the chapter on Metaphysical Stuff.

BODY CHEMISTRY

NUTRITION, HORMONES AND OTHER
FACTORS THAT IMPACT BODY BALANCE

This is an expansion of the section of "Student factors" that touched upon physiology.

NUTRITION

What goes into the mouth provides the building blocks for the body and energy to run the body. How these ingredients are processed within the body varies between individuals—it might be beneficial OR it might cause a reaction that isn't all that positive.

What might be "healthy" for one might cause an allergic reaction in another. Allergic reactions affect how an individual feels and therefore how the individual will be interacting with you ("moodiness"). If the body doesn't produce certain enzymes or produces defective enzymes, an overload of certain compounds in your body can cause disease conditions and illness. Illness affects behavior. This is something that needs to be kept in mind in the event you cannot deal with a behavior problem strictly with training.

HORMONES

(THE ENDOCRINE SYSTEM)

Hormones are compounds that the body produces to cause other cells in the body to do a wide variety of things. They affect perception (thinking processes), energy and behavior. This topic is very complex but I will just give you some key words so you can be aware and look deeper if you want.

We need to recognize that every hormone has profound effects on multiple systems of the body and can affect behavior, the way organs process materials and function or are able to recover from injuries. The use of hormones as supplements should not be taken lightly.

COMMONLY DISCUSSED HORMONES (AND DRUGS)
THAT AFFECT BEHAVIOR:

You'll hear these names in the news or advertisements.
You can easily look into their actions and triggers for their
release which is way beyond the scope of this book.

Oxytocin   Dopamine   Insulin
Serotonin   Melatonin   Thyroid hormone
Human Growth Hormone
Epinephrine/adrenaline/Norepinephrine
Cortisol/corticosteroids/dexamethasone/prednisone
Estrogen/Progesterone/Testosterone

The Autonomic Nervous System (Sympathetic and parasympathetic (aka Vagal) systems) as discussed earlier in this chapter is just one component in mechanisms affecting hormone levels and their effects.

One concept that is overlooked is that the body sometimes can't keep up with the demands of life. For example, people who endure chronic stress can actually deplete their cortisol supplies. Cortisol helps the body deal with stress. When you face long-term stress, cortisol stocks run out and your cortisol levels will drop so you'll suffer more illness and disease conditions.

Sex hormones (Estrogen, progesterone, testosterone/androgens) can have a profound effect on aggression and moods.) "Roid Rage" and PMS are very real and can dramatically change the personality of both people and animals. I have seen female dogs and horses act very differently when in heat, equivalent to PMS (premenstrual syndrome). I have several rams that run with the ewes year-round. I use great caution when entering the sheep pens and even more when the ewes are in heat and the rams' hormone levels are higher. These same rams were sweethearts as youngsters but now I must lock them out of pens where I want to work or risk bodily harm.

The severity of this effect will vary from individual to individual. I have found that there can be a genetic component to the impact of hormones: I had two miniature stallions from the same mother and father. Both turned into raging maniacs during breeding season. I castrated one who then was so good he gave pony rides at birthday parties. Stallions from a different mare remain well-behaved and controllable even in the presence of mares in heat. It should be noted that facing a male in "'Roid Rage" is never to be taken lightly and is one of the few situations that have me fight the emotion of

Dusty post-castration with Adam

FEAR. There is something terrifying about facing that kind of intense rage.

It can be hard to tell what portion of aggression is due to hormonal levels and what relatively permanent changes hormones made on the brain if the male is castrated after sexual maturity.

> I had a Jacobs ram, Joey, that was a wonderful pet until he matured. After he "got balls," anyone who entered the pasture had to be ready to run even when the breeding season was over. And even several years after castration, he was a force to contend with. The males that were castrated before a year were much nicer pets throughout their lives.
>
> The aggressiveness of intact males varies with the breeds. My Katahdin ram will come at me during breeding season but back off if I hit him with a stick (I still run.) My Katahdin/Jacob cross ram would not stop until I got out of his pasture. A friend told me to flip attacking rams on their backs when they run at you. Five flips and this one still came for more. I don't know what effect castration would have had on him because I got rid of him before the next breeding season.

There are herbal preparations that may help alleviate some of the problems caused by overreaction to sex hormones. Horse supply catalogs can give you an idea of what ingredients seem to work. For example, I used "Mare Magic" made of raspberry leaves which seemed to calm down the raging stallion I mentioned above. Castration may help reduce aggression if it's strictly a hormonal problem. Be aware that aggression has a strong component from learned behavior, so castration may play just a small role in reducing problems related to aggression.

NEUROTRANSMITTERS

Neurotransmitters are a class of hormones that make your nerves function. You need enough of these in your body to function properly. Nutrition plays a part in neurotransmitter levels, but so does how the individual's body is processing the nutrients to make these neurotransmitters.

Another element is depletion of these neurotransmitters when the body uses them faster than they can be made. In people, this can be caused by use of alcohol, recreational drugs, nicotine and prescription medications. It also can be caused by inadequate amino acids in the diet (or blocked absorption in the gut) which are needed to make neurotransmitter, Neurotransmitter depletion can manifest in people as migraine headaches, depression, panic disorder, anxiety. obesity, irritable bowel disease, fibromyalgia, eating disorders, Parkinson's disease, and premenstrual syndrome.

NEUROTRANSMITTER HORMONES:

Acetylcholine	Serotonin	Histamine	Nitric oxide
(N Glycine	Glutamate	Aspartate	Dopamine
Gamma-aminobutyric acid (GABA)		Endorphins (opiate-like peptides)	
Noradrenaline (Norepinephrine)		Adrenaline (Epinephrine)	

GLUCOSE

Glucose (aka blood sugar) provides energy for activity and thinking and thus behavior. What you eat, how much you eat and how fast you burn it off all play a role in the levels of blood sugar available for functioning. Eating too much can initially cause hyperactivity but the body's response to that high sugar level is to crank out insulin, which will cause the blood sugar to plummet.

Diabetes mellitus is a complex condition that prevents glucose in your bloodstream from entering the cells where they need to work. This is either because your body cannot produce insulin due to pancreas damage (Type 1 Diabetes) or your body does not respond to the insulin it can produce due to insulin receptor damage (Type 2 Diabetes, insulin-resistance.) This leads to too much sugar in your bloodstream which can lead to bladder infection, blindness, circulation problems and gangrene and a host of other damage. Insulin is also overproduced in insulin resistant individuals.

Food additives and chemicals in the environment can also have an impact on how blood sugar is handled. Some people are more sensitive to these compounds than others.

I will pause here for a PSA (public service announcement): Dr. Benjamin Bikman has discovered how insulin has an effect on every cell of the body and not just with glucose regulation. He presents the argument the overproduction of insulin in response to insulin resistance causes chronic inflammation and is the untreated root of many diseases like cancer, hypertension, weight gain, fatty liver, dementia, low testosterone, menstrual irregularities and infertility, and more. This means that high blood sugar is not the cause of all these other diseases but is a sign of a deeper layer that needs to be understood. His book and presentations on the internet are well worth watching.[24] Why is this mentioned in a book about behavioral intervention? Because your health and well-being impacts behavior, because these conditions affect us either in our own bodies or in someone we care about, and I would venture to say many physicians will not bring these connections up in the exam room.

---

[18] Bikman, B. (2020). Why We Get Sick: The Hidden Epidemic at the Root of Most Chronic Disease - and How to Fight It. Blackstone Publishing

My own reaction to sugar is so profound that I will fall asleep after eating an apple. I learned not to snack on one during a drive longer than 15 minutes. My kids knew this, so when they were tired of working on the ranch but I had energy to spare, they would say, "Here Mom, have an apple!"

HYDRATION

The amount of water in your body is of course dependent on what you take in, what you sweat out and what you produce in urine. Research has shown that hydration has a profound effect on learning and thinking as well. Thus, teachers should make sure their students get a long drink after recess before they sit down for class and lectures, especially on hot days. Animal owners should make sure clean water is always available and palatable. Some animals won't drink dirty water or water that's hot from sitting in the sun.

IN SUMMARY

I hope that I've adequately explained behavioral concepts and provided basic biology that can help you better understand why animals and people behave and respond the way they do. I have found that having a little more knowledge allows you to ask good questions and get better answers. You can ask real people in person or google it on the internet. It's amazing what you can find!

Be sure to read or watch videos of other trainers and therapists and see how they explain things, too. You will likely discover things on your own if you keep your eyes, mind and heart open.

PART V

THE METAPHYSICAL STUFF

THE METAPHYSICAL STUFF

A QUICK INTRODUCTION

I have a confession to make: I learned how to use Christian Science healing techniques and Qigong when I became frustrated that my knowledge from vet school failed to make animals well. As crazy as it sounds, the stuff works! What's even crazier is how you have to throw away all you learned about "the real world" and think in terms that are very foreign and honestly weird. But it works! I have learned that these concepts can resolve behavioral problems as well, which is what Whispering is all about. Hence, I needed to include this in my book for you.

I didn't know what Metaphysics was until recently. As I researched, I realized the broad application of Metaphysics:

- Metaphysics explains every other healing modality that mainstream medicine shuns.

- Metaphysics is how the Shaolin Temple martial artists perform amazing feats.

- Metaphysics is an integral aspect of every religious tradition and spiritual practice.

I am going out on a limb to present this information for these reasons:

- To open minds to the usefulness of "alternative" methods through scientific explanation of Metaphysical Law

- To give practitioners of "alternative" healing modalities higher success rates through understanding and application of Metaphysical Law

- To reduce the conflicts and fear-mongering between believers of different religious traditions through the understanding of their common link in Metaphysical Law

- To have an excuse to research and understand Metaphysical Law.

I'm introducing this topic a bit lightheartedly so that you won't take me as an evangelist wanting to convert anyone or presenting myself as an expert on this topic. I merely want to offer, as Sergeant Joe Friday would have said, "Just the facts, ma'am." This section is rather lengthy because there isn't much common knowledge about metaphysical principles. I had to pull what I've learned from many different sources to build an introduction and foundation for understanding.

If I haven't lost you, please enter a different realm of understanding with me with deeper discussion!

WHY TALK ABOUT METAPHYSICAL LAW?

Metaphysical Law operates in religious traditions, spirituality and traditional healing arts. The nuts and bolts of metaphysics bring real results for those who practice these things, which is why belief in them persists, sometimes in the face of persecution. Understanding Metaphysical Law gives you an ability to use these practices in more powerful ways to help yourself and others.

I have tried many different "alternative modalities" and seen amazing things happen with my own eyes. It concerns me how the scientific and medical communities demean techniques that are really helping people and animals. Practitioners and believers in these practices are stigmatized by the media and academic community. Not wanting to become a target of regulatory action, I've kept quiet about techniques I use. Now that I do not rely on my veterinary license to survive, I can be more open about non-standard protocols that work in my hands. I recently realized that Metaphysical Law explains why they work, and SCIENCE now has given me ways of explaining it, too. If that intrigues you, keep reading!

Different circles use different words for the same concepts. To help you connect the dots, I will use words with similar meanings separated by slash marks. This may be obnoxious, but it's a way to communicate concepts more efficiently. For atheists who wince at the word "God," just substitute the word "Good" anywhere you see "God." They are synonymous.

WHAT IS METAPHYSICS?

If you look up the term "Metaphysics", you will find wordy phrases and mind-numbing definitions. Merriam Webster's simple definition of Metaphysics is the easiest to explain: "a study of what is outside objective experience."

"Outside objective study" looks at things you can't detect with your 5 senses—sight, hearing, taste, touch and smell—and therefore refers to "subjective study." By default, "subjective study" refers to topics that are considered outside modern mainstream science.

But SCIENCE has come to the rescue! Another way to explain it is that everything we observe with our 5 senses (i.e., Objective study) can be described with the natural laws pertaining to matter—Laws of Thermodynamics, Gravity, Motion, Electricity, Pressure, Chemistry's Periodic Table, etc.

Subjective study is covered by Quantum Physics. Quantum Physics explains the Natural Metaphysical Laws pertaining to energy and physical matter. This is the study of particles smaller than atoms (subatomic particles) PLUS the properties of energy (vibrational frequency.) Atoms are 99% Energy and only 1% physical matter. These are the principles that describe phenomena which are not detectable and measurable by our 5 senses, and are the basis for taking "Deep Woo-woo" seriously. The Metaphysical Laws and Principles were described as far back as ancient Egypt by Hermes Trismegistus (described in detail in The Kybalion). They are utilized in what are considered Mystical aspects of every religious tradition, even Christianity.

Here is the basic take home message: Inanimate objects and living cells are made of energy. Thoughts and emotions generate energy in the form of electromagnetic waves. These electromagnetic waves affect the behavior of physical matter (at the level of subatomic particles) because physical matter also holds energy and responds to energy. Conversely, the energy held in inanimate objects affects living cells as well.

> *"Those who talk about life force are called victims of the "vitalist fallacy"*
>
> ~Robert Gilbert

Incredibly, your thoughts can have a real effect on the thoughts of others, on physical matter, on how your body functions and the outcomes of situations. (This is referred to as alchemy, transmutation, chemicalization, "Magic" without the rituals,) You can create with your thoughts! Some describe this as human beings carrying the potential power of the Creator God as part of their genetic heritage (actually co-creators, not gods in their own right). But I'm getting ahead of myself...

Metaphysics is the basis for religious beliefs, Mystery School teachings, of secret societies (Rosicrucian, Freemasonry, Theosophical Society, etc.), "magic", esoteric knowledge, and everything that's referred to (sometimes disdainfully) as New Age.

Metaphysical principles explain psychic phenomenon, traditional healing modalities, extrasensory perception (ESP), telepathic communication, remote viewing, intuition, animal communication, chakras, souls, life-after-death, near-death experiences, (NDE) consciousness, astrology, Tarot, crystal therapy, Reiki, Yoga and more.

Those who understand Metaphysical Law can recognize and appreciate the power behind these practices.

> *"Science and Religion are expressions of the same knowledge. To paraphrase Arthur C. Clarke: Any science sufficiently advanced is indistinguishable from magic."*
>
> ~Conny Mendez, "The Mystical Number 7"

"EVERYTHING IS ENERGY"

Metaphysics works on the level of vibrational Energy (also called Qi, Chi, and Prana) at the non-physical level which is explained by quantum physics. Dr. Robert Gilbert is a former U.S. Marine Corps Instructor in Nuclear-Biological-Chemical Warfare Survival. Since leaving the service in 1985, he has conducted independent research into the Geometric basis of modern science. He is Director of the Vesica Institute and offers lectures and courses on Ancient and Modern Holistic Sciences, Spiritual Sciences and Sacred Geometry. He explains how the non-physical dimension connects to the physical. Following is a distillation of his salient points from "Key Methods to Activate and Balance Egyptian BioGeometry" posted by FMBRTV Nov 10,2019:

Biogeometry is the study of the interface of energy and matter. Life energy animates physical matter and is measured in Scalar Waves on the Vibrational Spectrum. Description of this Vibrational Energy as based on the discoveries of the French School of Radioethesia. Without this life energy, a body is just a lump of tissue. This Vital Life Force/Vibrational Energy is responsible for sexual vitality, procreation, connecting the energy in the meridians of the body, and linking emotional and mental states to physiology. " Life force is referred to as Prana in India, Chi or Qi in China, Ki in Japan, and Etheric in Greece.

This is the vital life force and higher consciousness that operates on a higher level (different dimension) than the physical (3-dimensional) plane. In contrast, the Electro-Magnetic Spectrum is directly related to the physical plane.

When scalar waves enter and animate physical matter, they disintegrate into Hertzian waves in the electromagnetic spectrum of light, radio waves, microwaves, infrared (heat), UV, X-Rays and gamma rays.

The Universal Vibrational Spectrum has 12 Bands with power at the Physical, Energetic, Emotional / Mental, and Spiritual levels."

Different levels of this spectrum affect spiritual, mental, emotional/astral, vitality/physical.

Classical medical traditions (Traditional Chinese Medicine, Ayurveda, Tibetan Medicine, Shamanism, etc.) consider this vital life force the causative element for health and well-being on the physical level. Understanding this Life Energy is the key to all forms of traditional healing, and which is often referred to today as "Vibrational Medicine."

Entrainment with sights and sounds of specific frequencies can shift a person to different levels of vibrational energy. Examples of these practices are therapy with tuning forks, singing a certain tone (vocal toning), crystals, gongs, Tibetan singing bowls.

Additionally, a person can emit vibrations that entrain others. (This is how a calm Whisperer can calm an agitated person or animal!)

The more spiritual activity one does (blessings, prayers, and meditation) the stronger this vibration emanates from their energy fields.

Spiritual activity brings subconscious blockages into awareness on a spiritual level. Spiritual activity also brings energy from higher dimensional levels into the physical body.

Thoughts have energy and can change the functioning of your body.

The right brain locks into the intuitive while the left brain locks ("grounds") thoughts into physical reality (the logical realm).

Thoughts can have an impact on others. It can even change the ice crystals that form in a glass of water.

Modern medicine manipulates the physical level directly through physical (pharmaceuticals, surgery) and increasingly electromagnetic means. In other words, modern doctors treat the symptoms. Modern medicine does not address the root cause of the illness/disease which ultimately starts on the metaphysical level. This is why conditions that doctors have "cured" come back. In contrast, metaphysicians seek the cause in the emotions or what the patient is thinking to effect changes. "Alternative modalities" work on the energetic subjective level to nudge the body into correcting and repairing broken parts and processes. However, if the patient's circumstances or frame of mind stays the same, the illness has a higher chance of recurring or another system will be affected.

"But there is a motion that crosses the barriers between the physical and the spiritual, and this is vibration."
~Conny Mendez, *"The Mystical Number 7"*

> ### WORKING DEFINITION OF QI
>
> Basic universal *stuff,* found everywhere and in everything
> Also the *force* that causes change in the universe
> Simultaneously "that which makes things happen in stuff"
> and "the stuff in which things happen" (Nathan Sivin)
> ~ Dr. Ruth Rogaski, Vanderbilt University,
> UC Berkeley Elvera Kwang Siam Lim Memorial Lecture
> "What is the relationship between the air we breathe (in
> Chinese, kongqi) and the qi of Chinese medicine?"

Then there is this thing called **The Higgs Field/Higgs Boson and Higgs Effect.** I am not completely clear on the terminology but I recognize that they have something to do with energy becoming physical matter. Rather than make technical errors, I will just quote good old Wikipedia! Those with an interest in physics can research it more on their own:

> *"The Higgs field is a field of energy that is thought to exist in every region of the universe. The field is accompanied by a fundamental particle known as the Higgs boson, which is used by the field to continuously interact with other particles, such as the electron. Particles that interact with the field are "given" mass... Giving mass to an object is referred to as the Higgs effect. This effect will transfer mass or energy to any particle that passes through it."*
>
> ~From Simple English Wikipedia

BASIC METAPHYSICAL PRINCIPLES

Metaphysical Laws are natural laws with very real effects. To utilize Metaphysical Principles, one must accept some basic premises about existence. I've assembled concepts from a variety of sources so please focus on concepts and don't get stuck on terminology.

- **Other Dimensions:** We, as human beings, learn about the world around us through our five senses (sight, smell, touch, hearing, taste). This is 3-dimensional level information gathering, which allows us to think 3-dimensional conclusions. Physicists recognize that there are actually more dimensions (some say 11) but we cannot detect those with our limited five senses. Those who are familiar with religions and spiritual language speak about 5-D and higher. Some people are apparently sensitive enough to connect with communications on other levels. Jose Silva's Ultramind Method is said to train the human brain to have this skill by inducing slow brain waves associated with sleep and meditation while in the awake state.

- **The Mind** is the life essence of a human being. Some circles refer to this as the Etheric Body or Light Body. The Mind generates thoughts which take the form of electromagnetic energy

- **The Brain** and **Physical Body** are the instruments with which the Mind interacts with the physical 3-dimensional world through Thought/ Energy.

- **Thought/Energy** influences how the Physical Body functions. It can create illness through inducing malfunction of the physiological processes. Thoughts/energy can also heal through triggering reparative processes. Drs. Bruce Lipton and Joe Dispenza discuss Epigenetics, the turning on of genes in our DNA, as it relates to what we think.

- **God/Source/Cosmic Mind/The Force/Good**
  ("God" for short) **created everything in existence**.
  Physical and Metaphysical Laws govern all processes to run
  in alignment with Truth, Love, Balance and Harmony. This
  is a Unifying Principle of Existence. Any negative thought,
  condition or action is outside what is "God/Good". Any
  action, idea or item that brings happiness is a representa-
  tion/reflection of God/Good.

- **Human beings are derived from God** We are born
  with a "soul purpose" and are provided with gifts to do
  a particular job. We can consciously or unconsciously act
  as God's agents to bring Good to the physical plane ("as
  above, so below," "On Earth as it is in Heaven.") If we
  understand the Metaphysical Laws, we can utilize them
  to create all that is Good. Those who fulfill their purpose,
  follow the Laws and do good receive "employee benefits"
  of protection, adequate resources and a happy life. (Law
  of Dharma) Human beings who cause suffering and chaos
  will face repercussions. (Law of Karma).

- The Mind of each person is connected to the Cosmic
  Mind, aka God. It is also referred to as the Soul, Higher
  Self, and other terms. This connection becomes blocked
  through experiences in early childhood and the forgetting
  of this connection. Atonement is the reconnecting of our
  Mind to the Source.

- Theologically, Man is "made in the image of God"/is a
  child of God and also possesses the ability to "create" with
  his/her Mind/Thoughts.

- When the physical body dies, the Mind/Soul continues. In
  other words, the Soul never dies. (The Christian message
  of Eternal Life, Buddhist teachings of reincarnation) Some
  believe the Mind/Soul reincarnates (comes back to live

on earth in a new body) to learn new lessons. With each lesson, the Soul ascends to a higher level of consciousness/ dimension. This repeats until it does not need to go higher. Some do not choose to learn life lessons so they just keep coming back.

- All physical items (human beings, animals, plants, rocks, water) were also created by this Cosmic Mind/God and carries some level of Intelligence/Consciousness. Thus, all physical items can be influenced by Thoughts/Energy and conversely can emit energy (crystals, Feng Shui)

- Thought/Energy can also influence the thoughts of other people, events (synchronicities) and physical items. (**The Law of Manifestation**)

- Deviations from these Unifying Principles of Existence— illness, negative feelings, harmful actions against others— create imbalance in the harmony of the Universe. To bring the system back into Balance, **The Law of Karma** determines that those who harbor negative emotions and thoughts or do bad things to others will themselves experience a negative situation to rebalance the system. The balancing event may take place in subsequent lifetimes.

- Energy flow can be affected by shapes in the environment. (**Biogeometry, Sacred Geometry, Feng Shui**) The Pyramids around the world were built with precision to affect energy flow in specific ways. Energy flows in patterns around our planet along ley lines and through our bodies along meridians. Mineral deposits, like quartz, can be a focal point for energy.

EXAMPLES OF THOUGHTS AFFECTING PHYSICAL MATTER

Grover Cleveland "Cleve" Backster Jr. was a CIA interrogator who used a polygraph instrument to demonstrate that plants reacted to injury and thoughts. This is now called "The Backster Effect."[25] (The Wikipedia entry is a classic battle between the scientific community and those that believe in the unseen, stating "These claims have been rejected by the scientific community." Interestingly, further in the same entry "the Mythbusters" team reproduced Backster's experiments with the dracaena plant, yogurt, saliva and eggs. Experiments where the team employed the same model of polygraph machine used by Backster showed positive results with the plant reacting both to actual harm, as well as thoughts of harm." But then the article goes on to explain why these results were irrelevant. You be the judge.)

Bangladeshi researcher Jagadish Chandra Bose published the same findings in his 1902 Response in the living and non-living. [26]

Professor Masaru Emoto caused a stir in 2005 with his books detailing the impact of thoughts on the formation of water crystals. He uses the Japanese word, Hado, defining it as "the intrinsic vibrational pattern at the atomic level in all matter. The smallest unit of energy. Its basis is the energy of human consciousness." This essentially means that everything emits an attitude, or aura, and this affects the things around it. What's more, external stimuli can affect the vibration of certain entities, and thereby change the mood of those entities. Examples of such stimuli are music or spoken or written words. [27]

---

[19] Backster Cleve (2003) Primary Perception: Biocommunication With Plants, Living Foods, And Human Cells, White Rose Millennium Press

[20] https://medium.com/the-shadow/plants-read-your-mind-this-was-how-a-cia-interrogator-proved-it-3eaa5bde015

[21] https://thespiritofwater.com/pages/hado-the-energy-of-life

As far back as August 1974, Jose Silva spoke at a conference on how thoughts and feelings affect physical reality and gave the example of energizing water by focusing thoughts into it.

Daphne Beall describes her experiments with putting tomatoes in thought-energized water. Tomatoes that were put in energized water did not rot while those put in regular water did.[22]

Recent videos on YouTube by multiple home scientists can be found showing how tomatoes or cooked rice exposed to thoughts of Love vs. thoughts of Hate deteriorate at vastly different rates.

FOOD FOR THOUGHT: Prayers at our church gatherings always included a request to "bless this food we are eating." I never thought about the Metaphysical effects of this until now!

THE AMAZING TECHNOLOGY IN OUR BODIES

Our bodies have built in antennas to receive electromagnetic/scalar waves. Some researchers associate this with the Pineal Gland in our brains. We also emit electromagnetic/scalar waves through our brain (thoughts) and our heart (emotions, electromagnetic patterns) that tell others what we're all about. (HeartMath Institute produces much research on the latter.) My dad would like the analogy of a stereo system receiver, or even better, a karaoke machine which he pulled out at every party. These pieces of equipment take in electromagnetic waves (sound) through a microphone or radio antennae and shoot out sound through speakers. The sounds they emit can be prearranged through LP's, CD's or MP3 files just like our subconscious sends out vibrational frequencies based on our programming from when we were young. We can change the genre, album or song our subconscious is using with conscious effort if we are aware of what we are playing.

The ability of our antennas to receive certain frequencies is affected by our health and our own vibrational frequencies. Drugs,

---

[22] https://www.espsy.org/tomato_experiment.htm

alcohol and unhealthy foods impede our reception. If you engage in actions and emotions of higher vibrational frequencies, you will emit those kinds of signals. You will also lock into others (resonate with people) who are on your same frequency like the tuning of a car radio to a radio station's waves. Others will gravitate toward you if they have the same frequency. This is the **Law of Attraction**. If you engage in dark thoughts and emotions, you will attract those who are similar. Mastery of your life involves controlling your thoughts and emotions so you can be around people who are good for you. Your life will be less chaotic and more peaceful. This is the core of martial arts and spiritual practices.

MANIPULATION OF ENERGY

The energy in your body can be moved around by your thoughts. You can also transmit energy through your thoughts or from your body to someone else's body. The practice of Qigong, Reiki, Jose Silva's Holistic Faith Healing and other forms of energy healing operate this way by focusing energy in the practitioner's hands and applying/drawing energy to the patients' bodies.

Your mind can generate thoughts which can affect the energy in objects, as was demonstrated with the experiments I mentioned. My late friend Dennis Danielson at The Rock Shop would say about the use of crystals, "It's all about your Intention." In light of what I now know about energetics, it makes sense that if you send "healing thoughts" to your sick dog, the bag of crystals you tie to its collar can amplify the intended effect.

HEALING AND METAPHYSICS

The body was created with amazing capabilities of repairing injury and fending off infectious agents. Illness and disease are created by imbalances and blockages of energy that impede these protective and reparative functions. Unblocking energy pathways allows the body to heal itself. Eastern healing arts such as Qigong,

Shiatsu, and Acupuncture manipulate and balance the energy in a body through the meridians. The use of electromagnetic devices, crystals, essential oils, herbs, foods, etc. also works to unblock the body's impediments to repairing itself. Your own mind can turn on and turn off gene expression for reparative processes. Thus, the belief in the ability of a medication, food or treatment to heal is as important as the actual physical effect, even though scientists dismiss the Placebo Effect as irrelevant.

Healers who use Metaphysics are Metaphysicians. Those who do not utilize physical objects or materials are called Spiritual Healers, Faith Healers, Psychic Healers, etc. Metaphysicians recognize the value of directly fixing the body with modern medicine which promotes healing on the physical plane. When allowed, Metaphysicians happily work alongside medical doctors to address the spiritual aspects of disease. (Because he was charged with illegally practicing medicine without a license, Jose Silva recommended only providing "remote healing" to avoid problems with medical boards)

REMEMBER THE THRESHOLD CONCEPT!

There are usually multiple factors involved when someone gets sick or has a behavioral problem. In other words, there are many moving parts to a system that can break down. All effective medicines and therapies induce some incremental effect toward fixing the problem. Sometimes it will only take one medication or treatment to push the system over the threshold and "cure". Sometimes it takes multiple approaches to push the body past that threshold of illness/injury and into a cure.

Take the whole-istic approach and use every tool in your tool box. Spiritual measures work in conjunction with physical measures implemented by medical doctors and any healing modality. Every practitioner of every modality has different levels of skill. The failure of a measure to "cure" a case is not an indication of failure for that one treatment, but is a sign that other factors are impeding the complete healing or that the practitioner must evaluate their execution of that technique.

INHERENT RISKS: Every technique involves a risk. Herbs and compounds can be ineffective if not prepared right or be toxic if given in too high a dose. Instruments can also be ineffective or cause harm. I personally have heard of two people who went ended up with collapsed lungs after acupuncture treatment at a regular medical facility. It takes practice to fine tune any skill. The irony is that a person takes risks to get that practice. Practitioners should be applauded for being brave enough to get that practice so they can be of greater service to humanity and not penalized when unexpected consequences happen. That is, as long as they recognize their limitations and don't keep doing the same mistakes over and over again.

THE LAW OF KARMA

We've all heard the phrase "What goes around comes around." The Universe was created to operate smoothly as a well-balanced system. Anytime a disruption happens there is a response from the Universe to rebalance the system. This includes our actions and thoughts that have a negative impact: If we do something bad to someone, we will face some sort of action against us to balance that out. This is Justice. But Justice must be executed with compassion and without malice. It's not "punishment," it's just a rebalancing of the system to bring everything back into harmony. To allow restitution for damages done is Justice with Compassion. To meet an offense with anger or other emotion to punish is to continue the back and forth of disharmony. To break a karmic cycle of injury between two parties requires one party to offer forgiveness.

As a side note, the American "Justice System" has inherent problems: exacting punishment for an offense. In fact, my limited experience with our local justice system as a juror or participant in cases gave me the insight that there is a marked lack of compassion from the bench (and even a lack of regard for what the law says). The current execution of "justice" brings nothing back to harmony but rather creates more anger and suffering. Additionally, it is my understanding that the conditions in our prisons and jails can be inhumane but that many think prisoners deserve this. How many times do we hear of violent criminals finished with their sentences inflicting another horrible crime in anger as soon as they are released? It is reasonable to entertain a different approach if we wish to reduce the dysfunction in American society.

What does this have to do with Whispering? It underlines the importance of not reacting in anger when the person or animal you're working with tries to hurt you. It ultimately leads back to the notion of Unconditional Love, which is considered THE most powerful force in the Universe.

THE LAW OF MANIFESTATION/ATTRACTION

You may have heard about this Law of Manifestation or Attraction in "self-help" and "empowerment" presentations. You essentially become a co-creator with Good/God by making a request (a prayer) to fill a need: the acquisition of some material goods, a solution to a difficult situation, conflict or difficult relationship, the healing of a physical ailment. In my experience, it does work. It involves more than positive thinking and repeating "affirmations" you've taped to your bathroom mirror to achieve a stated goal.

This spiritual Law of Manifestation has its basis in what Neville Goddard calls The Law of Consciousness. His book, *Feeling is the Secret,* is one of the most understandable and easy to understand explanations of this phenomenon I have found. In short, conscious thought is made manifest (brought into physical reality) by the Subconscious when emotion is expressed.

> *"...a request for synchronicity without an assumption of timing (or what form) the request will be answered."*
> ~Lee Carroll/Kryon

Jesus Christ taught this to his disciples so they could perform "miracles" of healing as He did. It is also taught in what are called "mystery schools" and secret societies. In current times, you will see presentations on it by Dr. Joe Dispenza, Vishen Lakhiani (Mindvalley) and Gregg Braden. This Metaphysical Law is also integral in healing methods, such as Mary Baker Eddy's Christian Science healing, Ernest Holmes' Science of Mind, Jose Silva's Holistic Faith Healing System and Chunli Yin's Spring Forest Qigong. There are many books explaining the process and each one has a slightly different way of explaining. There are also many nuances that can't be contained in one presentation. I found it important to read from as many disciplines and writers as possible. I still have more to learn, but I will try to explain the basics:

THE LAW OF MANIFESTATION AS A 4- STEP PROCESS (by Dr. Sue):

1) Envision what you want to "manifest." This sends out the message energetically of what you want.

2) Feel the emotion that you would have when that goal comes to be. Generally, this means feeling joy about your success. This causes the subconscious mind to embed that vision as part of your experience and reality on the Etheric level and will engage with the Universe to make it real on the physical level. In other words, positive emotions elevate your vibrational frequency so your thought energy will be aligned and resonate with the people or "spirits" who are also positive and find you to help you achieve this goal.

3) Take actions to create a situation in which the desired result has a better chance to happen. This third step is sometimes omitted from discussions about manifesting, but it's important because taking action keeps you in the frame of mind that you are an active participant and not a victim of circumstances. One book used the analogy of needing to buy a lottery ticket if you want to win the lottery. If you just think and feel but don't take action, then you can indeed slip into "hopey-ism."

4) Watch for synchronicities and take action on them. Synchronicities are opportunities that the universe has offered in alignment to fill that request. If an opportunity arises that will move you a step toward your goal, take it. Sometimes manifestation is a process that will take several steps Make no assumptions about the specifics on how and when that answer will come. If you do so, you may turn away potential answers.

Have total faith—Faith with a capital "F". This phrase refers to not worrying about how things will work out. Know—have total confidence—that the Universe will present the most appropriate answer. It is important to not doubt the process because "doubt" and Fear are negative emotions that will block the process. It helps not to look at the progress and not be attached to the outcome. Recognize that there is a difference between Faith and Hope—Hope has an element of doubt.

Just know that whatever happens will be for your highest good even if it's not exactly what you envisioned. And be open to the concept that the best answer may not be what you expected.

> There is a joke about a man trapped on the roof of his house in a flood who prayed that God would save him. Three rescue crafts stopped by but he turned them away because he was waiting for God. The man drowned. When he got to heaven, he asked God why He didn't save him. God answered, "I sent you three boats!"

While this sounds simple, there are many nuances to understand to use it successfully. Every writer or instructor has a slightly different way of describing the details. Chunyi Lin of Spring Forest Qigong describes it as connecting your Heart to your Brain and gives exercises to achieve this in his book "Head to Heart: 18 inch Journey into Oneself." Jose Silva explains it as your Right Brain (the creative, intuitive side) working in balance with your Left Brain (logical thought focused on the physical world.) Silva uses deep relaxation of the body to relax the brain into slower Theta Waves to connect with The Other Side.

They all mention the elimination of Fear from your thoughts while doing this, because Fear and other negative emotions block any positive movement forward.

You will find many different descriptions and explanations about the Law of Manifestation. Don't sweat the details. Just try a version that seems plausible to you and see what happens.

*"Everything is energy and that's all there is to it.
Match the frequency of the reality you want and you
cannot help but get that reality. It can be no other way.
This is not philosophy. This is physics."*

~Darryl Anka, www.bashar.org

RELATIVE FREQUENCY OF EMOTIONS

The Beach Boys' song "Good Vibrations" is referring to Emotional frequency, which can be described in a relative scale as opposed to the duality concept. Emotional Frequency was first presented in *"Power vs. Force"* by David R. Hawkins, and was further popularized by Abraham Hicks. Each human emotion receives a "frequency" based on whether it cultivates a primarily positive or negative mindset.

To change your set point, you need to do with any bad habit or addiction you want to change:

1) recognize when you're doing it
2) when you catch yourself doing it, actively/consciously make yourself do something different
3) keep doing this until it becomes part of your programming and the new normal for you. (Repetition is key and can take days to months.)

The emotions are originally described as follows, ordered from higher vibration to lower vibration. There are charts showing numbers (Hz), but I was not able to find any documentation of instruments used to measure anything, so I will just present these emotions in a relative scale:

HIGH FREQUENCY/VIBRATION/COHERENCE
Joy, Appreciation, Empowerment, Freedom, Love
Passion
Enthusiasm, Eagerness, Happiness
Positive Expectation, Belief
Optimism
Hopefulness
Contentment
Boredom
Pessimism
Frustration, Irritation, Impatience
Feeling Overwhelmed
Disappointment
Doubt
Worry
Blame
Discouragement
Anger
Revenge
Hatred, Rage
Jealousy
Insecurity, Guilt, Unworthiness
Fear, Grief, Desperation, Despair, Powerlessness
LOW VIBRATION/FREQUENCY/COHERENCE

DUALITY/POLARITY

Duality or Polarity in the spiritual sense exists in everybody. In other words, we all have the potential for acting in a positive or negative way. Some will describe this as "good vs. evil." Christian leaders will refer to this as "God vs. Lucifer" or God vs. Satan." I will leave that discussion for later. Meanwhile, let's look at the concept:

I've compiled terminology from a variety of sources that represent these two sides. Some may surprise you and make you think as I had to think.

Every day we make choices that reflect one side or the other. The more we apply one over another indicates how we align ourselves. These are provided to be thought-provoking and not to place judgments.

The attributes and emotions associated with the list on the right are said to bring you calm so your thinking will have clarity and be able to think with the cortical brain. Those who speak the language of spirituality say these lead to "high vibrations" and "high frequency" which emanate harmony, good emotional and physical health and resilience. The list on the left brings disturbance and emotional upset so you are reacting with the reactive lower brain and this leads to "low vibration and low frequency" which leads to problems and unhappiness.

PHYSICS TALK: The attributes on the left are "higher vibration/higher frequency." "Unconditional Love" is at the top. The list on the right is "lower vibration/lower frequency." The lowest is Fear. Doing or thinking from either list raises or lowers your energetic level of frequency or vibration. The more you do of one or the other becomes programmed into your sub conscious brain until you don't recognize you are doing it. This becomes your set point, or resting level.

Those who believe in "God" will describe all the positive emotions and actions as "of God" and all the negatives as "not of God," "lacking God" or "outside of God."

Even non-believers should see the practical application behind this concept. In simple terms, if you try to emulate the qualities on the right, you will be a calmer, cooler person. You will be healthier because you will have less stress in your life. You will be the type of person who others will enjoy being with and trust more easily. Some would say that these are qualities a good leader would have.

The willingness of others to trust and accept your leadership is indeed the key to working in a Whisperer capacity.

Please understand that one should not use these lists to judge others or yourself. The qualities in the left hand column are not "bad" or to be completely avoided as they have value in our daily lives to get things accomplished or warn us of situations or elements in our lives that we need to contemplate. These are useful for Survival. We just should not spend too much time there as it is not good for our physical and mental health. If one believes in the Law of Attraction, the emotions attached to the column on the left are not good for our life path either.

Our alignment is the sum total on a given day. We can make conscious decisions to situate our lives so we experience certain emotions and project certain qualities. It also determines what "energy" we send out to others and the Universe. Some even go so far as to say we as individuals can shift the vibrational frequency of our planet by raising our own vibration. Just fun things to think about.

Darkness	Light
Negative	Positive
Chaos	Calm
Competition	Cooperation
Criticism/Judgment	Acceptance/Compassion
Confrontation	Reconciliation
Force	Resilience
Fear	Confidence
Anger	Forgiveness
Deceit	Truth/Transparency
Arrogance	Humility
Separation/Them vs. Us	Unity
Service to Self	Service to others
I help you, you help me	I help you even if you can't help me

FOR THE ESOTERIC-MINDED WHO DELVE DEEPER

Reverence for man-made	Revere the natural
Material/Worldliness	Spiritual orientation
3dimensional	5 dimensional
Scientifically created	Naturally evolved
(Solution by protocol	Solution evolves)
Follow ego/self	Follow Source/God)
Evil	Good
Ego	Holy Spirit

THE CHEROKEE PARABLE OF THE TWO WOLVES

An old Cherokee chief was teaching his grandson about life.
"A fight is going on inside me," he said to the boy.
"It is a terrible fight and it is between two wolves.
"One is evil - he is anger, envy, sorrow, regret, greed, arrogance, self-pity, guilt, resentment, inferiority, lies, false pride, superiority, self-doubt, and ego.
"The other is good - he is joy, peace, love, hope, serenity, humility, kindness, benevolence, empathy, generosity, truth, compassion, and faith.
"This same fight is going on inside you - and inside every other person, too."
The grandson thought about it for a minute and then asked his grandfather, "Which wolf will win?"
The old chief simply replied, "The one you feed."

A FEW WORDS ABOUT "FAITH" AND "FEAR"

FAITH is a word associated with religious belief and used disparagingly by non-believers and skeptics. However, Faith is not silly "hopey-ism"—a belief that something will happen if you wish hard enough for it.

Faith is a belief that something will happen based on KNOWLEDGE. Those who use Metaphysical Law to heal or affect events, indeed have faith that these will work. I will go out on a limb and say that I do have Faith in Metaphysical Laws because I have learned how to use them. I'm not always successful in attaining a hoped for outcome, but it's likely for my lack of skill or extenuating factors.

When we let go of an object, we know it will fall to the ground based on our knowledge and experience with the Law of Gravity.

If it doesn't fall as expected, we look for reasons why and don't question the validity of the Law of Gravity.

When we use a cell phone to visually talk to someone on the other side of the world, we don't know how it works but it doesn't stop us from using it. At the same token, if the phone doesn't work because the battery is dead or we don't know how to use an application, we don't say the technology is flawed.

Faith gives us confidence. Working with confidence means that you work without Fear. Actually, Fear is "faith" that the outcome will be negative! Additionally, because Fear blocks energy flow, being able to work without Fear expedites healing. Because Fear is a "negative" emotion, your energy will be less attractive and trustworthy to those you are working with and you will have a harder time "whispering" to an animal or person you're trying to help.

You need not be an adherent to any religion or belief system to benefit from applying metaphysical principles. Just understand.

RELIGIOUS TRADITIONS AND METAPHYSICAL KNOWLEDGE

The concept of metaphysical law is discussed in ancient and not so ancient religions but only by those who focus on the spiritual aspects of those religions. The *Kybalion* printed in 1908 and available on the internet presents a little discussion how interfaith metaphysical concepts trace all the way back to Hermes/Thoth of ancient Egypt, and in The Law of One (Ra). Christians may find it surprising that the miracles Jesus performed were based on metaphysical principles that He learned as a member of the Essene community and in his travels to other lands[23]. The Secret

---

[23] Jesud In India (a series) Paul Anthony Wallis & Erich Von Daniken (in conversation)
  – Paul Anthony Wallis

Teachings of Moses are based on the Kabbalah and Egyptian as well. [24]

Dolores Cannon and Edgar Cayce have brought forth understanding of different layers of existence/dimensions/consciousness in different ways but leading to the same conclusions.

Most religions refer to a single Creator God/Spirit/Force/Source. Dharma is the term used in ancient Hindu texts for the cosmic law that created the ordered universe from chaos. The Judeo-Christian Bible simply calls this "God."

I have found variations of these concepts in Buddhism, Taoism, Hinduism, Zoroastrianism, Rosicrucian, and Christianity from the sects that study mysticism. At the core of all these systems are three tenets:

LOVE GOD
LOVE EACH OTHER AS GOD LOVES US
DO GOOD IN GOD'S NAME

Each religion has its unique ways of expressing these principles. Each person has an even more unique way of living their lives. In a world of Free Will, even following these tenets is a matter of personal choice.

Rules of Conduct, like the Ten Commandments, are guideposts to living the right way and move toward closeness with "God." These guidelines for human behavior and ways of living prevent society, family and nature from descending into chaos.

Most religious faiths teach that doing good things and living the "right way" will bring you a harmonious life, a life of abundance (not lacking anything you need) and generally smooth sailing. Rituals and specific rules vary between religions and even

---

[24] Edmond Bordeaux Szekely, The Teachings of the Essenes from Enoch to the Dead Sea Scrolls 1978)

within faiths. Great discord and division are created when people want to argue about practices and which religion is "the right Truth." Erin Michelle Galito, like Paul Selig, Jayem, and many others, presents messages she says are from "Master Jesus" and "The Voice of God". For discussion here, we use the mantra: "Don't sweat the small stuff."

> *"The TEACHING appears in the Zend Avesta of Zoroaster, who translated it into a way of life that was followed for thousands of years. It contains the fundamentals concepts of Brahmanism, the Vedas and the Upanishads; and the Yoga systems of India sprang from the same source. Buddha later gave forth essentially the same basic ideas and his sacred Bodhi tree is correlated in the Essene Tree of Life. In Tibet the teaching once more found expression in the Tibetan Wheel of Life.*
>
> *The Pythagoreans and Stoics in ancient Greece also followed the Essene principles and much of their way of life. The same teaching was an element of the Adonic culture of the Phoenicians, of the Alexandrian School of Philosophy in Egypt, and contributed greatly to many branches of Western culture, Freemasonry, Gnosticism, the Kabbalah and Christianity. Jesus interpreted it in the most sublime and beautiful for in the seven Beatitudes of the Sermon on the Mount."*
>
> ~Edmond Bordeaux Szekely *The Teachings of the Essenes from Enoch to the Dead Sea Scrolls*

"The Law of Dharma or Purpose in Life: Everyone has a purpose in life . . . a unique gift or special talent to give to others. And when we blend this unique talent with service to others, we experience the ecstasy and exultation of our own spirit, which is the ultimate goal."

~Deepak Chopra

"Now there are varieties of gifts, but the same Spirit; and there are varieties of service, but the same Lord; and there are varieties of working, but it is the same God who inspires them all in every one. For just as the body is one and has many members, and all the members of the body are one body, so it is with Christ"

~New Testament 1 Corinthians 12

"Human philosophy has made God manlike. Christian Science makes man Godlike. The first is error, the latter is truth. Metaphysics is above physics, and matter does not enter into metaphysical premises or conclusions. The categories of metaphysics rest on one basis, the divine Mind. Metaphysics resolves things into thoughts, and exchanges the objects of sense for the ideas of Soul."

~Mary Baker Eddy, Christian Science

CONNECTING WITH THE DIVINE (AND THE OTHER SIDE)

The first step to connecting with "God" or anything on the spiritual level is acknowledging its existence. The next step is to follow the guidelines to bring your thinking into alignment with God et al. Some describe this as submitting/surrendering to "God," "walking in the Light," "the narrow path, "the road less traveled."

There are also meditations, prayers, rituals and other practices that "raise your vibration/frequency/consciousness" so that you can "ascend" to a higher level of Consciousness and closeness to God. Transcendence is another applicable word—to transcend the animal nature and become more God-like.

I have a stack of books that I discovered from the YouTube channel "Giving Voice to the Wisdom of the Ages/Audio Enlightenment". Each writer has a slightly different way of describing the process which adds texture and nuance to understanding. But the same 3 tenets apply, so it's always a good fallback to remember when the discussion gets too confusing.

NOTE: Connecting with anything "on the other side" (spirit guides, angels, Higher Self, interdimensional beings, even extraterrestrials) involves the same process as connecting with the Divine.

There are several approaches to working toward a heightened state: Dr. Stephen Porges's Polyvagal Theory explains it through the autonomic nervous system. Jose Silva's Mind Control Program speaks in terms of shifting your brain waves to access this state of clarity. Chunyi Lin of Spring Forest Qigong speaks in terms of "energy." My Whisperers' Tricks shift you into the Zen Zone. And of course, there are those who use drugs, mushrooms or herbal compounds to achieve an altered state. These are just a few ways of approaching Higher or Inner Knowledge

Consistently, the concept of Unconditional Love, Forgiveness and The Golden Rule (not harming others) is vital to this process. There are other concepts that are tied to what I call "walking in the Light" that help you connect to the Divine. I've listed them with their corresponding opposites in the chart on Duality.

This altered state brings higher intuition, serenity, inner peace, problem solving abilities and the ability to emotionally connect (empathize) with others. It is said by some that you are connecting with a Universal Wisdom, spiritual guides, angels, Inner Knowing, Higher Self or "God" who will provide you with the answers you need. It is like turning the dial on an old radio to tune into a specific frequency for your favorite radio station. The station is always out there but you will only hear it when you adjust everything correctly.

> *"I am repeating creative truths that have been around for millennia. These are truths that The Other Side wants us to know. They are in the ancient Taoist philosophy of the Chinese. They are in the Upanishads of India. The Kabbalah of Judaism. The Quran of Islam. The words of Jesus in the Gospels…(The Silva Method) help us to use our natural contact with The Other Side effectively to make this a better world in which to live. People who do their thinking, analyze their problems, seek help from The Other Side while*

at the alpha level are centered. Their awareness is connected to Higher Intelligence. These are people who are helping with creation instead of working against it. They have become partners with God, you might say, because they are helping God, and God is helping them. They are getting help from the Other Side by being at alpha level. It's that simple."

~ Jose Silva from *The Silva Mind Control Method for Getting Help From the Other Side*

PURPOSE IN LIFE=DIVINE MISSION

Clinically speaking, people who found and live what they consider their purpose in life are at much lower risk of suffering from depression. Thus, if you are working with a person who is acting out due to issues with self-worth or depression, you might want to read this:

Religiously speaking, we exhibit both characteristics unless we choose to be spiritually aware. Once we are aware/awakened, we can make a conscious decision to follow one side or the other. Most religions say we were created in God's image, which exhibits the attributes of Light. By aligning ourselves with those attributes brings us closer to our true Divine nature or closer to whatever concept we might call God. If we consciously choose to follow Good/God/the "Lightworker" path, our life will be easier. If we choose to follow Satan, described as "selling your soul," or Lucifer who is said to mix "a little bit of good to counter the little bit of bad" it can take us down a path with material gains but spiritual darkness. The two paths are described by the Hopi Prophecy as well as all major religions. The "unawakened" will go back and forth and be open to negative influences.

Following the Light also gives us an ability to tie into a kind of Universal Wisdom or gives us stronger intuitive insights. Notably, healers of all practices align with the concepts on the right as much as possible because negative thoughts and emotions block the ability to heal.

While some promote Jose Silva's programs as a way to material abundance, Mr. Silva had a decidedly divine mission to help humanity in mind for his work.

> **Jose Silva's Laws of Programming** The following laws are to be considered to make programming most effective (using the skills from his programs to change a situation):
>
> • Do to others only what you like others to do to you
> • The solution must help to make this planet a better place to live.
> • The solution must be the best for everybody concerned
> • The solution must help at least two or more persons
> • The solution must be within the possibility area

From https://silvanow.com/2esparld.htm#xl_Proj:32to:32Home:32Conditioning

MIRACLES, HEALING AND THE LAW OF MANIFESTATION

> *"Heal the sick, raise the dead, cleanse those who have leprosy, drive out demons. Freely you have received; freely give."*
>
> ~Jesus, Matthew 10:08 New
> International Version

God (at least according to the Old Testament) created Man in its own image. Some of the Christian faith believe Jesus Christ's purpose for incarnating on earth was to show Man how to do "miracles," which we can naturally do because we were all born with The God Factor. To get to this level, one needs to choose a spiritual path, shed his/her Ego/Monkey Mind/human nature and align with his/her own Higher Self/Divine Nature/God. In doing so, we are able to find the Divine Self or God Spark within each of us and apply the Law of Manifestation to heal disease and injuries, smooth difficult relationships, bring about synchronicities to create opportunities that will make our lives better give us the guidance to take the best actions.

> *"In the creation, God extended Himself to His creations and imbued them with the same loving Will to create... Because of your likeness to your Creator you are creative."*
>
> ~A Course in Miracles

> *"There is no greater power in the universe than human intent and Love with the energy of expectation. Intent is the action Love is the energy couching the action by how you act. Always intend and expect using love, not doubt fear or worry. Create a new reality... Light will find its highest level. Truth will find its highest level. It just takes time."*
>
> ~Lee Carroll/Kryon

WHITE KNUCKLING WHILE APPLYING
THE LAW OF MANIFESTATION

It has taken me decades to come to some sort of understanding of this process and I still have more to learn. But I will share with you my own observations so far: As a veterinarian and ranch owner, I am faced with situations involving serious injury or illness with a possible outcome of death. In these cases where it is hard to control the fear and doubt, I compare it to being on a roller coaster coming to the crest of the first peak. Your heart is in your throat but you've made the commitment to go through with the ride. You grip the guard bar so hard your knuckles turn white.

Here are some thoughts that help me through these times:

1) God/Good/Spirit /The Universe is in total control
2) I will project as much love as I can muster on the patient
   to connect him/her/it with God and bring harmony and
   healing in to the situation
3) I will take action to help that physical healing come about
   with appropriate medication and care.
4). If it makes me afraid, I will not look at the injury or the test
   results or the prognosis given by attending physicians.
5) To additionally control Fear, I think these thoughts:
   a) God will manifest the best possible outcome and it
      may not be what we are asking for or expect.
   b) Death may be the ultimate outcome but I will not
      fear this because the soul will live on in a different
      dimension and we will meet again
   c) Recite Bible scripture like Psalm 91 or Psalm 23 and
      lean into Faith.
   d) The outcome may not be restoration to physical health
      but the passing will be peaceful and love-filled. And
      that is enough.

I found that the more I used the Law to promote healing and developed a list of successes, the more confident I became. With confidence comes less difficulty controlling fear and doubt

THE CONTROVERSY:

"Science is the pursuit and application of knowledge and understanding of the natural and social world following a systematic methodology based on evidence."
~The Science Council

"A science involves a pursuit of knowledge covering general truths or the operations of fundamental laws."
~Britannica.com

Metaphysics is science, though Modern Science has chosen for the most part to scorn Metaphysical Knowledge. Reports of phenomena are too often discounted and dismissed as "not proven" or "anecdotal" even if they have been observed for thousands of years or reported by thousands of people. You see, if you are not in the club, your word doesn't matter.

An example is the war waged on Homeopathy by the American medical community trying to ban and criminalize the practice.

I have read enough research papers to realize that researchers who "debunk" alternative practices are not using techniques appropriately in their experiments. A study done by American researchers years ago concluded acupuncture was ineffective at inducing anesthesia for surgery and implied that acupuncture was not a valid medical procedure. I recall thinking "Don't they know that that's not what acupuncture is for?" This obviously would lead to a high failure rate. The ability for a person to utilize these concepts successfully takes deep knowledge and skilled hands. So, when you read a paper declaring a technique is bogus, see how much effort the researcher used to learn the technique from one who has mastered it.

On another note, governing professional bodies are prone to turf wars. They like to tell the public that only their club members should be allowed to tell you what is True and to do anything about it. In my state, this relates to any agency under the guise of Consumer Affairs. It has gotten so bad that I've heard offering nutritional advice at a pet store can be considered "practicing veterinary medicine without a license." People are afraid to make any health decisions and will wait for someone in a white coat to tell them what to do.

I have seen people who have a high success rate of helping others and haven't hurt anyone be targeted by governing bodies. Take for instance the Christian Science parents who were criminally prosecuted because they did not seek help from a hospital. How often do we see doctors criminally prosecuted when patients die from adverse drug reactions or negligence? I can't help but think that some of these governing bodies and the politicians who give them the power to prevent good people from doing good work have an element of darkness in their souls.

Evidence leads to theories. Theories warrant further testing.

I have an egalitarian perspective: It doesn't matter what station a person has in life, if they offer a testimonial and are not intentionally lying then this is Evidence even if they weren't participating in a "double blind clinical trial." Modern science and medicine has discouraged if not outright suppressed practices from traditional cultures. This has resulted in a loss of knowledge and wisdom that has helped people for thousands of years. I even see in veterinary medicine how practical techniques and strategies we used just a couple decades ago are not even being taught in veterinary schools and scoffed at by new graduates.

"People who say it cannot be done, should not interrupt those who are doing it"

~Bernard Shaw

Or

"Hold my beer..."

Thankfully due to medical professionals such as Brian Weiss (hypnotic past life regression), O. Carl Simonton (cancer treatment and mental imagery), Joe Dispenza (mind-body medicine), and Eben Alexander (Near death experience) who write and speak seriously about spirituality are leading to serious research. If you are interested in exploring the medical aspects of spirituality, Shenefelt's "Spiritual and Religious Aspects of Skin and Skin Disorders." This paper contains a wonderful summary of spiritual practices of many different cultures and religions with eye-opening examples that made me want to look even deeper into each.[25]

CONDEMNATION BY RELIGIOUS ENTITIES

Those who have faith in the unseen, such as "God" angels and spirit guides will have less difficulty in accepting these concepts. After all, Jesus Christ taught his disciples to perform "miracles." Ironically, many Christian leaders have deemed use of these principles "from the Devil" and "black magic," an attitude that came during the rule of Constantine who persecuted the Gnostic and Essene Christians who practiced this knowledge. Many have been burned at the stake for practicing these forms of "magic." I do believe that people with very dark hearts have used these principles to harm others. But like any tool, the knowledge can also be used for doing good and therefore should not be cast aside or ignored.

---

[25] Shenefelt PD, Shenefelt DA. Spiritual and religious aspects of skin and skin disorders. Psychol Res Behav Manag. 2014 Aug 2;7:201-12.

Some Christian leaders caution against looking into these topics because they are considered a slippery slope to Luciferian influences. However, it should be noted that Christian Science Healing is based on the New Testament and firmly in the Christian faith while applying metaphysical principles to heal (it is not "faith healing" or "praying for healing"). For those who are concerned about "negative entities," there are precautions that people "of the Light" can take to avoid dark influences: Recognize that Good is far more powerful than any negative intent and declare that you are working for the Light/God and will be protected (Old Testament Psalm 91). Just shining a light vanquishes Darkness. Above all, do not fear these entities because it's your fear that gives them their power.

Executing this on the spiritual level leads to manifestation on the physical level.

There are some who consider any use of metaphysical knowledge as "demonic" or "evil." I do believe that there are people who do use this knowledge to do bad things to others. However, it should be recognized that Jesus Christ was a master Metaphysician who taught these principles to his disciples. Mary Baker Eddy (Christian Science), Jose Silva Sr. (Ultramind Methods), Chun-yi Lin (Spring Forest Qigong) are devout Christians who emphasize the importance of using their metaphysical teachings to help mankind in the way God wants us to.

It should be highlighted that FEAR is the most negative, healing-blocking, lowest vibration emotion. Fearing evil "entities" and intents is what gives that evil power in our lives. Additionally, one cannot do God's Work if one lives with Fear.

WORDS GET IN THE WAY: Many Christian leaders teach that anything "Occult" (e.g., Tarot, astrology, crystals, Yoga, etc.) is associated with evil. In other circles, "esoteric knowledge" mystery schools and secret societies (Rosicrucians, Freemasons, Knights of Templar, etc.) are associated with people who use this knowledge for personal gain without regard for the well-being of others.

Because of these warnings, I avoided looking into these practices for a long time and viewed their practitioners with suspicion. Conversely, the terms "Spiritual" and "Religious" can trigger reactions of fear and loathing from non-believers and skeptics in the sciences. It's like how Islam is considered by some Americans as the religion of terrorists. It wasn't until recently that I started looking at topics associated with "mystery schools" and "secret societies" after I learned of Christian "mystics" like Anna Lee Skarin, Murdo MacDonald Bayne and Vivian May Williams. I actually never completely let go of my hesitations until finding Conny Mendez's book confirms the validity of the Kybalion. This knowledge is indeed powerful and creepy people indeed use it to do harm. Those who enter the realm of different dimensions do need to be cautious and know that they can open themselves up to evil if they have fear and emit lower vibrational frequencies. Of course, we are all potential targets of these bad actors regardless of our dimensional status. To protect ourselves, we can declare that we are of the Light and protected by God. At least this is what I've heard from numerous sources and I'll take that advice!

MY PERSONAL APPROACH TO APPLICATION OF METAPHYSICS

This is an area of deep nuances that I am still unpacking. I learn something new almost daily that helps me apply metaphysical law even more effectively. What I write here is just a snapshot of my understanding:

Metaphysical law can be very powerful. Like anything that is powerful, one should be careful with it because you can do serious damage. There are people who dabble with ritual and find themselves in circles where practitioners are doing what can be described as "evil." Because you open up energetic portals to other dimensions using rituals and tools like Ouija boards, people recount feeling like they were being followed by "entities" after participating in these activities without taking proper precautions. You can use the wrong herbs at the wrong dosage and get into toxicity problems. I've heard of several people who ended up with collapsed lungs or worsening of pain (probably from hitting a nerve bundle) after doctors in mainstream hospitals tried to use acupuncture on them.

I am adventurous but still cautious. As a result, most of my experience with the metaphysical is in the mental energetic area. I figured I can't do too much damage using "thought healings" and energy manipulations without any physical contact. However, because this method has such subtle impacts it takes a lot to see results and develop confidence in your ability to use it. This is where one needs to apply Faith before you see results. As I understand it more deeply, I find my efforts more productive. It is a difficult medium to work with because the language is very foreign to our everyday way of thinking. There are many nuances that need to be understood, too. Every time I read or hear the works of a different writer, my understanding deepens and success rates increase.

The following is a reiteration of what I went over in this chapter but with added depth for those who wish to venture deeper:

1) We are spirits/souls. The physical world we live in is "The Matrix", a dream or "An Illusion." The real world is the realm or dimension that we cannot see while we have human bodies.

2) God/Good/Source that created all the physical and meta-physical laws controls everything.

3) Our souls are part of this God. We merely need to open our eyes to this to reconnect with the source of power and understanding. This is how the term Atonement ("At-one-ment") is applied. In this thinking, you do not need to perform certain rituals to be "saved" or gain favor with "God."

4) This God Source only sees and does Good and works to bring everything back into harmony. By opening our eyes to this connection to the God Source, we can harness this healing energy and apply it to ourselves and others. This is how "As above, so below" and "On Earth as it is in Heaven" from the Lord's Prayer is applied.

5) As opposed to the concept of Duality (Good vs. Evil), there is only God. God is in everything and everywhere. God is only good, love, joy, harmony. Anything outside of God is Ego. Therefore, if any chaos, fear, anger, sadness, conflict, illness, etc. is not "OF GOD" (Some call this Unity Consciousness). Because the God Source is all powerful, it will overcome anything that is of Ego (anything negative.)

6) To apply Metaphysical Law to situations or conditions that are in need of fixing or healing, you must have your rela-tionship with the God Source solid. You must let go of Fear, worry, anger, sadness and KNOW (have confidence) that these metaphysical laws will work to bring the God power to heal from the spiritual realm into the physical realm. This means you cannot be concerned with what you see with your eyes or what people are telling you about the situation.

7) Make no judgment about anyone else. Do not even judge yourself if your efforts fail. Accept and love regardless. This is another way of saying don't let anything upset you and trigger you into anger, sadness, or any other negative thoughts and feelings.

I found that using the model of Good vs. Ego instead of Good vs. Evil helpful because it is more conducive to letting go of Fear.

While Metaphysics is powerful, we are not very skilled at using it when we are just starting to learn it. Thus, it is important to keep using the tools you already know (medicines, therapies, etc.) while you are building your ability to understand and use Metaphysical principles. This will not happen overnight. It is a process that can take years, even a lifetime. The more you practice, the better you get. Some refer to this as "Ascension."

One needs to be careful about following "Spiritual leaders" and "self-help gurus" to the point of worshiping them. These are human beings who too often have been found to be doing dark things to those who trust them too much. It is safer to listen to your "inner wisdom" to see if something sounds right to you before proceeding. This is Discernment. Anything you do that ends up harming another person in the process is obviously going to have karmic repercussions. Any time you are encouraged to do something that will manipulate the thoughts of another person to benefit yourself (e.g."Make this person fall in love with me") will infringe on their sovereignty and right to free will. This qualifies as "service to self" and also subject to "bad karma." To be safe, I stuck with teachings from what are called "Christian Mystics" until I felt comfortable about others, like Ra (Law of One). Additionally, if I stick with the Christ message which is consistently "of the Light," I cannot be swayed by dark influences. There are some circles that start off with noble intentions and have been infiltrated with leaders having-not-so- good intentions. Always be on the alert for this. Also, take care to protect yourself while participating in rituals or other manipulations of energy or are experiencing negative side effects from anything you take into your body.

For those who are interested in learning more, I highly recommend the YouTube channel "Giving Voice to the Wisdom of the Ages" and its audio book service AudioEnlightenment. The messages of everything here have been "Of the Light." There are others who channel the Christ message in different ways. You can tell they all lead to the one Truth/Source because their messages are all in alignment: fix yourself and align with God, everything else will take care of itself. It's a simple principle but takes lots of learning and hard work to execute.

I am a very private person with my spiritual beliefs. What I've written here is information I haven't shared with many (mostly because everyone thinks I'm nuts). But because it will help some of you help others as well as yourselves, this is my gift to you.

I'm sure that some readers will take me to task for using terms in "the wrong way." Please refrain from nitpicking and just mull over concepts. Be open to learning more but be diligent in staying alert to how the knowledge is being used and when/why words trigger a reaction in us. This way we can increase our knowledge without interference from background noise. You do not need to wait for an expert to test a theory. Within reason and if you are **capable of doing it safely**, by all means test a theory yourself. Learn to trust your own eyes. This is part of Sovereignty and Free Will. End of soap box speech.

I am not an evangelist who wants to prove to you that these natural laws run the world. I just want people to be aware of what took me a lifetime to discover and start to understand. I encourage you to explore these ideas on your own and try out what resonates with you. You may be pleasantly surprised!

> *"I do not like green eggs and ham! I do not like them, Sam-I-am."*
> *"You do not like them so you say. Try them, try them and you may.*
> *Try them and you may say."*
> *"Sam! If you will let me be, I will try them. You will see.*
> *Say! I like green eggs and ham! I do like them, Sam-I-am!"*
>
> ~ Dr. Seuss "Green Eggs & Ham"

For those who are curious, I was raised in a Chinese American Baptist church and follow the teachings of Jesus Christ. However, I found much written in the Bible incongruous with the concept of Unconditional Love and I focus my reverence on "God" rather than worshipping Jesus as Savior. I have been accused of "not being Christian" because of this. In my later years, I found that my beliefs are indeed aligned with the Apocrypha, which are texts that are not included in the Bible (Books of Thomas and Mary Magdalene and others referred to as the scrolls found near the Dead Sea and Nag Hammadi) and the practices of the Essenes, a community that raised Jesus. It doesn't bother me if others want to declare me "non-Christian." Also, I am not promoting these beliefs or trying to convert anyone. I am just giving you a point of reference for what I've written.

JOSE SILVA (1914-1999)

As I was proofreading this manuscript, I came across numerous suggested YouTube videos on The Silva Method. I got the hint and watched one. The premise was intriguing—training the brain to do amazing things. The more I delved into his work, the more I realized how relevant his techniques could be to those interested in "Whispering" and wished I had heard of the program years ago. I have given much time and ink to his works because they are not very well-known at the deeper levels and I believe his knowledge could help many people as well as provide ideas for further research.

Using the Laws of Metaphysics and the understanding of how the brain works, one could develop empathy, communicate effectively, problem solve through clear thinking, intuition and even psychic abilities, and help both people and animals on an individual level with great effectiveness. Jose Silva passed away in 1999 but his legacy lives on in his books, videos and the programs that are offered by many others as The Silva Method and Silva Ultramind, and Silva Everyday ESP. I will try to summarize what he discovered and how he applied them so the techniques could be taught to others.

Jose Silva's life story should be made into an inspirational documentary. He lost his parents when he was 4, dropped out of school to help his grandparents support him and his siblings. He never went to school but learned to read and write both Spanish and English, started a successful electronics business after taking a correspondence course for his local barber, researched how the brain functions and developed ways that could train average children and adults to remember and process information. He also discovered how to help them develop intuition, psychic abilities, problem-solving capabilities, perform healings on people with injuries or illness, harness the Law of Manifestation to change the course of events, and be able to perform remote viewing and telepathic communication. Pretty wild stuff if you ask me!

The brilliance of his findings are borne out by the number of people who have developed these skills through his instructors and home study courses, and the number of prominent people who have embraced and even teach his techniques, such as Vishen Lakhiani of Mindvalley and the late Dr. O. Carl Simonton, the oncologist who brought mental imagery to the world of cancer treatment.

The main premise of his works is associated with inducing the brain to shift into Alpha and even Delta and Theta waves while in the awake state, which produce health benefits also associated with the Polyvagal Theory: He determined using EEG that 90% of adults use primarily the Left Brain and Beta waves for problem solving and that only 10% of adults do. However, the 10% of the population that use the Right Brain and Alpha waves make up the people who are high achievers in business and positions of influence in our world. (It should be recognized that those that exhibit traits associated with the Autistic Spectrum also use the Right Brain and likely a lot of Alpha Wave thinking.)

Silva developed a guided meditation and the playing of sounds at 10 MHz to "condition" (entrain) the brain to shift into Alpha State (amplifying Alpha Waves) more often while awake. Students then learn techniques to trigger this state of awareness by holding a hand with 3 fingers together or through a shortened mental and physical relaxation exercise.

The Silva Method works like meditation (deep relaxation) and physical activity (exercise) to reduce stress, promote health, improve immune responses and support mental well-being.

Silva additionally developed "Active Meditation" whereby one could use specific thoughts and direct them to induce changes in the environment and the behavior of others (manifestation through metaphysics).

Practitioners of the Silva Method develop intuitive skills that include telepathy and mental projection (remote viewing), accessing guidance "from the other side" and better problem solving and decision-making by utilizing both the right and left sides of the brain.

Like Mary Baker Eddy who founded Christian Science, Silva believed he was divinely guided to receive the information he brought forth to benefit humanity. His original work, especially his Ultramind System, places great emphasis on using these gifts to help others.

Programs based on his original works that are currently available for home study are

Ultramind ESP System to develop intuition

Holistic Faith Healing to do laying on of hands and remote healing

Choose Success to remove subconscious blockages

Superstars Fitness Secrets—mental training for fitness and sports

Sales Power using ESP for Sales Professionals

ESP for Business Success

You can find organizations that teach his methods in various ways by just doing an internet search.

CONNY MENDEZ (1898-1979)

While I was working on this chapter on Metaphysics, I happened on a YouTube audio presentation of "Metaphysics for Everyone" by Conny Mendez. The 1:40 hour presentation was THE clearest, most understandable explanation of Metaphysics and esoteric knowledge and its practical execution I have ever heard.

Most of the information on a website about Mendez is in Spanish. My command of Spanish is limited to reading menus on taco trucks so I could only glean the following about this amazing person from various internet entries: Conny Mendez (Juana Maria de la Concepción Mendez Guzman), was a composer, painter, caricaturist, actress, stage director, and lecturer. She started studying Metaphysics in 1939 and became a student of Emmet Fox. In 1946, she founded the Christian Metaphysics Movement (Dynamic Christianity) in Venezuela and later The Brotherhood of St. Germain. She wrote many books and articles and lectured in major cities of North, Central and South America.

After much searching, I found *"Power Through Metaphysics"* in English translation on Amazon. This is a four-volume book that includes *"Metaphysics for Everyone."* I highly recommend this book for anyone who wants a good overview of Metaphysics in one book.

Volume 1 *"Metaphysics for Everyone"*: describes the basics of Metaphysical Law (from the Kybalion), Principles of Mentalism and an interpretation of the 10 Commandments.

Volume 2 *"Your Heart's Desire"*: explains the mechanics and execution of Manifestation/Alchemy/Transmutation

Volume 3 *"The Mystical Number 7"*: covers The 7 clauses of the Lord's Prayer, The 7 Aspects of God, The 7 Universal Principles, The Seven Rays of Light.

Volume 4: *"The Count St. Germain:"* Alchemy, transmutation, his incarnations including Proclus, Robert the Monk, Christian Rosenkreutz (Rosicrucian) Roger Bacon, Francis Bacon

IN CASE YOU'RE WONDERING...

How did I end up with these crazy ideas? Well, I was born into a family who understood that there is a spirit level operating around us. When family members died, we got clear signs that they weren't really gone. Like the night of my grandfather's wake while the family was spending the night at his home, the fuses blew out not once but twice. The fuses also blew out at the apartment building he once owned. So even though we went to a Baptist church, I never got the feeling that this Life After Death concept was something to be afraid of.

Our family gatherings included a friend who was a Qigong healer. She would work on people after dinner when they had aches and pains and those who got her help said they felt better. She also seemed to have psychic abilities and gave us messages from my mother who was in a coma for 3 weeks. I interviewed her with the hopes of publishing her story. While it never made print, hearing her life journey with spirit guides had a profound impact on my understanding and world view.

I took lessons in Qigong given by a Chinese foreign graduate student. He taught us how to focus energy in our hands, detect blockages in the bodies of others and move energy around to promote healing. While we meditated with our eyes closed, he would walk behind us and move his arms. I could tell by the surge of energy that swept through my body when he was behind me. When friends have allowed me to "work" on serious injuries, they tell me they feel something happen, the pain goes away and they function normally again. I recently learned about E.G Fricker, a healer from the U.K. who did the same for thousands of patients around the world. The Washington Post even wrote an article about this amazing man.[31] In books written by and about him, he describes energy flowing through his hands to bring about healing.

[26] Rovner, S. (1977, May 6). A faith healer's touch . The Washington Post. Retrieved June 24, 2022, from https://www.washingtonpost.com/archive/lifestyle/1977/05/06/a-faith-healers-touch/475e8331-9ffd-4038-9542-5cd834a0e7a0/

In the course of caring for animals, I also came across several talented animal communicators who could tell me details that nobody could possibly guess. I read several books on how to hone my own skills and took a workshop. I never reached the level whereby I could "hear" specific thoughts from animals but I do think the exercises made me more sensitive to what the animals want.

After graduating from veterinary school, I was frustrated with cases that didn't survive despite following protocols that I had learned at the number one veterinary school in the nation. I had picked up a copy of The Sentinel outside a Christian Science Reading Room. The stories of healing intrigued me. I learned the principles by reading articles in the Christian Science Sentinel magazine and the book *Science and Health with a Key to the Scriptures* by Mary Baker Eddy, and by hiring CS practitioners to work on animal cases that weren't going well. The concepts were difficult to wrap my head around but eventually I must have understood enough because I began having better success with patients. A turning point for me was when I developed a blistering rash on my forehead that had the appearance of cutaneous anthrax. This was an era where the fear of Anthrax was at its height and if I uttered that word at the hospital, I would have been thrown into quarantine. Instead, I decided to work on it without even antibiotics. Within hours, the blistering resolved. I still have a divot in my forehead which is characteristic of cutaneous anthrax.

I attribute my understanding of metaphysical prayer to my surviving being dragged under a horse by a strap around my neck for a quarter mile and over a barbed wire fence. Despite having a hoof print on my back, I walked out of the emergency room after this exciting event and worked in the clinics 2 days later.

I incorporate my understanding more and more in my work and life because I have seen their effectiveness. Up to now, I haven't talked about it much. When I offer to help people heal, they either politely decline or when they feel the energy moving it frightens them.

The backlash when these ideas come up in conversation has been harsh. A dean of the veterinary school told me "I don't believe in anything that isn't proven" when I asked his opinion of acupuncture in the 1980's. Another professor told me "I don't believe people can communicate with animals" when I offered to see if my animal communicator friend could help a bear that couldn't/wouldn't walk. (That sure shut down the conversation quickly.)

As a consultant with the veterinary board, I became aware how veterinarians can be harshly sanctioned if a complaint is filed and they haven't followed what is the current "standard of care." Punishment will be exacted whether or not the veterinarian did anything that would have harmed animals. Sometimes it's for doing things veterinarians did in the past but is no longer in vogue. I use a lot of unconventional protocols on the animals at Phoenix Ranch and for friends' animals if they promise not to tell anyone. The methods I use may work because I incorporate Metaphysic principles but might not for another veterinarian who doesn't. I just know that "old school medicine" I learned from veterinarians from the 1960's as well as things I've discovered on my own do a pretty good job in my hands.

I can be bolder about speaking of this now that I am retired from clinical practice and don't face threats to my career and finances.

My hope is that my testimony and explanations will create more awareness and openness to "alternative modalities." I believe every healing modality has its place in the hands of people with whom it resonates. When they don't work, it's because the patient or the practitioner are somehow blocking the healing. Often this is a sign from the Universe that we need to dig deeper to develop our skills and understanding. Sometimes a healing doesn't happen on the physical level but through healing on the spiritual level the patient "leaves the earth plane" in peace and surrounded by love.

I believe it is mean, not nice, sociopathic and even criminal to withhold information that could benefit people and animals. Our government systems are too broken to make this right but I do believe the Law of Karma will take care of things in the end. In the meantime, good people can do what they can to help each other and make this world a better place.

IN SUMMARY

If you took the time to read this chapter and aren't too triggered, thank you. I hope you found this information helpful and that it inspires you to look further into these alternatives.

There is so much to know about this area of knowledge. One key point is that to utilize it effectively to help others, one must get balanced mentally and learn to think along the right lines. It's that old adage "Physician, heal thyself." It doesn't matter if you use the spiritual path or knowledge of psychology to analyze yourself. Do it as an adventure. As Erin Michelle Galito says, "Don't take your spiritual journey–or yourself–seriously!"

> *"There are three classes of people: those who see, those who see when they are shown, those who do not see."*
> ~Leonardo da Vinci

And maybe all this talk is still just too weird for you. Don't worry about it. You can still do quite a bit with a good heart and the knowledge you develop on your own and the work you do should still be honored and celebrated.

PART VI

THE WHISPERING PROCESS
Deep Dive

Purpose of the process

Components of the process

Attunement

Build Trust

Build Communication

Build Confidence

Build Respect

BUD WILLIAMS (1932-2012)

I must give credit for this chapter to many ideas I learned from the writings of the quintessential whisperer Bud Williams. (www.stockmanship.com) Mr. Williams communicated with herd animals non-verbally and without contact to build trust. It's a unique concept that took years of dedicated practice for him to develop. Mr. Williams and his wife Eunice could herd just about anything into pens—including reindeer and poultry—without benefit of fencing or extra help and taught their technique internationally. Their work was a factor inspiring "low stress herding systems" for livestock and Dr. Sophia Yin's "Low stress Handling" for pets.

The Williams never published many books but held clinics and created a website with a wealth of information on all aspects of animal care and herding.

It took me a lot of rereading of his website articles to understand his techniques. His use of words is a little different but I finally came to understand what he meant. For example, he said that you must "work the herd" before herding them. I eventually understood that he spent a lot of time moving the animals around to see how they responded to how he moved around them. He made the point that each animal has their own "pressure points" and "points of balance" and don't read the diagrams you find in herding manuals. In Eunice's words, "Bud used pressure-release rather than fear and force to control animals. He always emphasized the importance of watching your animals, they will tell you if your position is right or wrong."

Bud Williams emphasized using "pressure" (rather than "flight") and staying in the "pressure zone" so the animal(s) are NOT frightened and move in a calm, controlled manner. Williams refers to this ability to keep control of the movement as "keeping contact."

Though it wasn't explicit, you can sense that he had a deep love and respect for the animals he worked with. His articles are full of wisdom about life as well as herding and are a delight to read.

Eunice Williams continues to offer their articles and videos on their website www/Stockmanship.com. His daughter Tina and her husband Tina Williams and Richard McConnell continue his legacy in imparting his techniques to those who wish to learn. (https://handnhandlivestocksolutions.com/)

THE WHISPERING
PROCESS

PULLING IT ALL TOGETHER

Horse whisperer Frank Bell's training techniques "embrace gentle handling with advanced communication." In the 1990's, Bell developed a series of steps to go through to make sure a horse has the right mindset before you get on its back. (www.horsewhisperer.com). He refers to this as his safety system—By getting attuned to the horse before you get on its back and making sure it is relaxed and willing, you are less likely to get hurt. As an older person learning to train a completely green horse, this seems like a great idea to me! The idea of letting a horse "buck it out" did not seem fun at all.

What I outline in this chapter is similar to what he does. The process I describe creates a relaxed scenario where bonding and learning can take place.

THE PURPOSE OF THE PROCESS

As mentioned in the introduction, The Process of Whispering gives you a game plan to

1) apply and practice your knowledge
2) learn how to apply this information as you interact (develop discernment) and
3) develop a Trust-based Relationship.

Use this order to develop a solid relationship.

THE COMPONENTS OF THE PROCESS

I've broken the process into 5 main components.

Attunement + Build Trust + Build Communication
+ Build Confidence + Build Respect

. These components are presented in the order I work, especially with troubled animals and people, to build the foundation for a healthy working relationship. If you already have a good rapport, you can breeze through most steps quickly then get right down to training. Working with untamed, traumatized or otherwise challenging cases will require starting from the beginning and patiently working through all the steps.

Each of these components could be a volume by themselves. In fact, there are whole books written about each of these concepts. This section is merely to point you in the right direction on how to integrate and prioritize them with some things I learned along the way. I delve into related concepts more elsewhere and encourage you to explore these topics in the works of other writers and speakers.

BUILDING THE FOUNDATION:

This is a concept taken from horse training and is sometimes referred to as "Foundation Training." Your relationship needs to be solid and is the "foundation" to get cooperation and learning. Work on the first step until you feel ready to move on to the next. As you work together, you will get into difficulties if there are holes in any one step. Difficulties are an indication that you may need to go back to the first or previous topic to work some more. The more effort you put into building this foundation, the more effective your training efforts will be.

ATTUNEMENT

get in tune with the person or animal you're working with. Like working on the same page, dancing to the same music, getting inside their head. Attunement gives you the ability to see the root cause of a certain behavior that you may want to change, be it aggression, shyness, etc. Attunement also allows you to know/ discern which teaching techniques would be most appropriate. The first step to becoming Attuned is recognizing its importance and making it a high priority.

For those who believe people can communicate with animals, instructors of this art tell their students to "send love" to the animal they wish to connect with. This might sound odd to a lot of readers. It does, however, have relevance with respect to your own vagal status. Those who believe in energetics will see it as a natural action to take. This is one of those "It can't hurt, doesn't cost anything and might in fact help" ideas.

Bud Williams' Low Stress Herding style is probably the most exquisite example of Whisperer's Focused Listening. It took me a few times of reading his blog with much between the lines to see this. Mr. Williams refers to this as "working the herd." He approaches the group and watches how they respond. He notices how his position, speed and other aspects of his actions change what the group does. During this time, he is building trust as well because if they start to move off too quickly, he immediately backs down. He doesn't try to get them going to their target pen until he is comfortable that they understand each other.

BUILD TRUST

Trust is required for cooperation. Trust is critical to the learning process because learning can only occur when they feel safe. Trust is required to keep your "student" in the Vagal/Zen Zone. (This is discussed in the chapter on neurophysiology) I started out writing a book titled "Trust-based Training," which shows how critical I think Trust is to the process. It still is central, but I'm rounding out the information a lot.

THE TWO MAIN FACETS OF TRUST

1) that you will not hurt him/her
2) that you will protect him/her from others. If they trust you, they will feel safer.

Sometimes you already have a decent level of trust, so this step goes very quickly. If you are working with a non-domesticated or feral animal, an abused/frightened animal or any other type of challenging animal, it will take longer.

It is VERY important not to cause physical pain or fear while you are building Trust, even when they do something bad or that you don't want. This is not the time for asserting yourself or making "corrections." FOCUS ON BUILDING THE TRUST FIRST.

They may challenge you but in all instances, avoid causing any physical pain during this trust-building process.

Another key point is to NOT take anything they do personally and not react in anger or fear if they try to hurt you. This breaks the cycle of them lashing out and getting into a battle with everyone who comes close.

Here are some ideas that help build trust:

Be a Protector When you take the role as a Protector, you make them feel safe and get what Karyn Purvis called "Trust Bank Deposits." Here are some ideas on how to do that:

Stop conflicts When there is a conflict, especially physical, you step In to stop it so that nobody gets hurt.

Stop the bullies When you see your subject bullied by another, you make it known that this will not be tolerated by reprimanding the bully. This puts you into the position of both a "Protector" and "Authority" for all involved to observe.

> When my kids, dogs, horses or chickens get into scuffles as they will over food or toys or attention, I make a loud noise or yell to make the altercation stop. With kids you have the added advantage of language. Getting to the bottom of how the situation started shows you really care about them, not just wanting to have peace and quiet. Fairness gains you respect, too.

> I keep my horses loose in a herd and they have an obvious pecking order. Some horses are afraid of others and won't go through gates if their bullies are nearby. So I will stand between them and the bully or make the bully go away so the horse has room to get through safely. This makes a deposit in my Trust Bank, as Karyn Purvis calls it, with the scared horse. It also asserts my leadership role with the bully.

Whisperers' Tricks to Build Trust: The Whisperers' Tricks trigger the Vagal system responses to facilitate the sense of safety, bonding and well being that are the foundations for trust as well as learning.

Please be sure to read the section on Safe Practices if you are attempting to work with potentially dangerous situations.

> **RESCUER EXERCISES** When I have to gain the trust of a parrot, I will startle them so they land on the ground (of course, their wings must be clipped first.) Parrots become afraid when on the ground because they feel vulnerable. They are more likely to step up on your hand because they are more afraid of the ground than of you. I find that each time I am able to get a parrot to "step up" from off the ground it becomes a little easier to get them to step up from the top of a cage because I am building Trust. If the bird has taken chunks out of me before, I still wrap my hand in a thick towel first, just to be safe. If I feel safe, I don't jerk my hand away if/when they try to bite.
>
> I also use this exercise with birds like cockatoos that are just plain bullies and delight in taking chunks out of hands.

REMEMBER: TRUST MUST BE BUILT
BEFORE ANY "CORRECTION" IS USED

This is especially important when working with traumatized, fearful or aggressive individuals. Control all interactions so that you will not be faced with needing to correct unwanted behavior. For example, don't take a dog out in public on a leash or get on the back of a horse until that trust bond has been built. You don't want to have to stop the dog from lunging at someone or a horse going where you don't want to go if you don't have that trust first.

Punishment/negative reinforcement/whatever you want to call it—is not to be used when working with fearful or resentful animals and people. Prematurely trying to teach new things can set you back quite a ways in building that trusting relationship that is so crucial.

In these cases, no reaction is the best way to handle what normally would warrant a "correction."

I learned this important point about not reacting to an outburst with Frankie the African Grey. He was psychotic from being locked in a tiny cage by his disabled owner. When approached he would alternately hide his head in a corner and mutter or face you and scream. Trying to pick him up for a nail trim was a nerve-wracking experience. One day he got out of his cage. I put my hand in front of him to see if he would step up on it. He latched onto my hand with his beak. I just left my hand in his beak and stared into his eyes. He stopped cold, looked back at me and let go. I was able to carry this now calm bird back to his cage and after that point I was his best friend. I have used this strategy with about every other species of animal with great success.

BUILD COMMUNICATION

Communication is the key to develop attunement and to teach/train/emotionally heal. You must understand what the animal or person is saying to you just as much as you must know how to convey clearly what you want them to learn or to do.

CLEAR COMMUNICATION TAKES EFFORT

Communication is very much a two way street that takes time to develop using verbal (words, sounds, volume, tone), visual (body language, gestures, facial expression, speed and direction of movement), tactile (touch, pressure as in cues for horses) and even telepathy/intuition. With people, words can have different meanings depending on your experience and culture.

It is important to make sure the messages are all in alignment so you aren't giving mixed signals. Think of the confusion to children given "Do as I say, not as I do" messages. (for example, a parent who smokes but tells their children not to because it's bad for their health.)

Mean what you say and say what you mean. Don't beat around the bush and make the other party guess what you're thinking (as in the case where a spouse gets upset that their partner chose "the wrong restaurant" after they said any place would be fine.)

SUBJECTIVE COMMUNICATION

Objective observation involves the 5 senses (sight, hearing, touch, smell, taste). Subjective observation comes through what we can't detect with those 5 senses but can FEEL them. This operates through the metaphysics and vibrational energy.

Thoughts and emotions convey energy and communicate on a metaphysical level. Therefore, remember to keep your thoughts and emotions in control and aligned with your words. Just feeling angry with someone is communicated. If someone says,

"I'm FINE" but feels otherwise, you can tell this is a mixed message. If you're trying to create a trusting bond but have reached a frustration level, take a break until you cool down.

It is your responsibility to make sure you are on the right track. This means putting out a message and watching to see if the message is understood. Too many times punishment will be doled out because someone assumed their animal or student was being disrespectful, when in fact they had no clue what the message meant. Don't be like one of those Americans who yell at people who don't understand English as if raising the volume will translate for you. Trial and error and persistence is the key. And don't forget Patience.

COMMUNICATION STYLES VARY BETWEEN SPECIES AND WITH INDIVIDUALS: With people, you can use words but there is a certain energy behind those words and body language.

Some people think talking to animals is silly. However, I found that animals respond to the tone of your voice as it conveys a message about your frame of mind. You can get a bunch of dogs (or kids) all energized by just talking with enthusiasm. The late dog whisperer Barbara Woodhouse wrote of being shameless when it came to talking with dogs like they were babies. I don't think it hurts to be demonstrative and make a difference. For example, Daisy is our grouchy rescue donkey who started greeting me at meal time when I cheerfully called out to her in my best Sesame Street voice. My horses respond to verbal commands combined with gestures as readily as my dogs.

A couple tips I use for getting the message across:

IMMEDIATE CONFIRMATION: when the desired response is performed: I make a huge enthusiastic fuss over a dog when they do what I asked them to do, especially in the training phase.

Clickers used in Clicker training work along this concept by providing a distinct signal when the response was the one desired.

"REWARD THE TRY" is a term used by horse trainers. It means even if they don't do it perfectly, reward any attempt in the right direction. If you "correct" them too soon, they may not understand where they are wrong and give up trying altogether.

This is particularly important with sensitive or timid individuals. For example, when I was paper training a terrier puppy, she would stand on the newspaper to potty but because her bottom was not always over the paper, she occasionally missed. After she was scolded for missing, she never would stand on the paper again. We ended up putting in a doggy door so she could go outside.

I've learned to be careful how to choose my words when pointing out mistakes to my student interns. They try very hard to learn an incredibly complicated job and feel bad when they don't do something right. I can tell that if I'm not careful, the sensitive ones might get discouraged and even give up.

TEACH BY OBSERVATION: When teaching my horses a new command, I will let them watch a trained horse hear the command then do the trick and get a reward for it. This allows them to process what you want when you give a command so that it's not a new scary confusing experience when it's their turn. It greatly accelerates the learning process as well.

REPEAT THE COMMAND UNTIL IT'S EXECUTED: When I give a command, I make sure it's executed before moving on. If you give a command and you go on even if it doesn't get executed, you're either not communicating clearly what you want OR if they know darn well what you are asking, you are communicating that it's not important they listen to you.

TIME/LOCATION ADDS MEANING: I mention elsewhere that the location and time of day add context to the meaning of your message. Thus, if you change where and when you are giving a command, it may take more effort to get the desired response.

In the Horse Training edition, I will have essays by Gerry Cox, Frank Bell and Bob Jeffries on Communication. These will give you different ideas on what you might try to communicate clearly as each has slightly different approaches.

For those who are open to the idea of Animal Communicators: Instructors of Animal Communication (Interspecies communication) all teach to "send thoughts of love or appreciation" to open the lines of communication with an animal. I can't say that I've been able to hold conversations with animals but it can't hurt and doesn't cost a cent.

ANIMAL COMMUNICATORS

In 1982 Penelope Smith came out with her pioneering book *Animal Talk* that explained how to communicate telepathically with animals. (www.animaltalk.net) I read it before I even applied for vet school. There are now many teachers and writers on that subject. I do not have the ability to work on this level but have used the services of two people (Marta Williams in California was one) who can give incredible insights into what individual animals are seeing and thinking. The advice they offered was dead on and saved me and the animals lengthy attempts to figure out health or behavioral problems. This amazingly was done over the telephone.

I participated in a workshop and realized that it would take me a lot of work to be able to do what some can do naturally. Nonetheless, learning about the communication process through websites, books and workshops can hone your empathetic connection with animals and people, which "whispering" is all about.

If you are in a tough situation, be open to contacting an animal communicator. Realize that, like with any services, the skill of the provider can vary greatly. Use your own discernment with any information and advice they provide. Do not expect 100% accuracy. If you keep these admonishments in mind, you may get the insights you need to fix a problem.

BUILD CONFIDENCE

You must feel confident and convey confidence in your request or ability to teach. If you show nervousness, it will affect your relationship. Either your student will not take you seriously OR will wonder why you are nervous and become nervous as well. "Fake it 'til you make it" can only take you so far but it might get you through long enough to build your own confidence with little successes.

Your student must feel confident that they can understand what you want and be able to do what you ask.

Lack of confidence creates anxiety and an increase in adrenaline levels. This reduces the ability to learn and if pushed too far leads to panic (crossing the threshold.) Negative response increases the anxiety so of course anything that could be construed as criticism should be avoided.

The key to building confidence is to slowly increase the difficulty while having a positive attitude. This is for yourself as the teacher as well as for your student. If you realize you've bitten off more than you can handle, or more than your student can handle, just back up and take smaller chunks.

Until there is both trust and confidence, negative responses must be used carefully to avoid setbacks in the relationship.

It is important to envision the student as capable of doing what you want them to do and that you are capable of getting them there. This mental picture will help immensely in making it a reality.

BUILD RESPECT

Respect is a complicated topic. It is a key component for a good working relationship. A Whisperer strives to maintain control of the situation at all times through Respect. This is taking your place at the top of the pecking order, pack, or hierarchy. This is both so that your teaching is efficient and for personal safety. It is not to feed an ego. A horse must go where the rider asks to go whether or not it really wants to. An out of control horse is a dangerous horse.

Even if you have the communication part down cold, an animal or person will only do what you ask or accept your teachings consistently if you have their respect.

You must be willing to assert yourself and correct behavior in a timely fashion. When you are able to stop a behavior, you are asserting your position in the hierarchy. With horses, the one with higher ranking will make the one of lower ranking move out of their path. Sometimes there are little scuffles but generally this order is accepted.

The appropriate level of correction is important. Don't use a chainsaw to prune a rose bush. Don't use a butter knife either. One will destroy your rose bush, the other will leave one of you frustrated and disrespected. Dr. Karyn Purvis of TBRI (Trust-Based Relational Intervention®) developed guidelines which I included in the "Soft Science" chapter.

The Purely Positive approach used by Clicker Trainers is a wonderful technique that works for the vast majority of individuals. However, you can get seriously hurt if a large animal chooses not to comply with your request to not come at you with teeth bared or stop running with you on the other end of a leash being dragged down the street.

While this is especially critical when working with alpha personalities that have aggression issues, respect comes into play in most relationships. You cannot teach nor lead without the respect of the other party. Even if you don't face physical hazards, a person or animal will not abide by rules you set if they don't respect you. This is how parents who want to be the equal friends of their children can get into difficulties when the children reach the rebellious teenage years.

Insisting on Respect is sometimes called "dominance" which has become a politically incorrect concept in this era. However, there are specific ways to assert your status as the dominant "top dog" without becoming an obnoxious tyrant or bully. You don't have to yell or fuss, you just need to out-stubborn them.

Years ago when I was in veterinary school working on my Masters' project, I was staying with a family in China. The 4 year-old son was rather spoiled and would refuse to cooperate though there was a lot of yelling at him by every adult in the household. I was given the opportunity to take him outside for some playtime even though I didn't speak much Cantonese and he spoke no English. When it was time to go inside, he refused to put his sandals back on and wanted to go up the stairs in bare feet. This was NOT a communication problem. I did the Stand Your Ground strategy: We weren't moving until those sandals were back on. He eventually put them back on and we went up the stairs. When it was time for me to go back to California, he asked when I was coming back again. I think I was probably the only adult in his life who didn't yell at him. Of course, he was not my child and it was not my place. But I think I got more respect from him because I was just plain stubborn

There are, of course, times when you should indeed do a bit of yelling to get a message across that non-compliance is not acceptable, as in when they are blowing you off disrespectfully. It takes practice to learn the difference.

One way to be a good boss is to show that respect goes both ways. Remember the Golden Rule—treat them as you would wish to be treated. To get respect, the other party must also feel their interests are respected as well. Taking into consideration their desires and showing kindness at all other times helps immensely. In a healthy relationship, respect is established through interactions until boundaries are agreed upon. This is where attunement comes into play as well.

You only need to act tough enough to stop unwanted behavior in its tracks.

ILLUSTRATING THE COMPLEXITIES
OF IMPULSE CONTROL

I had never had problems with dogs chasing and killing chickens after the first few encounters until I had dogs with Border Collie blood. The one that was half Kelpie turned out to be guilty of killing ducks when I wasn't watching her. One I got as a puppy started killing chickens at about 6 months old and no amount of scolding stopped her from killing when I wasn't watching.

And there are breed differences: I never had problems with dogs taking down sheep after months of training them. Then I got young German Shepherds. No amount of training would ever break them of these proclivities. I realized that they got excited when playing with each other or seeing something that triggered excitement. One time the shepherd must have gotten over excited by the smell of newborn lambs because she jumped a fence she'd never jumped before and killed one. It was not a Respect thing; it was an impulse control issue. (In my experience, the challenges drop off greatly once they hit about 5 years old and about 2 years for small dogs.) I learned to manage this by rehoming the Border Collies and tethering the Shepherds when we're at the sheep part of the ranch or whenever I anticipate them getting overly excited about anything. Moral of the story: Great dogs are still great dogs but be aware of potential challenges with any breed and be prepared to deal with possible consequences.

Impulse control issues are totally separate from Respect issues. While you still need to stop bad behavior dead in its tracks as part of the training, punishment for actions taken on impulse is not an appropriate consequence. If they acted on impulse, they are not thinking of the consequences and punishment just creates resentment or fear. If impulse control is the root of the problem, the long-term solution is to manage their exposure to triggers/temptations. Do not leave a bowl of candy out where the kids can reach them. Do not let a dog off leash where they might see a cat and want to chase it. Understand where unacceptable behavior is coming from. Some might think it a stretch to say animals understand the concept of "Fairness." However, I know that I must frequently assert my status with reprimands for breaches in the rules I've set. There is no degradation in our relationship if I do this right and for good reason.

HEALING THE EXTRA HARD CASES

Difficult cases—ones that are over-reactive or behave badly even after you've tried your best—are often results of emotional trauma or inappropriate corrections. In cases where bad behavior has been going on a long time, the constant battling itself creates emotional trauma. Keep in mind that chronic or severe emotional trauma creates changes in the brain and wiring. Healing involves returning it to normal function so that responses will become normal again. It's the same basic process as described before with a few extra considerations and more finesse.

Here is a short list of the additional considerations. You can insert your own words to fit whatever situation you are working with.

1) **Look for the root of the problem**. Don't stop at just changing the behavior. That is only a temporary fix, like putting tape on a leaking pipe. Look at all possible reasons then hone in on the most likely ones. OR Hone in on one but be willing to look at others if that doesn't work out.

   With people, you can use what Dr. Gabor Mate calls "Compassionate Inquiry." He says that the root of any sort of addiction and many mental illnesses comes from childhood trauma. (Trauma includes abuse on the physical, mental or emotional levels, inappropriate sexual contact that creates shame, living through war or gang-controlled neighborhoods, watching parents fight, needs not being filled due to neglect or the parents' inability to connect emotionally or demands on their own lives.) It takes work to dig out the event(s) that create this since many bury these memories or are very young when they happened. His work deserves a chapter on its own.

Like with the strategies for building communications, you need to be open to trying everything necessary to get the job done.

2) **Test your idea:** Find the threshold for overreaction, make a small change, then test again. If there is a response for the better, keep in that direction. If it doesn't seem to be working, try something different.

3) **Take baby steps and watch closely:** Make those changes little. This way you can watch for subtle changes in your student that tell you that you're approaching the Threshold for blowing up. You can then decide if you should take a different approach or take even smaller steps. Going slow and making adjustments along the way allows your path to develop organically. This is in contrast to the protocol/cookbook strategy of rigidly following a plan. If you miss those signs and slightly cross that Threshold into a reaction, generally the reaction will be easier to stop. It is NOT A MISTAKE to cross that Threshold.

4) **"Reward the try":** This is a term heard in Natural Horsemanship circles. Encouragement goes far in the push toward healing as well as building that bond. If appropriate, celebrate the little victories. Even if they don't succeed, celebrate the attempt itself.

5) **Keep a 360 perspective:** Even as you focus on one thing at a time, keep your peripheral vision on so you can catch clues on what other factors might be in play. I can assure you there may be many simultaneously. You can cure the

problem and kill the patient with the cookbook approach supported by evidenced-based research.

6) **Never give up:** When I was involved in advocating for students being bullied at our schools, I heard school counselors and teachers say "You can't help everyone." In my honest opinion, they did not really care very much. I saw the fruits of their indifference in the children who self-harmed and dropped out. Those who are dedicated are like loving parents who do all they can. These are the cases where Unconditional Love comes in handy. And be authentic! You cannot be effective unless you are.

When the dedicated reach the limits of their own capabilities, they work hard to seek outside help or make sure the case goes to good hands. You may not have the outcome you are hoping for but at least this one individual knows that someone in this world loves and cares for them. And who knows, you may hit the jackpot!

> *"If you are defiant, I will get you. I will figure out what makes you work. I might not get tremendous growth…but I'm going to get something out of you…I am the key to every door."*
> ~Kelli, a teacher from The Best Teacher In You

> *"Children need at least one person in their life who thinks the sun rises and sets on them, someone who delights in their existence and loves them unconditionally."*
> ~Pam Leo

In summary, I develop a specific type of relationship by hitting on all these principles but focusing on this order of priorities. Each of these principles have many facets that you only discover when you try to implement them. I will give you a head start by sharing what I've learned about accomplishing them.

You can start training/teaching at any time but, as mentioned before, it is important NOT to use any scolding until you have a level of trust built into the relationship. Anything perceived as "punishment" used before there is trust will set you back in your relationship. Too harsh a correction at any point can cause a setback in confidence and trust. There is a discussion of "corrections" and appropriate levels of response in the Soft Science chapters

The Threshold Concept and the Polyvagal Theory are important to understand. These really help you interpret what is happening in front of your eyes without the services of a psychic.

Each of these components has multiple layers. When you run into problems in training, it is a sign that there is a deficit in one of these layers. Go back to this list and see where you have a deficit so you can work on the problem effectively. If you still have difficulty finding the root of the problem, search through the other chapters for clues. Sometimes it requires much trial and error to find the specific issue. One key Whisperers hold is that they are stubborn creatures and never give up.

PART VII

WHISPERERS' TRICKS
Deep Dive

Positional Triggers
    The Hamilton Hold For Babies (Human):
    Laying Horses On Their Sides
    Sheep Tipping (sitting them on their rumps)
    Flipping Sharks, Rabbits, Chickens On Their Back
    Neck Flexing/Bending Exercises

Skin Pressure & "Body Work"
    Massage
    T-Touch by Linda Tellington Jones
    Working the Happy Spots
    Pole-Taming For Wild Mustangs:

Deep Breathing
    Pranayama Yoga exercises
    Running/Physical Exercise

Meridian/Acupuncture Points
    Tapping/Emotional Freedom Technique (EFT)
    Endotapping for horses
    Sucking On Lollipops to Stimulate Labor Contractions
    Tongue Pressure on Roof of Mouth During Breathing
    Exercises
    Ocular Compression
    Rolling the Eyes Upward
    Horse Twitching Lip Twitch/ Shoulder Twitch/Ear
    Twitch
    Mouth T-Touch or "Working the Tongue:"
    Massaging the Gums
    Paul Williamson's TAP
    Massaging Points On and Behind the Ears
    Cat Scruffing ("Clipnosis")
    A Rope Around the Left Front Leg of a Horse

Other Methods
  Occupational Therapy Tools
  Mindfulness
  Vagal Maneuvers
      Carotid Sinus Massage
      Mammalian Diving
      Valsalva Maneuver
      Hang the Child Upside Down
      Do a Handstand for 30 Seconds
  Acts Of Kindness / Service To Others
  Reflex Integration
  Sound Frequency
  Rhythm
  The Magic Of Music
  Dancing
  Animal Assisted Therapy

WHAT ARE "WHISPERERS' TRICKS"

Whisperers' Tricks are techniques that can be used to calm, encourage trust and promote a positive relationship. Most are techniques that utilize the Vagal response. Some, like music, are ways of engaging the individual and luring them into activities that get them to let down their psychological walls between you two and participate in learning activities that help them physically and mentally. If done correctly, these techniques are easy to use and handy to know But ALWAYS REMEMBER THE THRESHOLD CONCEPT .

These techniques will sometimes appear to have miraculous effects and provide breakthroughs. They are really just one factor that edges you and your patient/student toward that threshold where a desired change will be seen.

There are no Magic Bullets. The failure of a technique to work is not an indication of failure but is a sign that 1) the one executing it needs a higher level of skill or 2) there are other factors preventing this technique from working and those must be addressed as well. Just like the time my car wouldn't start and I thought the repairs we spent lots of money on had failed. I just needed to put gas in the tank!

My goal is not to teach you how to do these techniques but to make you aware of their existence and encourage you to look further into ones that intrigue you. Exploring is a lot of fun because you will discover some really neat ideas. Maybe you will create some of your own!

PRACTICAL APPLICATIONS
OF WHISPERERS' TRICKS

As mentioned before, Robert Redford laid down a crazy trau-matized horse in the movie "*The Horse Whisperer*" and when it got up it was healed. It's not magic. Whisperers routinely use techniques to get animals and people to calm down and feel good things toward them.

We now recognize that many of these techniques have their basis in the autonomic nervous system and the Polyvagal response, though the exact mechanisms may still need to be worked out.

These are not just parlor tricks. Sometimes the subjects will enter an altered mental state mimicking sedation without needing drugs. This has useful applications as anyone who has wrangled an uncooperative animal will agree.

USE IN DESENSITIZATION

The added benefit of a calm or even sedated state associated with some of these techniques, in some cases, is being able to desensitize while they are immobilized. In other words, you can expose the subject to something they normally panic over without them actually panicking. This is accomplished by changing the threshold for panicking or overexcitement while exposing them to "that scary thing." If you do this right, the subject will later be okay with that scary thing even without sedation.

For example, Buck Wheeler uses his "Stablelizer" halter which hits calming acupuncture points, to train skittish horses to load into a trailer. Professor Beery and John Rarey in their old-time horse training courses will lay fractious horses down, (some give a massage for additional relaxation/sedation) then make all sorts of commotion around them with whips, power tools, etc. to effectively desensitize them to these noises and activities. (This is what my horse trainer did before he took my horses on the road with carts.) When these horses get up, they are safe and easy to ride. Bill Richey of the National Mounted Police Services told me those years ago, horses in training would be given a light dose of acepromazine to get them through their first Mardi Gras as part of the "bomb proofing" process. After that initiation, the horses would be fine in crowds of revelers without any medication.

USE IN SELF-REGULATION

The late Dr. Karyn Purvis developed Trust-Based Relational Intervention (TBRI) for children in foster care or adoption who had relational trauma. She writes: "In one of our learning groups (called a Nurture Group) we will practice several skills for self-regulation, such as deep breathing, using fidgets, and pressing the parasympathetic pressure point just over the middle of their lip. Due to the holding of their finger sideways to press across the top of their lips, the children[27] call this activity the "magic mustache."

---

[27] Purvis, K. B., Cross, D. R., Dansereau, D. F., & Parris, S. R. (2013). Trust-Based Relational Intervention (TBRI): A Systemic Approach to Complex Developmental Trauma. Child & Youth Services, 34(4), 360–386. http://doi.org/10.1080/0145 935X.2013.859906

USE IN HEALING PTSD AND OTHER EMOTIONAL OVERREACTION

Emotional trauma etches itself into the subconscious through the limbic system of the brain. When a triggering event or sight is encountered again, it creates a reflexive emotional response.

Some hypnotherapists have their patients with PTSD recall "the scary experience" as an uninvolved onlooker. This helps the patient mentally process the experience without triggering the emotional response and they are able to heal (See the websites of Mark Tyrrell and Marisa Peer) Of course, you can't talk animals into hypnotic states and mental imagery but these techniques likely work in the same way.

WHY THE SPOTTY SUCCESS RATES?

Some of these techniques come under fire for being "ineffective" or "inhumane." A lot of techniques are not effective because people aren't using them correctly. When these techniques aren't working, some people keep trying without make corrective changes and the techniques get a reputation for being "abusive." There are even scientific research papers concluding that equipment like electronic collars (aka "shock collars") and scruffing cats should not be used. [28,29]

When you read the research methodology, it is clear that the researchers must have a low level of experience or knowledge of the appropriate use of these techniques.

It would be beneficial if knowledge were better conveyed. For example, "I would guess that fewer than 5 percent of experienced horse handlers, including equine veterinarians, know how to use

---

[28] Overall, K. (2007). Why electric shock is not behavior modification.(editorial) Journal of Veterinary Behavior, Vol3, Issue 4,171–175.

[29] Moody CM, Mason GJ, Dewey CE, Niel L. Getting a grip: cats respond negatively to scruffing and clips. Vet Rec. 2020 Mar 28;186(12):385. doi: 10.1136/vr.105261. Epub 2019 Oct 5. PMID: 31586939.

a twitch effectively," says Sue McDonnell, PhD, certified applied animal behaviorist of the University of Pennsylvania School of Veterinary Medicine in Philadelphia. [30]

Indeed, I was not taught the mechanics and application correctly in the number one veterinary school in the country! I recall a story told by an instructor at the vet school: a professional athlete asked to hold the chain lip twitch on his own horse while the veterinarian worked. He was so nervous he applied too much pressure and almost tore off the lip of his poor horse.

The improper use of these techniques results in failure to restrain/sedate, injury to the subject or handler, and outcry against the use of the technique altogether. One tragic case involved caregivers wrapping an out-of-control child in a blanket and sitting on him because they were told that this would calm him. The child died by suffocation and the caregivers were charged with manslaughter. This of course leads to people being reluctant to use this "risky procedure" though "common sense" would tell us that we need to make sure the child can breathe. In our litigious culture (especially California) it is best to assume there is no such thing as "common sense."

Understanding the science will hopefully encourage people to take these techniques seriously and seek adequate training to use them safely and correctly.

PLEASE NOTE: I've provided this information so that you can research them further using "key words" if you find ideas intriguing. I do not claim to be an expert on any of these techniques. Some techniques can be risky to both the trainer and subject. They should not be tried without doing your research and getting appropriate training.

---

[30] McDonnell, S. (2017, September 25). Using the twitch properly. The Horse. Retrieved October 21, 2021, from https://thehorse.com/15767/using-the-twitch-properly/

In case that wasn't clear enough, I will say it using other words: Just because you read about it here does not mean I encourage you to try something at home. Be sure to research a technique thoroughly before attempting anything. If possible, have someone with experience demonstrate the technique to you and if you can, have them watch over your shoulder while you try it yourself.

ROUNDUP OF
WHISPERERS TRICKS

Here is a list of ways to get your subject to calm down, cooperate, learn better and even like you more. In short, these alter mental and physical states. Most of them involve the vagal response. Some facilitate neural rewiring. Others operate on the Metaphysical level.

These are also ideas for dealing with stress in your own life. If you're like me, you have plenty of opportunities to see if they help.

This is an attempt to open eyes on the incredible range of things you might try. My daughter just received her doctorate in Occupational Therapy and is learning Reflex Integration, which opened up a whole new world to explore. All these years, I thought occupational therapy was for getting people back to regular life after debilitating injuries or illnesses. Occupational therapists actually work with special needs children as well. Many of the ideas in this chapter are from websites for occupational therapists and parents of children with difficulties. Even if your child is not diagnosed with a condition, many of these ideas can help for those times when they are threatening to have a meltdown or challenging you with misbehavior. You might use them for yourself or the animals in your life as well.

I include techniques I find useful for calming down uncooperative animals so you can get a job done (horseshoeing, nail trims, injections, wound tending, etc,) with less chance of getting hurt. I've grouped by what seem to be the main mechanism that triggers them.

These techniques are ADJUNCTS to training, not to replace training. In other words, these will help you get the job done or a lesson learned more easily but you still need to do work to get misbehaviors adjusted.

I go into more detail on certain topics especially when there is little written information about them. I encourage you to explore ones that intrigue you. I hope this chapter will spark some ideas in those who think creatively.

Again, this is not an invitation to go out and try anything I've written about. It is an effort to increase awareness of available techniques and their mechanisms so that if you hear about them, you'll understand how they work. There are too many great products that get bad reputations because people just aren't using them properly. Pets get hurt or emotionally damaged by well-meaning owners.

BE SAFE! Be sure to research and seek out more knowledge from those with experience before you try it. Do it for short periods of time and watch for the response. If they fight it, don't push it. You might try again using a different amount of pressure or changing the speed.

SENSORY INPUT/CONTROL

SENSORY OVERLOAD

ELECTROCONVULSIVE THERAPY (ECT) formerly known as Electro shock therapy used in human medicine for psychiatric treatment. This seems to reset the circuitry in the brain. Current techniques use much lower voltage than the levels used in the past that caused alarming seizures and violent muscle convulsions. While there is seizure activity in the brain, there are no muscle convulsions at current levels. Depression sufferers report they feel much better afterward these treatments

OPOSSUMS & FAINTING GOATS—When scared or overly excited, these animals will become unconscious and fall over ("playing 'possum") Of course, I don't know if they wake up happier. While there aren't any training benefits in making an opossum faint, I wanted to include this as examples of what I've referred to as the "Vagal freeze" involving the primitive dorsal Vagal system. It is in fact a component of Paul Williamson's TAP technique for horses.

"CONFUSED CONSCIOUSNESS" IN HORSES—When horses in training are walked backwards, they can go into an "obtunded" mental state where their legs buckle under them and they stumble. Trainer Gerry Cox coined this term and uses it in his training program. It may involve sensory overload and a dorsal vagal activation but could involve a complex mechanism which I don't think anyone has researched. I hope by writing about it, someone

will be inspired to study this reaction and maybe find even more useful applications for it.

"CONFUSED CONSCIOUSNESS"

Confused Consciousness is a phenomenon that horse trainer Gerry Cox of Mountain House Stables, Corvalllis, Montana sees in horses just entering training. When he gets a new horse in for training he will first teach it to walk backward without a saddle on until it "feels soft on the face and free in the feet." Then when he puts the saddle on, he will ask it to move a hip sideways and then back up, even if it is just one step. In many cases, the horse will appear to go into an altered mental state to the point of their legs buckling under them and almost having to lie down. He has named this response "confused consciousness."

Cox says he will repeat the request to back up until the horse is again "soft in the face and free in the feet." When the horse has this been put through this exercise several times, it will stop responding this way. Cox says that this is because it has learned that it is easier to accept the saddle and understand that backing-up is easier than to sag or consider lying down! However, I suspect this is an involuntary response that doesn't involve choosing to sag or to walk normally. Rather, I hypothesize that walking backwards with all this new equipment is new stimuli that when used all at once overloads the brain and, similar to opossums and fainting goats, throws it into primitive vagal freeze. I believe that after enough repetitions, the novelty has worn off and these neural responses stop happening. But this is just my best guess. Perhaps if we understand the mechanisms involved, we can utilize this response for training or diagnostic purposes. I look forward to hearing what anyone else finds out!

Photo provided by Gerry Cox

NEUROLINGUISTIC PROGRAMMING
(HYPNOSIS AND GUIDED MEDITATION)

Hypnosis utilizes a relaxed mental state and Alpha Brain Waves to change the neural patterns of the limbic subconscious brain and alter the way it responds. I discovered two practitioners who work in the style of Whisperers and highly recommend a peek into their websites.

Uncommon Knowledge www.unk.org has many worthwhile articles and videos on the use of hypnotherapy with an exceptionally compassionate approach. Mark Tyrrell uses conversational, Ericksonian hypnotherapy on "solution-focused therapy and making unconscious changes through hypnosis" He heals PTSD with one application: By using words with a particular tone and rhythm, he puts people into a state of deep relaxation (neurolinguistics). Once there, he has them revisit the triggering experience like an uninvolved bystander so that the emotional response is not triggered. This allows a processing of the memory without the physical reactions usually associated with it and rewiring of the limbic system. If done correctly, future exposures to the triggering event will not cause those disturbing reactions associated with PTSD.

Marisa Peer uses a similar process that she calls "Rapid Transformational Therapy.' She describes RTT as a combination of psychotherapy, hypnotherapy, Cognitive Behavioral Therapy (CBT) and Neurolinguistic Programming (NLP). She also provides online training for this (www.marisapeer.com). One special application she uses to treat depression is developing the patient's sense of self-worth with the simple phrase "I am enough." Well-meaning parents who set high standards for their children can inadvertently set their offspring off for internalized feelings of failure (children's brains are impressionable and easily programmed until the age of 7.) I can see from personal experience how hypnotherapy may be useful in getting us to embrace this phrase because the programming can be so deep. This is also a cautionary message to be sure your children know you love them unconditionally even if they can't meet the high goals you show them.

Neuro Linguistic programming has also been used by the American government in unethical and cruel military mind control programs and by marketing companies to sell you things you really don't need. I trust that the readers of this book would not ascribe to this path of manipulating people for your personal gain.

The Silva Mind Control Method was developed by Jose Silva in 1944 and presented to the public in the 1960's He described this process as "dynamic meditation," which involves relaxing the body and quieting the mind, letting the slowed brain-wave frequency (Alpha waves) engage the Right Brain. Silva describes the Right Brain as "in touch with the rest of intelligence in the Universe, the Creative Source that creates." (His books also use the terms, "Higher Self," and "the Other Side," This intelligence finds solutions to problems, heals abnormalities and creates harmony, The intuition can be used by business owners to make the best decisions, medical practitioners more accurately diagnose and treat patients. His technique even assists in "sending healing energy" to individuals who need it (more in "Everything is Energy"). I find his discussions of neurophysiology and rewiring the brain highly informative. His method is currently being promoted in expensive self-help programs but you can easily find videos on YouTube and copies of his many books to learn these techniques on your own. (SEE ARTICLE in Metaphysical Stuff)

Guided meditations have become a popular way people get into a relaxed state by listening to audio presentations. This allows them to work on "rewiring" their brains to change undesirable responses to ones that are more beneficial and socially acceptable. Many websites offer meditations for free or as purchases.

Covering The Eyes / Working In Darkness—If an animal can't see what you are doing, it will not get upset and react to your movements. In technical jargon, this takes out the visual input that can trigger an excitatory response. You are essentially moving the threshold for excitement by reducing the number of excitatory inputs

I also knew that covering the eyes of out-of-control animals calms them down. Throwing a towel over the eyes of sheep and cattle is a stockman's trick to get things done. I use towels on every fractious animal I work with. On smaller ones, you can control all the limbs and cover the teeth and eyes all at the same time.

Daisy the Donkey was a rescue that I have not been able to touch in the 6 years she's been on my ranch. Norman Eggert is the only one who has ever been able to help me trim her feet. He has the patience of a saint and has gained her trust.

This photo shows how he used the lab coat I was wearing to cover her eyes after he got her tied to a fence rail. It took quite awhile to get her tied the first time. . She didn't struggle while he worked on her hooves.

I'll take the opportunity to point out that Norman is a neighbor who renovates and manages residential rental housing. He has to be one of THE most talented animal handlers I've ever met. We have been friends for 25 years and I only learned this about him in the last few years when he started helping me with Daisy. Just an example of how talents can be so well hidden in humble people.

Birds do not see well at night. When I need to catch chickens, I work in the dark because they do not fly away as readily. My son Andrew even taught me how in the dark they will step up onto your hand and calmly sit as you walk them over to where you need them.

Once when I lost an African Grey parrot and found her 12 ft up in a neighbor's tree. I waited until nightfall and was able to catch her because she could not see what I was doing and was afraid to fly in the dark. I was glad this worked because I had to use a ladder at 8 months pregnant with a toddler in tow!

The Thundercap

This product is produced by Thundershirts. It "reduces the visual stimulus that can make a dog agitated by filtering its vision." You can see by the packaging how this product and strategy can be used.

The Ram Shield Premier 1 makes a "ram shield" to keep people

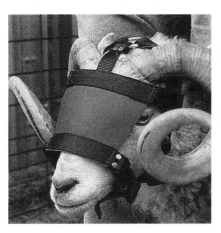

and other sheep safe from aggressive rams. (www. premiersupplies.com) "Ram shields are used to block the ram's forward vision—which prevents rams from charging humans or other rams." We used one on our Jacobs ram. It gave us some lead time to run before he figured out where we were and tried coming at us.[31]

---

[31] **Ram shield for horned breeds Photo courtesy of Premier 1**

DEEP PRESSURE STIMULATION

There are a number of ways we've been calming animals and people without realizing it. Pressure receptors in different parts of the body elicit the Vagal response and subsequent releases of calming factors. In recent years, the need to alleviate stress of living in our modern world and the rise in autism has spawned an industry of research and product development. A good history of deep pressure stimulation techniques, including the Grandin Hug machine, strait jackets and weighted blankets can be found on this website article https://truhugs.com/research-science/do-weighted-blankets-work-temple-grandin-hugging-machine/[32]

Here is a rundown of techniques that use this mechanism. I added details where I had opportunity to communicate with people who actually use or studied these techniques:

SWADDLING BABIES: Tightly bundling babies keeps them calmer. In hospital neonatal units, you will see rows of babies wrapped like little mummies

Asian baby carriers that hold the baby tightly on the back do the

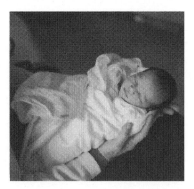

same. I used the Chinese version to carry my children

while I did my housework. It was a square piece of cloth the size of a bandana with straps sewn on to each corner. They are a bit tricky to use so the baby doesn't fall out

[32] V. (Ed.). (2020, December 19). Temple Grandin Hug Machine: How Did Weighted Blanket Research Begin? Retrieved March 24, 2021, from https://truhugs.com/research-science/do-weighted-blankets-work-temple-grandin-hugging-machine/

so you need to get the hang of getting it adjusted. I would set the carrier up in a chair, put the baby on top of the carrier, back into them both then tie them on. These carriers are now on the market as "Meh Dai" Bei Dai, Mei Tai or just "Asian baby carriers". If they got fussy, I could bounce the baby on my back and they would calm down, even go to sleep so I could finish the vacuuming. I considered it an essential survival technique for mothers with babies and too much to get done. (See also the "Hamilton Hold")[33],[34]

BURRITO-WRAPPING SMALL ANIMALS:

This is a favorite technique of veterinarians and vet technicians who have to do something to an uncooperative small animal or parrot.

Like swaddling babies, it involves wrapping an animal in a towel so they cannot move their limbs to get away, kick or bite you. If you've done it right and they aren't in pain from the way their limbs are positioned, they will stop struggling. It does take a bit of practice to get good at it. One must take care to make sure it is not so tight that it restricts breathing and that the nose is not covered so much air cannot enter. **Always make sure the chest is moving. Continued struggling may be a sign that the position of the limbs may be painful or they cannot get enough air to breathe.**

With really wild ones, you can throw a thick towel over them then proceed to roll them up in the towel. This keeps them from seeing your hands reaching for them and your hands are protected from claws and teeth if you do it right.

I also have used home-made or commercially produced "cat bags" when I needed to do procedures like

---

[33] **My daughter at 1 day old when she didn't**
[34] **My son Andrew when he was small enoug**
   "oi-dai."

fluid administration without help on cats that were not inclined to cooperate. My bags were made of heavy canvas with strategically placed zippers to access limbs or other parts of the body. I recently found them for sale as "cat grooming bags. While it would need to be tightened to produce whole body pressure, it might be easier for some people to keep on a cat than a towel." That said, it can also be tricky getting a cat into the bag as opposed to the ease of letting them out. (Sorry, I could not resist making this joke)[35]

BENGKUNG BELLY BINDING OF POSTPARTUM WOMEN: In a Malaysian ritual, women who have recently had a baby have their mid-sections wrapped tightly as part of a caretaking ritual. Belly binding classes and services are now offered in the United States as well. Not only does this support their stretched out muscles but they feel emotionally better through the deep pressure on vagal receptors. Postpartum depression is not reported in these cultures, likely for many reasons but this can add a physical factor.[36]

This brings to mind those old-fashioned girdles. Maybe wearing one did more than give women an hourglass figure. Not many of us just had babies and need postpartum support, but many of us have stress and perhaps a girdle would be worth trying.

TEMPLE GRANDIN'S HUG MACHINE:
Dr. Grandin, who has autism, realized that she calmed down and felt better when she put herself under the weight of sofa

---

[35] **The Cat Sack by Campbell Pet Company**

[36] Clark, B. (2018, March 07). The art of the sacred belly bind. Retrieved April 02, 2021, from https://www.birtharts.com/the-art-of-the-sacred-belly-bind/

cushions. She developed the "squeeze machine" to achieve the same effect for others that might benefit from this effect. According to Wikipedia, "A hug machine, also known as a hug box, a squeeze machine, or a squeeze box, is a deep-pressure device designed to calm hypersensitive persons, usually individuals with autism spectrum disorders. The therapeutic, stress-relieving device was invented by Temple Grandin while she was attending college and was used on college students in a study".

WEIGHTED BLANKETS FOR PEOPLE—These are now being marketed to help people sleep better, especially if they live stressful lives or are on the autistic spectrum. TruHugs in San Diego, CA is a company that makes them. Their website www. truhugs.com also provides many good research articles about the benefits of deep pressure stimulation.

WHEAT PRESSURE BOX FOR HORSES:
A horse is loaded into a container which is then filled with grain until only its head is exposed. It has the greatest calming effect on high strung fearful horses. Mustang trainers use this technique to calm down horses as part of their training process.[37] I have heard of a similar to putting a horse into a pool of water

NEWBORN ANIMAL SQUEEZE SEDATION:
When newborn or very young animals are held tightly around the chest, they will fall asleep and go limp. In veterinary literature, it's called "squeeze-induced somnolence." I'm personally partial to the rancher term "the flop reflex." Interestingly, we did not learn about this in veterinary school that I recall and there isn't anything I could find in American veterinary journals. I first learned of this

---

[37] Grandin, T. (n.d.). The use of the wheat pressure box on horses (equine restraint system). Retrieved April 02, 2021, from https://grandin.com/behaviour/tips/equine.restraint.html

phenomenon because Dr. John Madigan of UC Davis utilized this technique to address a condition called "dummy foal syndrome."

I eventually tracked down his colleague Dr. Derek C Knottenbelt, Director of Equine Medical Solutions Ltd, who told me it was a well-known restraint method by stud farm owners in the U.K. and that he used it in college many years ago.[38]

This phenomenon has been documented in foals (horses), calves (cattle), crias (alpacas) and even piglets. Dave and Sheila Scroggins of Colusa Riverside Alpacas told me this works in crias up to several months old. Ellen Jackson of Victory Rose Farms in Vacaville tells me it works in foals up to 10 days old.

I presume that the mechanism for this is similar to the reflex that causes horses and sheep to go into a sedated state when they are laid down or sat on their rumps. I am mentioning this because I see valuable practical applications for this phenomenon in restraint of babies without using drugs that carry risks. I'll go into more detail here because there is very little in the literature about it.

---

[38] (personal email 4/8/2021) OBE, BVM&S, DVM&S, DipECEIM, DACVIM, MRCVS (Recognised RCVS and European Specialist in Equine Internal Medicine)

THE MADIGAN FOAL SQUEEZE

Neonatal Maladjustment Syndrome (NMS) aka "Dummy Foals" occurs in 3-5% of baby horses. They are born acting dazed, don't seem to recognize their mothers and won't nurse. 80% survive with intensive medical care, which is costly and labor intensive. Generally, these are treated with intensive management of feeding and careful monitoring with the hope they come out of it.

Dr. Madigan from University of California Davis School of Veterinary Medicine has done research on what is now called "Madigan's Foal Squeeze Procedure:[46][47][48]

Dr. Madigan associates dummy foals with cesarean sections and quick births when the babies don't go through the compression needed to drop the blood levels of hormones that have a sedative effect to keep them quiet while developing inside the mom. His research has shown that the chest compression causes slow wave sleep and drops in the progesterone associated hormones that are thought to keep babies asleep until they are born and out of the womb.

The researchers used a rope around the chest in loops like ranchers use to make cattle lay down (this is called "casting a cow."). When they pull the rope backward toward the tail the baby is simultaneously squeezed and pulled down.

---

[39] (Pickles, K., Madigan, J., Torske, S., & Aleman, M. (2014). Use of squeeze-induced somnolence for routine plasma administration in healthy neonatal foals. Equine Veterinary Journal, 46, 4-4.

[40] *Madigan J.E., Restraint and Handling of Foals" in Manual of Equine Neonatal Medicine by Madigan J.E. Updated: AUG 25, 2016

[41] Toth, B., Aleman, M., Brosnan, R. J., Dickinson, P. J., Conley, A. J., Stanley, S. D., . . . Madigan, J. E. (2012). Evaluation of squeeze-induced somnolence in neonatal foals. American Journal of Veterinary Research, 73(12), 1881-1889.

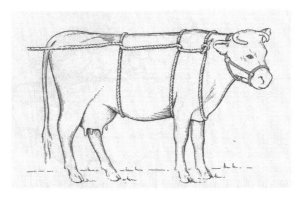

Rope squeeze on a cow from *"Restraint of Animals"* **by John Leahy & Pat Barrow 1951**

After 20 minutes, the length of time it might spend in the birth canal, the rope is untied. The baby usually gets up onto its feet, is more alert and often immediately starts nursing. Madigan says this is effective in the first 24-48 hours. He has collaborated with researchers of autism. You will be able to find many videos and articles through an internet search on "Madigan Foal Squeeze."

The same condition occurs in calves, goats and alpacas with different presentations and different names (PSR/Poor Suckle Reflex, "Weak Calf Syndrome") This technique has worked in a calf that was a difficult breech birth where likely too much time was spent in the birth canal. Thus there are other reasons for the "obtunded" (dazed) presentation than just too little time in the canal. While I could not find other case reports of this technique's use in calves, the veterinary literature recommends repeating this multiple times if necessary, so it must have been tried by others.

Interestingly, a month old kid (baby goat) recovered from this condition after a goat in labor licked it incessantly for hours, which is basically a full body massage. This is additional evidence suggestive of a Vagal-responsive component to this condition.

Colusa Riverside Alpacas use this idea for crias that were born "not quite right". They were concerned about breaking ribs of a crias (baby alpaca) with a rope so they gave the babies a bear hug squeezing it around the chest. This provided the same response as with the rope technique with several "dummy crias". They said this technique can sedate babies up to several months old in contrast to foals where the technique stops working at a much earlier age.

Neonatal squeeze performed on a "dummy cria" (baby alpaca) Photo courtesy of Colusa Riverside Alpacas

PRACTICAL APPLICATION OF THE FOAL SQUEEZE

Ellen Jackson of Victory Rose Farms in Vacaville CA part-nered with Dr. Madigan in his foal squeeze research. She uses the technique routinely with a custom designed harness to administer plasma and medications to day old Thoroughbred foals at her breeding facility.

The harness has straps that wrap about the chest, across the rump and around the shoulders. Ellen was kind enough to have me watch the process: When she tightened the chest straps the foal got groggy and in minutes lay down to take a nap. She said the straps are more comfortable than the ropes so the foal stays asleep better. They use lidocaine and do anything else they can to minimize arousing the baby from slumber while they work on it. "We give all our babies a liter of plasma the day after they are born. The squeeze certainly sedates them but they still hear noise and feel pain so the addition of a small amount of xylazine (sedative) overcomes that. Also covering their eyes helps. It works up until about 10 days old. Some foals are much more receptive to it. Some need a small amount of additional sedation, xylazine. But ½ cc works really well in conjunction with the squeeze."

I had the opportunity to watch this procedure. I would think that every vet, technician and horse owner would want to know about this trick so they can work with babies much more easily.

MY LITTLE DUMMY CALF STORY

As a side note, we had a calf born here who may have had a mild case of "dummy calf syndrome." He had a fairly normal birth which took about 2 hours from when I first saw front feet poking out to a baby on the ground. While he apparently nursed okay after birth and followed mom normally for the first day (animal people will be relieved to know he must have gotten his colostrum), the baby increasingly became weaker and more tired. I found it trying to nurse on his dad, Jed, who shares their pen. I got Lenny on a bottle and for the next three days, I milked mom out just so we could bottle feed him. While I was milking Boo Cow, Lenny would suckle on my face and arms. In between milking attempts, I would guide his mouth to a teat I had handy. Each feeding time he took it for longer lengths of time. He finally transferred back to mom for full meals after those 3 long days. Thankfully.

I shared this story to show a possible contrasting presentation of NMR with a normal delivery length (veterinary journals won't accept case history reports anymore) and thought you might enjoy the visual of me under a cow trying to milk her while a calf is latched onto my face. I wish I had thought of trying the rope trick to see if it would have shortened this process.

STRAITJACKETS: A **strait jacket** is a garment shaped like a jacket with sleeves that are then tied behind the wearer's back to keep the arms from moving. It was originally used for restraining people who may cause harm to themselves or others. Once the wearer slides their arms into the sleeves, the person restraining the wearer crosses the sleeves against the chest and ties the ends of the sleeves to the back of the jacket, ensuring 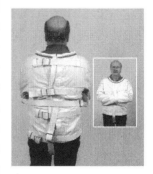 the arms are close to the chest with as little movement as possible. It does provide some calming effects through deep pressure.

However because it was used by facilities who just didn't have enough staff to properly care for patients and just left them on so they could get work done, straitjackets became associated with inhumane treatment or even torture. Thus, straitjackets have been relegated to Halloween party costumes, zombie movies and props for escape artists and magicians. Interestingly, you can find "straitjackets for babies" on the internet which are a form of a swaddling garment. Hopefully, recognition of the benefits of straitjackets and proper guidelines will lessen the stigma attached to their use.

"THUNDERSHIRTS" FOR DOGS:

A dog garment made of stretch knit fabric and a Velcro-adjustable flap is on the market at time of publication. The tight fit provides the pressure to calm fearful dogs (as in during a thunderstorm.) (www.thundershirts.com)

T-TOUCH BODY WRAPS: Dr. Tellington-Jones has developed several ways of applying elastic wraps to the body of horses, dogs and people to elicit the calming response through light skin pressure and triggering proprioception receptors for better body awareness and coordination. Books on this technique are available on their website. (www.ttouch.ca)

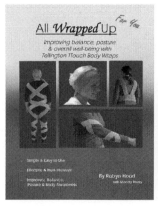

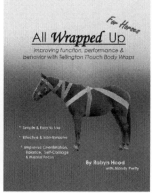

POSITIONAL TRIGGERS

I believe (hypothesize) pressure receptors in the chest and abdomen (intrathoracic/intra-abdominal) are triggered by the shift in weight from the internal organs. So these may be a variation or subset of Deep Pressure Stimulation.

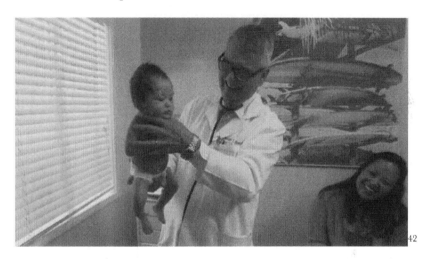

THE HAMILTON HOLD FOR BABIES (HUMAN): Pediatrician and baby whisperer Dr. Robert Hamilton is author of *7 Secrets of Newborns.* In this wonderful book, he includes a magical hold for soothing an upset, crying baby. I'm sure it triggers the Vagal response. I wish I knew this when my children were tiny and think every new parent or caretaker would love to learn this trick!

Dr. Hamilton says this can be used during the first 2-3 months of life while they are light enough to do this safely. He demonstrates in his video how to support the baby with its arms folded across its chest, supported on your forearm. You hold its bottom with your other hand. Gently bounce and jiggle it. Most babies will stop crying and look around. Videos of this technique are available on

---

[42] **Dr. Robert Hamilton with a baby calmed by the Hamilton Hold.**

the internet as well. By the way, I highly recommend his book for even more great information on helping babies develop mentally and physically and how parents can stay sane in the process.

LAYING HORSES ON THEIR SIDES: When horses are laid on their sides, they go into a trance, sleep or sedated state (in vet school, they called it "obtunded.") and stay that way even after restraints are removed. This technique was demonstrated in the movie Robert Redford movie *"The Horse Whisperer."* You can find these techniques described in books by JR Rarey and Professor Jesse Berry that came out in the last century. After the horses wake up and get back on their feet, they are calmer and easier to work with.

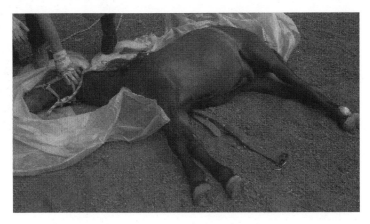

Our miniature horse Sylvie after being laid down with a Running W rig. This was part of the "bomb-proofing" process used before taking her on city streets with a cart

There are several techniques to make horses lay on their sides. This is a process that needs to be done carefully so that neither the horse nor the handler gets injured. Sadly, some trainers have been harshly criticized for using this technique. Several trainers have told me they no longer do it because observers see the horses struggle as they are laid down and file complaints with animal services. Admittedly, there are some trainers who are just not as gentle as they could be but in the hands of a good trainer this is an excellent technique, as the famed trainer Tom Dorrance demonstrated. It can be executed with gentleness and sensitivity. The real trick is getting them to lie on their sides without the handler or the horse getting hurt in the process if the horse fights going down. It is definitely not something for a beginner to try.

A horse trainer from the Amish community using the old Professor Beery method of horse training got 5 of my spoiled pet horses on busy city streets pulling carts within 2 months. He used this technique to bombproof them before they went on the road: He would lay them down using a running W rig. After they were on their sides, he ran leaf blowers, cracked whips, shook cans of rocks and other things to make lots of noise and dragged tarps across their bodies. The horses all lay perfectly still and unreactive during this process. Watching my horses trained with this technique and the profound physiological response I saw is actually what got me wanting to write these books.

SHEEP TIPPING: Sitting sheep on their rumps for shearing or hoof trims causes them to go limp and stop struggling. Professional shearers all use this technique and get the job done in an amazingly short time.

Premier 1 has designed a chair you can actually set the sheep into so you can trim feet and do other procedures. As you can see, the sheep is pretty relaxed! I had a ram actually fall asleep on us when we had him sitting like this. I did see mention in the French Clipnose article that shepherds found prolonged times in this position can cause mortality. This is likely because of the pressure caused by the weight of the rumen

stopping blood flow through the caudal vena cava. Just mentioning this risk so that nobody thinks it's safe to leave a sheep sitting in a chair like this for long periods of time and to watch for signs of trouble.[45]

---

[43] **Beatrice getting shorn by Judd Redden**
[44] **Jacobs wether Bidi being shorn by John Maral**
[45] **Sheep deck chair photo provided by Premier 1**

FLIPPING SHARKS, RABBITS AND CHICKENS ON THEIR BACK

This is a parlor trick that you can find in many online videos. Certain species become "hypnotized" or fall asleep when flipped on their backs. Of course, not many people use this technique to train bunnies or sharks but it is a great example of how positions can trigger these neurological responses.

NECK FLEXING/BENDING EXERCISES—"Lateral flexion" is an exercise horses are put through while in training. It can be done by pulling on reins or lead rope to a halter. It can also be done by holding a carrot to the side so the horse wraps its neck around your body (I call this the "Big Hug" trick.) Some trainers put horses through these exercises to "make them soft." (i.e., more responsive to commands.) Frank Bell refers to this as a body position of bonding as when a mother horse looks at her nursing baby. One could compare this to yoga stretches for horses. As a matter of fact, turning the neck to the side in all directions is used in yoga to alleviate tension and neck pain.

A study that showed elderly people fall more when they turn their heads while walking (neck flexion) because of the vasovagal effect.[46]

The carotid sinus baroreceptor (pressure receptor) is on both sides of the neck. Pressing on this receptor (carotid massage) works with the vagus nerve to slow the heart rate and drop blood pressure. Thus, it makes sense that turning the neck to the side could have this effect.

---

[46] Schoon, Y., Olde Rikkert, M. G. M., Rongen, S., Lagro, J., Schalk, B., & Claassen, J. A. H. R. (2013). Head Turning-Induced Hypotension in Elderly People. PLoS ONE, 8(8), e72837. https://doi.org/10.1371/journal.pone.0072837

Martial arts techniques and Dr. Spock on Star Trek use pressure on this area to cause fainting, syncope or unconsciousness.[47, 48]

Horse people will recognize pulling of the head to the side as "the one rein stop" aka "the emergency brake." It's quite interesting that not only does this keep a panicking horse from taking you where you don't want to go, it works to calm it as well.

Neck flexion is one of three components in Paul Williamson's TAP that is discussed in Whisperers' Tricks

**Intern Lizette getting a
Big Hug from Dakota**

[47] Yartsev, A. (2020, August 15). Function of baroreceptors and clinical relevance of the baroreflex: Deranged physiology. Retrieved April 02, 2021, from https://derangedphysiology.com/main/cicm-primary-exam/required-reading/cardiovascular-system/Chapter%20492/function-baroreceptors-and-clinical-relevance-baroreflex

[48] Zimmer, H., Bennett, T., Gardiner, S., Ravassa, S., & Karemaker, J. M. (2017, December 21). How does carotid massage stimulate the baroreceptors? Retrieved April 02, 2021, from https://www.researchgate.net/post/How-does-carotid-massage-stimulate-the-baroreceptors

      PM;, L. (2016, February 22). [The risk of death caused by cardioinhibitory reflex mechanism is very small]. Retrieved April 02, 2021, from https://pubmed.ncbi.nlm.nih.gov/27063201/

SKIN PRESSURE, SKIN STIMULATION AND "BODYWORK"

"Bodywork=The application of physical therapy methods such as massage, yoga, exercise, and relaxation techniques for the purpose of promoting physical and emotional well-being."

MASSAGE:

We all know how good that feels! Horse trainers like Frank Bell and Gerry Cox use facial massage as an integral part of his horse taming and bonding routine. Being aware of the acupuncture points on the head and other parts of the body and using this knowledge can make your work more effective.

T-TOUCH BY LINDA TELLINGTON JONES:

Dr. Tellington-Jones has developed a whole system of moving your hands across the body to alter the emotional and mental state to one conducive to relaxation, a sense of well-being and learning.

One of her signature moves involves using the fingers to make circles (1-1/4 rotations) on specific areas of the body at specific pressures and speeds to evoke desired reactions. The website www.ttouch.ca

says that the method for people "supports cellular communication and enhances the healing potential of the body" For horses and dogs, T-touch is used to "improve behavior, enhance performance and health and teach a dog to learn willingly. It helps establish a deeper rapport and more effective connection and understanding between humans and their animals." Many books and videos are available on this method.

FINDING THE "HAPPY SPOT":

Every individual has several places on the body that when scratched in these places they will turn into butter in your hands. With my dogs, scratching them on their back over the hips will make them thump their back foot. My pig Oscar will flop over on his side if you scratch him in his armpit. With Beatrice the ewe, over her shoulders or on her chest gets her neck stretched out and eyes dreamy. With my horses the spots vary—you have to search around for the place that makes them stretch out their necks or do what I call "twitchy lips." Most people I know love having their shoulders or neck rubbed. (I made a lot of friends in college this way.)

I am not sure if these are specific points on a meridian or neurological receptors but it's obvious that doing this makes them happy, which gets them to like you more. This is "bonding." It might take a few minutes to find each individual's happy spots. After that, you can go straight to those specific areas

I found Beatrice's Happy Spot!

You can relax a tense animal or person this way so they aren't as jumpy about the next thing you want to do with them. These activities don't take much time and no equipment at all. I try to throw a few "happy spot" sessions in as I pass by an animal during the course of the day just to keep relationships on the positive side.

POLE-TAMING FOR WILD MUSTANGS:

A technique developed by Jim Sharp and promoted by Frank Bell involves rubbing wild mustangs with long poles to calm them down enough to be handled. The poles are effectively scratching and petting the horse from a distance. When sufficiently relaxed, they can be approached and eventually handled.

BODY MOVEMENT

Kinesiology, Yoga, Pilates, Tellington-Jones method

These are all systems that utilize body movement with specific exercises and postures to enhance mental and spiritual well-being. These are each very involved systems with distinct philosophies and approaches. I cannot do them justice by trying to describe them here but they are definitely interesting and worthwhile to consider.

Dancing

Body movement (kinesthesia) combined with hearing music (auditory) and feeling the beat work together to amplify the effects.

DEEP BREATHING

The increased pressure from taking deep breaths triggers baroreceptors (pressure receptors) in the chest to fire and release Vagal-associated hormones. This is accomplished in yoga, meditation and mindfulness exercises.

RUNNING AND OTHER PHYSICAL EXERCISE: The

deep breathing required for exertion also triggers those baroreceptors and is likely the reason for "runner's high." Making kids run laps around the playground or lunging horses (making them run around the pen or on a rope) are common practices to settle them down for lessons.

MERIDIAN/POINT STIMULATION

Acupuncture is the Chinese medical practice of inserting fine needles into the body to stimulate points along meridians. Americans tend to think of it as for pain relief or anesthesia, but in reality it involves complex mechanisms that take years of study to master.

Angela Lee, Lac is a Licensed Acupuncturist who provides services through Antara Medicine and teaches Qigong at UCSF and Kaiser Permanente Hospitals. She describes acupuncture and other modalities used in Traditional Chinese Medicine (TCM) as ways of "moving energy through the body." One needs to understand the complexity of the meridians (energy channels) and all the systems each point affects.

One of the systems it works on is the ANS and therefore the Vagal response. You don't need needles to stimulate acupuncture points. Here are a few ideas:

SPECIFIC ACUPUNCTURE POINTS

There are a number of techniques like T-Touch, acupuncture, light therapy and other ways of stimulating acupuncture points to get therapeutic results for specific conditions. I was never able to master any of those and have great respect for the skill and knowledge of those modalities. But I do have hands and like to give massages. (I did massage the point between the tail and anus of several horses to get the gut moving and pull them out of impaction colics!) Knowing where points that trigger relaxation are allows you to put special attention on those areas. And it can't hurt!

I originally planned to provide diagrams of where these points are, but found great variation in diagrams that are available. This illustrates how complex the mechanisms are. Rather than offer incomplete information, I advise you to get a good book or look up the information on the internet.

TAPPING OR EFT
(EMOTIONAL FREEDOM TECHNIQUE)

Rhythmic tapping along acupuncture meridian lines is a self-help technique said to release fear, deal with anxiety, phobias and stress, and enhance the body-mind connection. It is being used in the treatment of PTSD and emotional trauma. Some coaches use EFT to help people remove psychological blocks to make their lives better. Though some skeptics say it's just the placebo effect, it costs nothing to do, people can use it on themselves whenever and wherever they feel the need and does show lowering the physical stress response.

ENDOTAPPING: Rhythmic tapping on a horse' body causes the horse to relax and be conducive to training;

JP Giacomini is a trainer originally from France who now works in Kentucky specializing in Classical Dressage and Horse-manship. He developed the technique of using a foam ball on the end of a dressage whip to rhythmically tap on the body of a horse starting on the back. This causes the horse to relax and drop his head. The emotional state and thinking process is altered. Horses can be trained to drop their head and relax in response to tapping, as well as changing gaits and posture for Classical Horsemanship training. It can be used to calm an agitated horse on the trail if it's trained to this response. Giacomini's website is www.equusacademy.com. His videos using this technique can be accessed on YouTube.

Paul Dufresne is a horse trainer in British Columbia, Canada incorporating many disciplines into his work. In his foundation training for in-hand, liberty and riding, he rhythmically taps in the specific zones on the horse's body to cause it to relax through the parasympathetic response. This response 1) calms the horse 2) allows relaxation of the poll (the joint between the head and the neck) and 3) relaxation of the jaw. These all work together to further support a calm mindset. The relaxed horse can then be trained to bend and hold its body to the desired shape with balance. This produces a better relationship with the handler, while speeding up learning and physical training. The tapping is then used as a cue for relaxation and resetting to a positive mental state at any time. Dufresne says "The technique is user friendly. Even beginners can get an improvement in their horses' emotional outlook while having tons of further nuances in refining training as they increase their skill level."

Dufresne provides excellent articles and videos on endotapping as well as other good strategies for training on his website (www.pauldufresne.com)

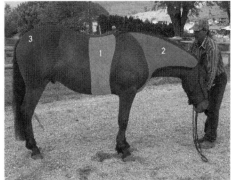

Zones for Endotapping
Photos provided by Paul Dufresne

LOLLIPOPS TO STIMULATE LABOR CONTRACTIONS:

Some midwives will instruct women to suck on a lollipop to induce or promote labor contractions. This presses on an acupuncture point in the roof of the mouth (the hard palate) which causes the release of oxytocin that stimulates uterine

Endotapping on a foal

contractions. Perhaps child caretakers might want to see if having their charges suck on lollipops in this manner harnesses the power of oxytocin to make the children easier to work with!

TONGUE PRESSURE ON ROOF OF MOUTH DURING BREATHING EXERCISES: Dr. Andrew Weil has a breathing exercise to promote wellness which includes pressing the tongue

to the roof of the mouth just behind the upper front teeth. " Dr Weil claims that there a number of incredible health benefits to the technique: "After two months, three months of regular practice, there are very significant changes that happen with the physiology…This lowers heart rate, it lowers blood pressure, improves digestion, it's a very powerful anti-anxiety measure, much more powerful than anti-anxiety drugs."[49]

It should be noted that in Yogic breathing exercise Kechari Mudra the tongue is placed as far back on the palate as possible, though starting on the hard palate behind the teeth may be where beginners start. I also heard in passing that placing the tongue forward and focusing on the feeling from touching the teeth enhances intuitive abilities. There seem to be a lot of things the tongue helps us do other than expressing an insult when being stuck out of the mouth!

OCULAR COMPRESSION: Lightly pressing down on the eyeball causes Vagal triggering. The aspect that slows the heart rate is called **Oculocardiac reflex**, also known as **Aschner phenomenon** and **Aschner reflex**. Yet another associated term is "vasovagal maneuver."

I use this technique to calm agitated animals since it triggers the vagal response. I worked with an Anesthesia-free dog dentistry service when they first started up. RVT Darlene Osborne created her "ocular calmer" incorporating both these concepts. She and other technicians are able to scale the teeth of dogs and cats using the hood to cover the eyes and applying gentle pressure to the eyeball through the cloth on occasion when it's necessary.

---

[49] https://www.thesun.co.uk/living/1255135/is-this-the-latest-cure-all-health-miracle-simply-touch-the-roof-of-your-mouth-with-your-tongue-and-breathe/

My first experience with eyeball compression was using it on a rescue horse that had a very bad attitude toward people. Svali, an Icelandic Horse, was hard to catch and threw off anyone who got on his back. After just one short session with ocular compression, his attitude toward me completely changed to one of submission and cooperation and I became his best buddy.

I also used ocular compression on my uncooperative cow to get bandage changes done. (See the story in "Massaging the Ears")

Pressing on the eyeball with the palm of the hand. Brace the heel of your hand against the cheek bone and your fingers on the bone above the eye to avoid excess pressure.

Ocular compression is also effective in stopping seizures in dogs. It stops seizures in the prodromal stage from progressing into a full seizure and shortening the duration of seizures in progress.[50]

Owners who have used it report impressive responses. One article describes gently applying pressure for 5-8 seconds at a time. Researchers used 10-60 seconds. I think that a longer pressure application may be uncomfortable because a colleague reported her horse getting fussy after 15 seconds. I'm sure the amount of pressure can be a variable, too. As such, results can vary. Veterinarians will admonish there are no real studies done. I am of the school that thinks when you are faced with an

---

[50] Speciale J, Stahlbrodt JE. Use of ocular compression to induce Vagal stimulation and aid in controlling seizures in seven dogs. J Am Vet Med Assoc. 1999 Mar 1;214(5):663-5. PMID: 10088014.

individual in the middle of a full blown seizure it's definitely worth trying.[51]

More information can be found on this webpage: www. canine-epilepsy.com

I have read about researchers using this in diagnostics for people using instruments to measure the pressure applied. Articles describe veterinarians using their fingertips to press against the closed eyes of dogs for controlling seizures.

My personal technique is to place the palm of my hand against the eye with the heel of my hand on the cheek bone and my fingers above the eye socket. This way you can't damage the eye with too much pressure. I gently press with the palm of my hand, count to 5, then release. For those who use mental manipulation of energy, you can think of calm thoughts and energy being shared. I watch for relaxation and may repeat if I think it would help.

I have not been able to find any information about the use of ocular compression techniques for seizures in people. I hope research will be done to determine its efficacy and, if it does work, provide safety guidelines. Imagine how helpful this would be for first aid training when you witness someone in an epileptic seizure and medical professionals with anti-seizure medications are not handy!

> My cousin's son has had seizures all his life. When he has one at home, they learn to clear the area so he doesn't hurt himself on furniture and leave him alone to ride it out. But if he has one in public, people will call an ambulance because it upsets them to witness the event and they don't know what to do. His mother is then handed a bill for $5000 which she is obligated to pay. He hasn't had a seizure in the past few years but if this simple technique were effective and training provided like with CPR, she would have been much happier.

---

[51] Moreno, D. (2002). Ocular compression (OC). Retrieved April 02, 2021, from http://www.canine-epilepsy.com/Ocularcompression.php

LOOKING UP—Since we are on the topic of the eyes, rolling your eyes upward while they are closed shifts your brain into alpha waves. This is a technique from Yoga

Alpha waves are emanating from the brain in the relaxed awareness of a day dreaming mind. An alpha state is the intermediate ground between waking and sleeping. It has been said that alpha waves provide a bridge between the conscious and subconscious mind as well as between the left and right brain hemisphere and processes. Alpha brain waves allow for vivid, lucid imagery and assist in creativity and intuition.

HORSE TWITCHING—Horse trainers have developed many ways of dealing with animals that greatly outweigh them. Here is a brief list of ones that are used. More details will be available in my horse training edition.

The Lip Twitch:

The lip twitch is an appliance (sometimes with a chain) that squeezes the upper lip. To the uninitiated, they look like medieval torture devices.

They are commonly used to get a horse to hold still when you need to give injections, treat wounds and do other things they might not like. These can indeed do damage if not used correctly. This is why people need to understand the mechanism and timing so that it works effectively and you don't hurt the horse.

A Lip Chain Twitch

The Shoulder Twitch:

The shoulder twitch on a horse involves grabbing a hunk of skin at the shoulder. It is generally used when giving injections or otherwise needing a horse to hold still for a few moments. The calming effect may be associated either with an acupuncture point or a "pinch-induced behavioral inhibition" response.

The shoulder twitch

The Ear Twitch:

Holding the base of the ear has been used as a form of restraint. You do need to be careful not to damage the ear cartilage and nerves. I personally haven't tried it because I'm too short to reach most horses. However I have used a version of the ear twitch on a cow which I discuss in "massaging the ears."

"THE STABLE-LIZER" is based on the Native American "war bridle" which runs a rope under the lip and over the upper gums and according to Buck Wheeler was used by Native Americans to steal horses from the US Cavalry. The rope presses on acupuncture point GV 26 and acts to calm a horse. Similar appliances can be found described in books by JR Rarey and Jesse Berry. The Stabilizer is designed to also press on acupuncture points behind the ear (TH 17). The inventor, Buck Wheeler, told me that The Stable-izer is used in racing thoroughbreds and in the United Kingdom for minor surgeries. It can be used alongside the riding bridle and tightened when calming is needed. He reports that some horses learn to enjoy the feeling that the appliance gives them (a "natural high"). It is important to realize that training an animal to wear and respond to it greatly improves your success with this piece of equipment. It takes from 3 to 4 minutes for it to work properly, when applied as directed. In cases where veterinarians and farriers are in a hurry, it helps when the horse owner has applied and used The Stablelizer® on the horse before it's really needed. On the Buck Wheeler YouTube channel, "The Stablelizer" provides an impressive video on how to incorporate this device into all phases of training and tips on how to use it most effectively by incorporating knowledge of natural horse behavior and social interaction. (https://udderlyez.com/stableizer.php)

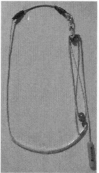

ILLUSTRATION 95
Excelsior Bridle

Jesse Beery's Excelsior War Bridle

Videos of this product can be found online and on Mr. Wheeler's website.

MOUTH T-TOUCH OR " WORKING THE TONGUE:"

Tellington-Jones says that because of the muzzle's direct connection with the limbic system, "working your horse" muzzle—mouth, gums and nostrils—can change a multitude of attitudes and emotional responses, such as biting, nipping, stubbornness, inflexibility, unpredictability and resistance to training."

Frank Bell (www.horsewhisperer.com) has developed his 7 Step Safety System for making sure the horse is in the right frame of mind before you get on its back. He incorporates manipulating the tongue while "working the head" (massaging the face and ears) to relax a tense horse. This is likely caused by the triggering of the many acupuncture points that are associated with increasing the vagal tone.

MASSAGING THE EARS:

MASSAGING THE EARS: There are also many acupuncture points on the ears. Some people have earrings placed so they can conveniently tug on them to stimulate those specific points for things like stopping smoking. We already have seen how one point is used in the Stable-izer apparatus and the horse ear twitch. Linda Tellington-Jones and others recommend ear massages for horses stressed from colic and other health issues. I recall a Qigong master would have students rub their ears at the end of an exercise set. As I mentioned previously, Angela Lee explains that the working of the ears is like working the whole body because all the meridians are represented here.

Thus, consider including the ears when you are doing "bodywork" to restore balance and well-being to someone's body and mind.

Anyone who has a cat has noticed how they enjoy having you rub the back of their ears, in particular where the ear attaches to the head and the cartilage bends when you push on it. Dogs like it, too. I think this is one of those soothing spots that feel good and help them relax. Maybe it will work on people, too, so they can self-soothe!

EAR MASSAGE ON A COW

My Jersey cow, Boo, had a horribly deep cut above her back hoof that required bandage changing. In each episode, my intern Jared and I spent about 45 minutes getting the old bandage material cut off because she would kick, poop, and whip us with her muddy tail even with her head tied and her body squeezed between fence panels. It was not fun. After a couple weeks of these shenanigans, I got the idea to massage the back of her ears, a combination of what cats like and the horse ear twitch, while Jared cut the bandage off. Lo and behold she didn't kick at all! To change things up a bit, I rotated from massaging the back of the ears, to the ear flaps to the face and a little eyeball compression. Bandage changes became less of a dreaded event. Knowing and applying this information certainly made life easier for everyone

PAUL WILLIAMSON'S T.A.P.
(Temporary Attitude Persuader)

Full TAP Photo provided by Paul Williamson

Paul Williamson is an Australian horse trainer in Japan. He has a method of horse training called Hybrid Horsemanship which starts horses bareback. One unique technique he discovered and incorporated into his training program is called the TAP (Temporary Attitude Persuader). He found that a horse that is excited will go into a state of sedation and even unconsciousness when 1) its head is turned to the side (lateral flexion) with 2) a snaffle bit hitting point ST4 on the roof of the mouth 3) girth pressure applied with a girth strap or saddle . This hits the baroreceptors in the neck, palate of the mouth and belly. He can apply this technique from either side on the ground or even in the saddle

Riders will recognize this flexing of the neck as the One Rein Stop though likely have never used it for this purpose. Now we can understand the added benefit of using it in emergency situations to increase the vagal tone.

The technique called the Full Tap using all 3 triggers is used primarily to lay dangerous horses down. When they wake up, they are calm and rideable. He emphasizes that this is a technique that should only be used by experienced trainers due to the risks involved.

The Half TAP is a variation of the Full TAP with or without the saddle. It can be used to calm and immobilize horses during the training process so they can be mounted. He also recommends using the Half Tap as a replacement for twitching in giving injections, cleaning wounds, and other procedures. Williamson says that this technique works in ALL horses if executed correctly.

Williamson reports that veterinarians from the Japanese Racing Association evaluated horses with heart monitors during this process and determined that no ill effects occurred. These techniques have been used successfully by a number of American trainers like Joe Fernandez of New Mexico.

Videos of this remarkable technique can still be viewed on Youtube.com on the Endospink channel or by searching on Hybrid Horsemanship. His book "Cool Change: Starting Horses the Easy Way Using the Half Tap" is available on Amazon in Kindle format and in print through www.Bookbaby.com

PINCH-INDUCED BEHAVIORAL INHIBITION "Pinch-induced behavioral inhibition (PIBI)" is the involuntary response when the skin along the back of the neck is pinched. Most commonly, pet lovers recognize how when you pick up a cat by the back of the neck, they generally curl up and stop struggling like a kitten picked up by its mom and refer to this as "scruffing a cat."

In rat studies, it has been called "the immobility response" or "maternal oral transport response." [52] In a 1978 French research

---

[52] Gianluca Esposito, Sachine Yoshida, Ryuko Ohnishi, Yousuke Tsuneoka, Maria del Carmen Rostagno, Susumu Yokota, Shota Okabe, Kazusaku Kamiya, Mikio Hoshino, Masaki Shimizu, Paola Venuti, Takefumi Kikusui, Tadafumi Kato, Kumi O. Kuroda, Infant Calming Responses during Maternal Carrying in Humans and

paper titled "L'Hypnose Animale" (Animal Hypnosis) referred to this as "clipnose." and describes how it works in cattle, sheep and young horses.

This tradition of using obscure terminology certainly made it a challenge to research phenomena using keywords!

While searching for photos of "cat clipnosis" to use in this book. I was surprised to find this photo of a cow. I could only find one video and an article in French showing how obstetrical clamps on the back of a cow made it lie down. [53] Fortunately, my French-speaking son-in-law gave me a quick translation of the eye-opening article by P.L. Toutain…[54] The video can be viewed if you search YouTube for "Hypnose (clipnose) chez l'animal."

Because you might not have a French-fluent son-in-law, I will present the details from the video and article here as best as I can:

Obstetrical Clamps (locking pliers with rounded tips) applied to the skin on withers (above the shoulder), back and sides will cause a calf or cow to go into a stupor and lie down. The effect appears to take place with the first clamp on the shoulders and becomes more profound the more clamps you apply. He wrote that it happens faster if the animal is afraid, (calves raised by mom and not handled by people rather than bottle babies) which

Mice, Current Biology, Volume 23, Issue 9, 2013, Pages 739-745, ISSN 0960-9822, https://doi.org/10.1016/j.cub.2013.03.041.(http://www.sciencedirect.com/science/article/pii/S0960982213003436)

[53] http://physiologie.envt.fr/1978-animal-hypnosis-clipnosehypnose-clip-nose-chez-lanimal/

[54] Toutain PL (1978a) L'hypnose Animale. Revue Medecine Veterinaire 129, 1289e1304 (in French)

suggests the dorsal vagal phenomenon since adrenaline amplifies/ potentiates the response and makes it easier to trigger. (Similar observation seen by Paul Williamson.)

In this report, adult horses will not respond this way but young foals will. (Adult horses do respond to the "shoulder twitch," which I discuss later.)

Sheep will respond to clips on the back and flank. There is mention of a patent pending for this clips but I could not find anything further. There were no photos of how these clips were placed or what type of clamps. I was unable to reach Dr. Toutain or anyone in the French veterinary circles to find out what other information they had about this technique.

CAT "SCRUFFING" and CLIPNOSIS: People who handle cats for a living (shelter workers, veterinarians and their staff, pet groomers) routinely grab the back of the neck to keep a cat from running off while they are doing something to it. In most cases, it works pretty well because the cat can't go anywhere.

If you can grab the back of the neck in the right place and hold the skin with the right tension so they can't turn around, at least the claws with be pointed away from you. In most cases the cat will stop struggling, too. I don't think many of us thought about the vagal mechanisms involved!

> If you are picking up a large cat, be sure to support the body with the other hand so you don't pull too hard on the scruff. I can tell you from personal experience that if you are working with a wild one, it's wise to be prepared with protective gear if you want to try scruffing as a restraint. Be prepared to get a few battle wounds while you develop your skill and technique.

In a study published in 2008,[55] Dr. Tony Buffington at Ohio State School of Veterinary Medicine studied this phenomenon that he heard about from a French colleague of applying 2 inch binder clips on the back of the neck just behind the ears. (Those French vets!) His team found that this particular amount of pressure in this location caused immobilization and relaxation in 30 of 31 cats the first time the clips were applied. In some cases the response included purring and kneading with their paws ("making biscuits".) A few will fall over and get "cat-atonic." (my attempt at injecting a little humor). Buffington said, "Cats generally seemed more content, sometimes even purring, and less fearful during veterinary procedures when clips were used instead of restraint by some other means,"

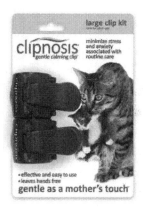

Clips work best when applied BEFORE the animal gets excited and upset. (similar to horse twitching appliances working better if the horse is calm when the appliances like the Stable-izer is applied.)

Note: This contrast from the situation with cattle needing to be excited for them to pass out indicates two different mechanisms of action. Perhaps the cats who go "catatonic" are using the mechanism seen in livestock.

The calming response tended to improve after repeated clippings over three months, suggesting the technique can be used over the course of a cat's lifetime for such procedures as physical examinations, blood draws, and vaccinations. Ohio State even patented a product to calm cats, and to provide a "3rd hand" for restraint during minor procedures like nail trimming, blood draws

---

55 Pozza, M. E., Stella, J. L., Chappuis-Gagnon, A.-C., Wagner, S. O., & Buffington, C. A. T. (2008). Pinch-induced behavioral inhibition ("clipnosis") in domestic cats. Journal of Feline Medicine and Surgery, 10(1), 82–87.

and ear cleaning. Some cats do NOT like this handling technique at all. Dr. Buffington adds, "I test cats by manually pinching the cat's scruff with my thumb and forefinger laid parallel to the body (to increase contact area) first. If I feel the cat relax, I apply the clip(s); if the cat tenses, I do not."

Scruffing cats is commonly used in animal rescue and shelter situations to move them between cages

Animal welfare advocates have voiced the opinion that scruffing and clipnosis is cruel. I hope that this information will alleviate those concerns. The reviews of the commercial product range from "doesn't work" to "works great" which suggests more information needs to be provided on how to use the clips for the best results.

I certainly would love for a graduate student to take on this concept in the various species as a research project so that the results will be more consistent

> Having to deal with uncooperative is not fun, and can cause injury to both the animal and the handler. That risk grows as you work with larger and heavier animals. Of course, anything you do to restrain them can cause injury, too. Techniques like this would save a lot of people and animals injury and frustration.
>
> I tried the cat method of 2 binder clips on the necks of 2 month old lambs but got no change in behavior (i.e. it didn't work.) Perhaps there isn't enough pressure from binder clips and a tighter clamp is necessary. Also, instructions to place the clips/clamps on the back are rather vague. If the mechanism requires getting close to acupuncture points, users need to know how to find those points. The amount of skin that needs to be pulled up might be a factor (some animals have looser and thinner skin than others.) All these questions would make for great student research projects. Let me know what anyone finds out so we can put it to use and spread the word!

A ROPE AROUND THE LEFT FRONT LEG OF A HORSE—

Horse trainer Joe Fernandez of New Mexico told me about a trick a farrier (horse shoer) taught him years ago: If you put a loop of rope (what dog people call a "slip lead") snugly around the left front leg of a horse just above the knee, the horse would settle down. He said this trick is useful for vet visits and farrier work. It doesn't take long to take effect and you hold the rope snug until the procedure is finished. If the horse does start fidgeting, you can tug on the rope to remind him you still have control of his leg. Interestingly, a rope around the right front leg will not have the same effect. The difference between the right leg and left leg is likely associated with the way the vagus nerve runs in the body. It would be interesting to see if a light tourniquet or rubber band around the left upper arm of a person or dog's left front leg above the knee would have the same calming effect!

Photos provided by Joe Fernandez

VAGAL MANEUVERS (FOR HEART PALPITATIONS)

I came across a fascinating article on a pediatric emergency medicine website about the use of vagal maneuvers for heart arrhythmias (supraventricular tachycardia to be specific) in children. [56] I'll briefly mention and describe these maneuvers in case you would like to look them up. While most of us will never face a child with an irregular heartbeat, it's worthwhile to be aware of how vagal maneuvers work and possibly these techniques for calming and bonding, too. You can look up these terms/key words if you want to learn more about the specifics:

Carotid sinus massage—located on the side of the neck by the Adam's apple. This is a spot that can trigger a lot of different reactions if you aren't doing it right (like cutting off blood flow to the brain) so be sure to research this one before trying it! I did find videos on how to do it safely and effectively. You want to actually massage the vagus nerve that runs parallel but to the outside of the carotid artery (which is where you feel a pulse.) In animals, this is "dorsally" to where you feel the arterial pulse. This stimulates the vagus nerve and increases parasympathetic reactions.

Mammalian diving reflex—immersing the face in ice water or covering the face with an ice pack for 30 seconds

Valsalva maneuver—"exhaling against a closed glottis" like blowing your nose while pinching the nostrils to make your ears pop when going into higher altitudes" bear down like you are having a bowel movement" or in case you don't a child to actually have "an accident" have them: blow into a straw or tube that's plugged.

Upside down—Hang the child upside down or have them do a handstand for 30 seconds—this increases venous return and

---

[56] Fox, S. M. (2019, March 15). Upside down vagal maneuver for SVT. Pediatric EM Morsels. Retrieved October 10, 2021, from https://pedemmorsels.com/upside-down-vagal-maneuver-for-svt/.

suddenly stretches the atrium (heart chamber) to trigger the vagal response.

Shortly after coming across the article about Vagal tricks for SVT, I came across an article about **"The Benefits of Hanging Upside Down for Kids"**![57] The article outlines the vagal actions to calm, focus and prevent meltdowns as well as working the vestibular system for better balance and coordination. Maybe those Gravity Boots that adults use to hang upside down in were a good idea! Or we can revisit our childhood by installing monkey bars in our backyard and use them after a rough day of work.

Moral of the story: "Therapy" doesn't have to be dull. In fact, I have fun memories of younger days when my uncles would hang us upside down when we were playing around.

Take ideas that have a practical application for one purpose and if you know the mechanisms of action you might find a use for them in a related need. So be creative and even have fun getting kids to settle down! Maybe kids would think it fun to put ice packs on their face, too.

My daughter is an occupational therapist working with children on the autistic spectrum. She told me that some of them "like being inverted" which is a fancy way of saying they will lie down with their head hanging off the couch or they sometimes do kind of a bear walk. Perhaps this is an intuitive self calming technique.

QUICK COHERENCE TECHNIQUE

This is an easy two step process you can use (and teach your student) to bring about Heart-Brain coherence: (I have mentioned this technique two other places in this book but think it's just so elegant and simple I wanted to make sure readers don't miss it.)

---

[57] Day, A. N. (2021, July 9). The benefits of hanging upside down for kids. Raising An Extraordinary Person. Retrieved October 11, 2021, from https://hes-extraordinary.com/hanging-upside-down.

1) "Shift your thoughts to your heart instead of your thinking brain and slow your breathing"—In other words, focus on your physical heart. Some people actually put their hand over their heart. Slowing down your breathing signals to your body that you are in a "safe place."

2 "Activate a positive feeling in your heart and radiate the feeling it evokes to the rest of your body"—Think of something, someone or a situation that brings about feelings of compassion, gratitude, love or appreciation. This could be the sunset, your dog, getting a hug from grandma… Gregg Braden suggests reciting what he calls "A Wisdom Code" like the Lord's Prayer Psalm 91, Vedic Prayer of Refuge or Buddhist Refuge Prayer…and send that feeling to your limbs and head.

Notice how your body feels, the physical sensations. This is the physical response. Do this for 3 minutes to lock your physical body into this emotionally coherent state.[58]

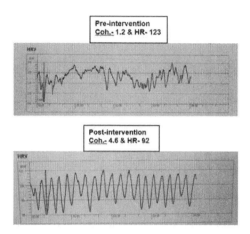

HUMMING: Humming is an even easier way to stimulate the Vagus nerve and bring your body into coherence. Many interesting videos can be found by searching the internet for "HUMMING HEALING."

OTHER METHODS OF INDUCING COHERENCE AND A PROSOCIAL MINDSET

OCCUPATIONAL THERAPY TOOLS

I always thought occupational therapists just helped people with debilitating conditions relearn basic life skills, like teaching

---

[58] Graphs used by permission from Jasubhai, Shilpa. (2021). Effect of Quick Coherence Technique on Psychophysiological Coherence, Heart Rate, Stress, Anxiety, Depression and Feeling State in Young Adults in India. Journal of Psychology and Neuroscience. 10.47485/2693-2490.1042.

stroke victims to hold a spoon to feed themselves. It wasn't until my daughter actually got her OD in the field that I learned it is much more.

Occupational therapy (OT) is a branch of health care that helps people of all ages who have physical, sensory, or cognitive problems. Occupational therapists help with barriers that affect a person's emotional, social, and physical needs. To do this, they use everyday activities, exercises, and other therapies. Many of the techniques I mention in this chapter are actually ones used by occupational therapists.

People who work in occupational therapy and with clients on the autism spectrum have a huge repertoire of things that help calm and focus their clients. I will list a few here but do seek out websites and books on these topics for more details.

Many behavioral problems have their roots in physical or cognitive problems because of the frustrations an individual deals with. Websites for parents of "spectrum children", teachers and occupational therapists offer many ideas that are worth exploring as well. Not only do they have ideas for overcoming limitations, they offer ideas for calming when frustration is exhibited. www.ottools.com

I encourage you to check these resources out even if your child is undiagnosed with a condition and not "disabled".

"To define is to limit"
~Oscar Wilde

A NOTE ABOUT "DISABILITIES": I personally don't like the label of "disabled" because of the stigma attached and the lowered expectations that come with the label. I have many animals that are missing feet or other body parts but do just about everything the other animals do. They just adjust so they can keep up. They don't receive sad feelings of pity from us, just the joy of life like everyone else. Our role as caretakers is helping them find a way to belong.

Nubs, a Congo African Grey parrot, had both his feet chewed off by his nervous mom when he was just hatched. He climbs and perches like all the other birds and gets into more mischief than most. He's eating breakfast on top of a tall cage with his cockatiel friend Doodles. I didn't help him get up there.

MINDFULNESS

"Living in the Now" is a phrase you will hear in the "New Age" and Buddhist circles. These concepts are usually associated with the practice of meditation. Dr. Jon Kabat-Zinn created the Stress Reduction Clinic and the Center for Mindfulness in Medicine, Health Care, and Society at the University of Massachusetts Medical School and has done much to increase the acceptance of this concept as a therapy modality.

I am not a student of this practice so this is my attempt at interpreting Mindfulness as an outsider and how it can apply to real-life situations: Mindfulness is slowing down and paying attention to what you are feeling, then sorting out why you are feeling that way about what someone did or said, or the situation you are in.

Being to fidgety and busy to sit still to meditate quietly for extended lengths of time, I don't have much personal experience with meditation, but "mindfulness" is an integral part of self-evaluation, which I do all the time, and eventually leads to self awareness, which is never a bad thing.

Here's the basic premise behind Mindfulness: What you think about can trigger emotions that manifest in physical responses. If you think about sad, scary or things that make you mad, your body will shift into the Adrenaline Zone. If you think happy thoughts, your body will shift into the Vagal or even Zen Zone.

"Living in the present moment" means that you react only to what is happening right now. Generally speaking, rough times are just transient. You might have to be in the Adrenaline Zone for a relatively short period of time while it's happening but can revert to the Vagal Zone when the threat or problems resolve.

Some people are stuck mulling over past injustices or trauma that keep them angry or afraid. Some people worry about the future and the worst case scenarios of what might happen. Both of these groups will live in a physiological state of Stress. We know that long-term, chronic stress predisposes us to illnesses and even cancer. On other hand, people who frequently recall good memories or are optimistic about the future will stay more in the Vagal Zone. These people are healthier and resilient to challenges to their health and heal faster.

So it really depends on what you want to think about and consciously choosing where to focus your attention. If you are optimistic and remember good stuff, then go ahead and live in the future or the past. If you have horrible memories of trauma or are faced with possible dire straits, of course you must act to get yourself out of the path of a coming train but keep your emotions in the present so you don't remain in a state of anxiety or fear.

> *"I am happy because I want nothing from anyone. I do not care about money. Decorations, titles or distinctions mean nothing to me. I do not crave praise. I claim credit for nothing. A happy man is too satisfied with the present to dwell too much on the future."*
> ~Albert Einstein, a smart man

It is important to have goals so that we can grow and do good things in the world. Just don't get so wrapped up in achieving those goals that you become disappointed in yourself or feel like a failure because you have not hit milestones you created for yourself. The key to balance is loving yourself and seeing yourself as worthy of your status as a human being regardless of material circumstances. To help others, you must be healthy and balanced yourself so you can be a model for those you want to help.

Remember, negative emotions cloud your ability to think clearly. If you step back from your emotional reactions and take an impartial view of a situation, you will be more able to control your emotions. I've heard of it described as standing on a balcony watching you acting out your life on a stage below. You can choose how to look at it and then how you feel about it. When you think clearly without being triggered emotionally, you can make better choices for yourself. This is a message you can give to those who need emotional healing as well as trying to practice it yourself.

ACTS OF KINDNESS / SERVICE TO OTHERS

Dr. Alex Huberman, a neuroscientist, cited research on how feeling the gratitude from another person is even more powerful in evoking vagal responses than thinking of a memory or person who triggers your own feeling of gratitude.

This is why it is helpful for those who are suffering from depression to become involved with service projects. There is a physiological change, not just getting your mind off feeling sorry for yourself. Those who can rise above their depression incrementally are better able to perceive and react to life events in a healthier way.[59] [60]

---

[59] Fox, G. R., Kaplan, J., Damasio, H., & Damasio, A. (2015). Neural correlates of gratitude. Frontiers in Psychology, 6. https://doi.org/10.3389/fpsyg.2015.01491

[60] Hazlett, L. I., Moieni, M., Irwin, M. R., Haltom, K. E., Jevtic, I., Meyer, M. L., Breen, E. C., Cole, S. W., & Eisenberger, N. I. (2021). Exploring neural mechanisms

REFLEX INTEGRATION

Reflex integration is discussed in the Hard Science Deep Dive but I am mentioning it here in case you skipped that section. The premise is that primitive reflexes have not developed normally into conscious motor coordination and responses. This leads to behavioral outbursts and behavior that frustrates their caregivers and the children themselves. Children diagnosed with special needs like autism and sensory processing problems seem to benefit from the exercises and therapies offered in these programs.

Even if your child isn't diagnosed with anything, it is worth looking into if they exhibit behavioral problems. There are specific programs, like the Masgutova MNRI method but also books on Amazon that give you reflex integration exercises you can try at home. It is possible that taking the time to calmly and gently engage in these exercises with the child is at least beneficial through the loving one-on-one attention and positive reinforcement (encouragement) they receive while doing these activities.

SOUND FREQUENCY

SOUND FREQUENCY listening to certain tones affects the brain wave patterns. A number of companies such as Smart-Sound, Hemi-Sync and Sacred Acoustics provide products that shift the listeners' brain into desired brainwaves.

Githa Ben David has developed a healing modality based on finding and singing a single note that resonates with your body's frequency and creates "a bridge to your soul." Ben David calls this The Note from Heaven. (http://githabendavid.dk/eng/pages/about-the-note-from-heaven/what-is-the-note-from-heaven.php) She also has developed a method of "scanning" a patient's body and to find the appropriate frequency necessary to "release

---

of the health benefits of gratitude in women: A randomized controlled trial. Brain, Behavior, and Immunity, 95, 444–453. https://doi.org/10.1016/j.bbi.2021.04.019

emotional trauma" and allow the body to heal. I would be too self-conscious to use this method but the YouTube videos on her method are fascinating to watch.

Gamma: learning, concentration, and self-control

Beta: increased energy levels, focus, alertness and clear thinking

Alpha: help with tension headaches, memory, mild-anxiety and creative flow states. Connection to the spiritual realms, intuitive abilities

Theta: may assist emotional processing, deep relaxation, intuition, memory consolidation, hypnosis

Delta/sub-delta: may assist pain relief, immune function, healing and deep sleep[81]

Dr. Ian Cook of UCLA and colleagues published findings in 2008 of an experiment in which regional brain activity in a number of healthy volunteers was monitored by EEG through exposure to different resonance frequencies. Their findings indicated that at 110 Hz the patterns of activity over the prefrontal cortex abruptly shifted, resulting in a relative deactivation of the language center and a temporary shifting from left to right-sided dominance related to emotional processing. This shifting did not occur at other frequencies. This is interestingly enough the frequency that resonates in the Oracle Room of the Hypogeum in Malta and other ancient sites creates[62] fractal nonlinear reso-

---

[61] From Brainwave frequencies and effects. NeuroSonica. (n.d.). Retrieved October 17, 2021, from https://www.neurosonica.com/the-science/brainwave-types-frequencies.html.

[62] https://www.ancient-origins.net/news-history-archaeology-mysterious-phenomena/ experts-unravel-sound-effects-malta-s-hypogeum-hall

nance which has the ability to alter matter and is a new frontier of research.

Some of the creative modalities incorporating sound frequency include humming, chanting, biosonic tuning forks, Tibetan singing bowls, gongs, and voice. It is easy to see how music had its place in traditional healing practices.

BINAURAL BEATS: A binaural beat is an illusion created by the brain when you listen to two tones with slightly different frequencies at the same time.

I came across this term in connection with guided meditations that induce relaxation. Some even strive to lead to altered consciousness. **The superior olivary complex** in the brain stem, the superior olivary complex processes sound input from both ears and synchronizes various activities of the many neurons in the brain.[63]When you listen to one frequency of sound in one ear that's slightly different from the frequency in the other ear, the Superior olivary complex interprets them as a single beat with a completely different frequency called a Binaural Beat.

For example, if you are listening to a 440 Hz tone with your left ear and a 444 Hz tone with your right ear, you would be hearing a 4 Hz tone.

It should be noted that if you listen to these same two frequencies through a loudspeaker, they blend OUTSIDE of the ears creating what is called a Monaural Beat which have an even greater measurable impact on entraining brain waves. The company Hemi-sync produces products and explains their technology this way: Signals act together to create a resonance that is reflected in unique brain wave forms characteristic of specific states of consciousness. The result is a focused, whole-brain state known as hemispheric synchronization, or Hemi-Sync®, where the left and right hemispheres are working together in a state of

---

[63]   https://www.webmd.com/balance/what-are-binaural-beats

coherence... The production of synchronized, coherent electro-magnetic energy by the human brain at a given frequency leads to a 'laser-like' condition increasing the amplitude and strength of the brain waves. It's evident that a "highly integrated brain," a brain in which both hemispheres are functioning in symmetry, synchrony, harmony and unity, is a key to peak states and peak human performance. When you listen to binaural beats, your brain activity matches the frequency set by the frequency of the beat This is called "the frequency-following effect" or Entrain-ment. In short, you can use binaural and monaural beats to entrain your mind to reach a certain mental state.

Companies such as Hemi-sync and Sacred Acoustics also provide information and products to try.

BENEFITS OF BINAURAL BEATS

- Increased creativity and cognitive enhancement
- Reduced anxiety
- and improved mood
- Helping you enter a meditative state
- Improved sleeping habits
- Helping to improve focus, attention, and memory retention

OTHER TECHNIQUES USING SOUND FREQUENCY
TIBETAN SINGING BOWLS

TUNING FORKS—applied to specific areas of the body Vocal

TONING—singing a specific note to resonate with one's own body and bring into harmony

HUMMING—the vibrations from the throat stimulate the vagus nerve as well as many other responses beneficial to health and well-being.

CYMATHERAPY (aka Electric Acoustic Massagers)—audible sound waves applied to tissues through a transducer. Has been used to heal race horses with torn tendons. In people it has been used for stress relief, pain relief, relaxation.

RHYTHM:

An excited individual in an adrenaline state can be calmed by having them listen to or feel a rhythm that is slower. Perhaps this works through entrainment of their own body's rhythm to shift them into a vagal state. You can do this by having them listen to music, speaking in a slower pace, play music, participate in drum circles, or ride a horse with a slower gait.

The Science: Here are excerpts from "Feeling the beat: Symposium explores the therapeutic effects of rhythmic music" by Emily Saarman (Stanford Report, May 31, 2006 https://news.stanford.edu/news/2006/may31/brainwave-053106.html

"Rhythmic music may change brain function and treat a range of neurological conditions, including attention deficit disorder and depression...

"Musicians and mystics have long recognized the power of rhythmic music. Ritual drumming and rhythmic prayer are found in cultures throughout the world and are used in religious ceremonies to induce trance states

"A small but growing body of scientific evidence suggests that music and other rhythmic stimuli can alter mental states in predictable ways and even heal damaged brains.

"There is a growing body of neuroscientists who support the theory that if there's a physical correlation of conscious experience, it has to be happening in the brainwaves.

"Music with a strong beat stimulates the brain and ultimately causes brainwaves to resonate in time with the rhythm, research has shown. Slow beats encourage the slow brain waves that are associated with hypnotic or meditative states. Faster beats may encourage more alert and concentrated thinking.

"Studies of rhythms and the brain have shown that a combination of rhythmic light and sound stimulation has the greatest effect on brainwave frequency, although sound alone can change brain activity. This helps explain the significance of rhythmic sound in religious ceremonies.

"It's too easy to forget how fundamental rhythm is in so many things and how important musical rhythm can be," said symposium participant Patrick Suppes, the Lucie Stern Professor of Philosophy, Emeritus, at Stanford, who studies brain waves and language cognition.

"Harold Russell's studies found that rhythmic stimuli that speed up brain waves in subjects increased concentration in ways similar to ADD medications such as Ritalin and Adderall. Following a series of 20-minute treatment sessions administered over several months, the children made lasting gains in concentration and performance on IQ tests and had a notable reduction in behavioral problems compared to the control group, Russell said.

"Thomas Budzynski found that rhythmic light and sound therapy helped students achieve a significant improvement in their grades. And could improve cognitive functioning in some elderly people by increasing blood flow throughout the brain. "The brain tends to groove on novel stimuli," Budzynski explained. "When a novel stimulus is applied to the brain, the brain lights up and cerebral blood flow increases." To maintain the high blood flow, Budzynski used a random alternation of rhythmic lights and sounds to stimulate the brains of elderly people. The result: Many of the seniors improved performance on an array of cognitive tests."

THE PACE OF YOUR SENTENCES MATTERS

My friend Alison is a caretaker for her mother who is able-bodied but has early onset dementia. Alison told me that if you speak to her mother too fast and energetically, her mother will get agitated, not seem to understand what you are saying (confusion) and speak irrationally. This also happens when people are having conversations when they are laughing and having a good time. However, when Alison speaks slowly and calmly, her mother calms down and can understand words and speaks more clearly.

This is an example of using the rhythm/pace of the spoken word to entrain another into coherence. It is also an illustration of how the "Adrenaline Zone" stalls out thinking abilities and the importance of using techniques to apply the vagal brake which keeps the body from entering that "Adrenaline Zone."

THE GAIT OF HAFLINGER HORSES

Haflingers are a small breed of horse with a distinctive rhythmic gait. Ty Nitti of Double R Ranch told me that just 20 minutes of riding on the back of a Haflinger has created a shift in the body enough to induce what he refers to as "breakthroughs." He just leads the horse with the child in the saddle and the spotter walking alongside to catch the child if he/she starts to lean to one side. One case was an 8 year old girl who never spoke until this ride. Her father was brought to tears to hear her talk for the first time.

Nitti said that Haflingers and some Quarterhorses were the only horses he had seen to provide this effect.

THE MAGIC OF MUSIC

Music is such an easy, inexpensive way to use both rhythm and sound frequency to shift the vagal and coherence status in a fun and inexpensive way. The more I researched, the more profound the benefits appear to be.

I asked a friend to write down his ideas of how music can be used as therapy. His remarks really opened my eyes to how deep the effects of music can be. I learned later that he comes from a long line of musically talented people. It is clear that music fills the souls of some in ways others can't see. This is an illustration of how it is beneficial to talk to those who have a passion for something and live it and not rely totally on researchers who look at it from a strictly clinical perspective. Here is a synopsis of his words:

"Music was a great outlet for me throughout my life. I just always played music the way some people play video games or sports. I am constantly hearing various kinds of music in my head and I just want to grab an instrument and start bringing the idea into reality.

"Whether you are learning music theory on piano, or playing around with a relative's bass, harmonica, or guitar. I believe it's a powerful thing that can be used and understood in many different ways.

"Music, tone, and vibration have a lot of layers. Absolutely everything is vibrational. I do feel music can help in a wide range of fields that are unexpected to some people. For example when someone says "it's not what you say, it's how you say it" that is due to different vibrations or tones.

"Figuring out how the vibrations, rhythms and intensity of music works makes it a useful tool in life."

"I just see sound as a multitude of things. Entertainment, a distraction, a tool, something that can make some situations better or worse, something to help people connect, or background noise to help you focus on something else

COMMUNICATION: Sometimes kids who are misbehaving respond well to a father's loud stern voice. Dogs seem to listen to people with deep voices over people with high pitch voices.

SOCIAL CONNECTEDNESS: The music community gave me a family, a rather large one, of people similar to me.

"Music that has great rhythm can be used at a social gathering to help everyone connect with each other: Someone looking to have a few friends over for drinks and games may want to have some mid volume, upbeat music. Even letting everyone take turns picking out songs. Live music is a chance for artists and fans to share this love of the music and connect with each other.

"When I am jamming with people regularly, it's like my therapy. It helps me get my mind off life for a little bit, gives me another language to communicate in, and feels like it's what I'm supposed to be doing.

EMOTIONAL RELEASE THROUGH EXPRESSION: I could compare it to someone who is having a group discussion and has a point they really want to make. The point is rattling around in their head and they are waiting for the right moment to get it out. The point they made may not be life changing or even make sense to anyone else. But it felt good for them to get that out. My life would have been more frustrating without music.

"If someone is looking to use music to help felons or recovering drug addicts, I'd say hands on learning an instrument would probably be the best choice

"Even listening to loud performances creates this emotional release

MOOD ALTERING: The ability to alter moods is why music is used as a tool to cope by people dealing with trauma, overwhelming emotions, or mental illness.

"If someone has been through something traumatic, it may be easier to talk about/ process it in a quiet room with soft ambient music playing. If someone seems to be a little manic and is having a hard time focusing, concentrating, or getting a break in the mania, talking to them in a soft, monotone, slow voice without high pitches or rambling could be a way to help calm them down and think clearly.

"Music is also connected with memory. It is up there with smell. A song you loved as a child heard years later will take you back to those days. Music is used in movies, TV shows, commercials and in stores to create a certain experience and convince you to buy products. It is good to understand this so you aren't tricked by advertisements.

"I really don't know what my life would have been like without music, it's just something that pours out of me. It's part of me."

~ Anthony Milani

If those wonderful words aren't enough, here are more reasons from a Science perspective on how learning and playing a musical instrument makes you use and strengthen multiple brain parts.

I paraphrased this list from a meme "THIS IS YOUR BRAIN ON PIANO." I don't know that my mom considered this information when she signed me up for lessons that I had to take all through grade school. I always thought it was our duty as good Chinese kids. Perhaps if I understood she was developing my brain, I wouldn't have grumbled so much!

- **VISUAL PROCESSING:** Sight-reading on the piano involves reading two lines of music, each in a different clef. (Visual Cortex, Occipital Lobe)

- **MANUAL DEXTERITY:** Both hands often play intricate rhythms independently from each other (Primary Motor Cortex/Prefrontal Cortex/ Cerebellum) Pianos also require the use of all 10 fingers which is an additional level of complexity.

- **AUDITORY PROCESSING:** Pianists listen to notes being played and adjust their playing accordingly (Auditory cortex/ Temporal Lobe)

- **RHYTHM PROCESSING:** Keeping time requires synthesizing and synchronizing all sensory input and motor output. Sometimes it requires subdividing the beat in multiple ways , which is actually using math without thinking about numbers (Prefrontal cortex/ Cerebellum)

- **SPATIAL ORIENTATION:** Pianists learn where all the notes are on the keyboard and can play without having to look at their hands (Prefrontal Lobe/Cerebellum/Right Hemisphere)

It should be recognized that "music therapy" is a broad label that covers any use of music to achieve therapeutic goals. Because these studies do not incorporate the same methodologies and ways of using music, they compare apples to oranges. This is why some researchers declared music therapy "ineffective" while others found significant positive results. The success of a music therapy program lies in the skill of the practitioners to be attuned to their clients and choose a modality that meets those needs.

This paper presented a summary of studies on the effect of music on mental states. The authors of this article trace the recognition of music and mental health back to Plato (428-347 BC) who considered that music played in different modes would arouse different emotions. The Indian Vedic Age (c. 1500 - c. 500 BCE) presented the concept of 7 notes associated with 8 emotions and particular arrangements of these notes associated with psychological reactions.[64]

Below are some of their findings in modern research:

PERCEPTUAL PROCESSING: Students with a specific reading disability receiving music therapy improved significantly on word decoding, word knowledge, reading comprehension.

EMOTIONAL PROCESSING: One researcher designed three methods of music training for children with special needs: 1) Music with rapid fire orchestral rhythms has to increase the participation and alertness and manage anger; 2) music without rhythms to induce relaxation; 3) and repeated rhythms to regulate the emotions.[65]

---

[64] A 2014 paper in the Indian Journal of Psychiatry gives an extensive review of studies on the impact of music on mental health. *Tikka, S. K., & Nizamie, S. H. (2014). Psychiatry and music. Indian Journal of Psychiatry, 56(2), 128. https://doi. org/10.4103/0019-5545.130482*

[65] Sairam TV. Music therapy: Designing training methods for the mentally retarded (MR) children. In: Sairam TV, editor. Music Therapy: The Sacred and the Profane. Chennai: Nada Centre for Music Therapy; 2006. pp. 74–8.

AUTONOMIC PROCESSING

- Induce relaxation

- Alter pain perception

- Alter blood pressure, heart rate and oxygen saturation through the autonomic nervous system

COGNITIVE PROCESSING

Students with a specific reading disability receiving music therapy improved significantly on word decoding, word knowledge, and reading comprehension.

BEHAVIORAL OR MOTOR PROCESSING

- Music triggers the body to move, as in dancing or moving with the beat.

- Music enables therapists to engage patients with substance use disorders (addictions) into other usual therapies.

HEMISPHERIC HETEROGENEITY: This refers to the brain processing rhythm on the left side of the brain and melody and the emotional impacts are processed on the right side of the brain.

NEUROCHEMISTRY: The following could be raised or lowered depending on what music was listened to: norepinephrine, β-endorphin, adrenocorticotropic hormone, cortisol and growth hormone

PROGRAMS USING MUSIC THERAPY

With older adults to lessen the effects of dementia.
With children and adults to reduce asthma episodes.
With hospitalized patients to reduce pain.
With children who have autism to improve communication capabilities.
With premature infants to improve sleep patterns and increase weight gain.
With people who have Parkinson's disease to improve motor function.
(from the American Music Therapy Association website)

In short, dancing and playing or listening to music are additional ways to affect the body with rhythm and vibrational frequency

It is not difficult to turn on a radio or play music to calm the mood of a tense individual or crowd. Conversely it can be used to energize people to work and be more productive. You can offer musical instruments to play. You can offer people lessons on musical instruments so they can self-soothe when upset.

Music even has an effect on non-humans. Studies have shown that cows give more milk and chickens lay more eggs when they listen to particular types of music. Happy relaxed animals are more productive—It's Science![66]

---

[66] Halliday , A. (2014, February 25). *A playlist of music scientifically proven to increase cows' milk production: REM, Lou Reed & more*. Open Culture. Retrieved October 30, 2021, from https://www.openculture.com/2014/02/music-scientifically-proven-to increase-cows-milk-production.html.

Israel: Classical music encourages chickens to lay more eggs: Ap archive. AP. (1997, September 30). Retrieved October 30, 2021, from http://www.apar-chive.com/metadata/ISRAEL-CLASSICAL-MUSIC-ENCOURAGES CHICKENS-TO-LAY-MORE-EGGS/6d88335c9b7498dd459427d3e827752b.

Bottom line is that incorporating music into the interactions can be a cost effective aid; doesn't hurt; can help. It certainly meets Dr. Sue's Gold Standard for Techniques Worth Trying. I sincerely hope that these positive aspects become recognized so music will be used as more than entertainment.

ANIMAL ASSISTED THERAPY

The use of animals in therapy work comes in many forms. For some, it entails certifying an animal as "a therapy animal" and taking them to people who benefit from their presence, such as hospital wards and care facilities. In my experience, the healing effects of animals on people is greatly underestimated and underutilized. I have seen a grown man tear up while holding a baby chick.

As director of CETA Foundation/Phoenix Ranch I provided opportunities to engage with animals through hosting ranch visits, petting zoos and pony rides at children's parties, trips to schools and elder care facilities and participation in community events. I always had enough well-trained volunteers with me to make sure the animals would be safe as well as the people, so we never had any problems.

Ty Nitti of Double R Ranch in Apple Valley, CA, offered opportunities for inner city youth and special needs children to experience the magic of horses—until like me, local agencies made it too difficult to continue operating. In our discussions, I learned that we were among the rare people who would put children with physical disabilities on a horse. We both were careful to choose a horse with the right frame of mind and have people surrounding the horse and rider to physically hold them in the saddle and had control of the horse at all times. Neither of us have ever had an injury but we saw the wondrous changes in a child that blossomed through this experience. It is a shame that these services are not encouraged.

Fear of liability is the main obstacle for animal-assisted therapy implementation. In fact, insurance companies discourage this "exposure." I worked with Progress Ranch Treatment Services for years without realizing that the director was going out on a limb by having me provide opportunities for the children in their care. Apparently contact with animals is discouraged within the child services industry. Even my daughter, an occupational therapist, is reluctant to bring clients to the ranch for fear of an incident and potentially losing her hard-earned license.

This is not an unfounded concern, especially in states like California where attorneys are anxiously waiting for cases and clients are happy to provide them. One woman who let visitors meet her ranch animals had an attorney threaten to sue her because a sheep stepped on his sandal-clad foot even though he sustained no injury. There were many things I did on the ranch that my insurance company made me take off my website under threat of policy cancellation.

I took the advice of a woman who ran a pumpkin patch petting zoo: "Your best insurance is knowing what you're doing". I always had volunteers carefully watching every interaction and I watched things like a hawk. If I saw red flags of animals getting stressed which might cause them to act up, I would remove the animal from that activity. I rotated animals out of petting zoo set ups before they got tired. For this reason, we never had injuries. This allowed me to try new things and make some great discoveries, which I hope to write about in another book.

Exposure to animals, especially through touch, is just a therapeutic device that shifts the physiological and mental state of a client into a calmer, more social state. To get the most out of this "device", the therapist should engage the client while in this new state. For example, when I had student interns take ranch dogs to an eldercare facility, I have them invite residents to pet or hold the dogs. The dogs were never forced on anyone, but waited for an invitation to come closer. Then the students would engage in conversations with the resident, who would speak of their pets from years ago. If the residents weren't verbal, you could tell in their eyes that something about this opportunity sparked a special place in their hearts. **The connection provides the healing.** One student told me that doing these visits actually helped her with her own emotional struggles from the stress of university studies. She volunteered to organize other students to continue the visits when I was unable to participate due to time constraints.

Another thing that happens when people engage with animals is the exhilaration of the creation of a Trust Bond. You will see this in their eyes when an animal takes food from their hands or relaxes enough to fall asleep in their arms. This is why at petting zoos, feeding the animals is one of the favorite activities.

I see magic happen when an animal takes food from the hands of a person. An elderly engineer came to the ranch to advise me on where I could put windows in a newly purchased building. He and his assistant saw the sheep and learned that the sheep liked mulberry leaves off my tree. After feeding a few that had fallen on the ground, the engineer got so excited he climbed on the picnic tables to cut down more leaves to feed the sheep. A minister came with his family to see the ranch. He didn't have much experience with animals. After giving the horses a few treats, this normally formal middle-aged man turned into a little kid with excitement on his face wanting more treats to feed. Watch the faces of people who are interacting with animals and you will see something special happening.

This is also a great confidence builder for those who are initially afraid of animals. One graduate student (male, about 6'2" tall) had to be coaxed by his classmates to hold a chick during a class visit to my ranch. When he finally wrapped his hands around the little ball of fluff, you could see tears in his eyes. I believe he overcame his fear of hurting little things. I have had several caretakers tell me that the children who would not touch the animals out of fear during their visit later asked when they could come back again. I think they see how much fun everyone else is having that they want to try it next time. And of course we know that with confidence comes greater self-esteem.

In short, I encourage people to use animals as therapy tools creatively and effectively. Do more than "pet the dog sessions." With careful monitoring of the reactions of both the animals being used and of the client, this can be done safely and with incredible benefits. Also, agencies should not be too concerned about "certifications." From my personal observation, there is little correlation between the training programs a therapy handler and animal went through and what they offer. Those programs do not develop the Heart.

I plan to write a separate book on animal-assisted therapy to expand on what I've learned in the many years of experience and observation. Until that happens, I will do what I can to support others in developing this service for their communities.[67]

[67] **A Progress Ranch resident. Photo provided by Morgan Ong**

THE SILVA METHOD

W hile I was in the last proofreading of this manuscript, I came across the Silva Method on YouTube videos. The premise was intriguing. The more I delved into his work, the more I realized how relevant his techniques could be to those interested in "Whispering." Using the Laws of Metaphysics and the understanding of how the brain works, one could develop empathy, communicate effectively, problem solve through clear thinking, intuition and even psychic abilities, and help both people and animals on an individual level with great effectiveness. Jose Silva passed away in 1999 but his legacy lives on in the programs that are offered by many others as The Silva Method and Silva Ultramind, and Silva Everyday ESP. I will try to summarize what he discovered and the techniques he developed to teach to others:

Jose Silva's life story should be made into an inspirational documentary. He lost his parents when he was 4, dropped out of school to help his grandparents support him and his siblings. He never went to school but learned to read and write both Spanish and English, started a successful electronics business from taking a correspondence course paid for by his local barber, researched how the brain functions and developed ways that could train average children and adults to remember and process information. He also discovered how to help them develop intuition and problem-solving capabilities, perform healings on people with injuries or illness, harness the Law of Manifestation to change the course of events, and be able to perform remote viewing and telepathic communication. Pretty wild stuff if you ask me! Additionally, he developed courses so others could learn these skills.

The brilliance of his findings are borne out by the number of people who can attest to their successes, and the number of prominent people who have embraced and even teach his techniques, such as Vishen Lakhiani of Mindvalley and the late Dr.

O. Carl Simonton, the oncologist who brought mental imagery to the world of cancer treatment.

The main premise of his works is associated with inducing the brain to shift into Alpha and even Delta and Theta waves while in the awake state, which produce physical and mental health benefits associated with the Polyvagal Theory: He determined using EEG that 90% of adults use primarily the Left Brain and Beta waves for problem solving and that only 10% of adults do. However, the 10% that use the Right Brain and Alpha waves make up the people who are high achievers in business and positions of influence in our world. (It should be recognized that those that exhibit traits associated with the Autistic Spectrum also use the Right Brain and likely a lot of Alpha Wave thinking.) Silva used guided meditation to induce deep relaxation and the playing of sounds at 10 MHz to "condition" the brain to shift into "Alpha State" (amplified Alpha brain wave activity.)

Concepts and Attributes of the Silva Method

Physical and mental well-being through stress reduction and improved immune responses,
Better problem solving and decision-making by utilizing both the right and left sides of the brain.
Telepathic communication to affect the thoughts and behavior of another.
Mental projection/Remote viewing
Guidance "from the other side"
Manifest a synchronicity to change a difficult situation using the "mental video" technique
Healing of others remotely and by energy sent through the hands.

Like Mary Baker Eddy who founded Christian Science, he believes the information he brought forth was divinely guided to benefit humanity. His original work, especially his Ultramind System, places great emphasis on using these gifts to help others.

Silva left behind many books on his various methods. A number of Silva Method training programs are available, each with slightly different emphasis. Inexpensive home study programs that he developed are still offered. Access to all of these is readily available on the internet.

RATED "R"—(FOR RELAXATION)

Sexual activity is a Vagal Trigger. I watched a stallion fall asleep on the back of the mare after a breeding session. I am mentioning this just to make the discussion of Vagal Triggers complete. Because this book might be read by tender eyes and minds, this is all I will say about the subject. You can take it from here.

IN SUMMARY

Shifting into a calmer vagal state can be done in many ways that are surprising. If you understand how these mechanisms work, you can get creative and see if you can achieve calming and bonding by variations of these techniques in other situations.

These are not "Magic Bullets" that will fix a problem completely but tools that can be used to shift the threshold between the Adrenaline State and the Vagal State so that your other efforts to teach or heal will be more effective.

You don't have to put on a serious face and make things boring to calm the kids down. As you can see, just playing the right music, hugging them or hanging them upside down can make a difference between meltdown and sanity. With animals, finding a way to reach them might mean the difference between staying in a loving home or euthanasia.

PART VIII

IN CONCLUSION

THANK YOU

I f you made it through this lengthy book you are likely a person dedicated to helping others. I hope you found the information in this book helpful, interesting and an enjoyable read. I encourage you to explore topics on your own because there is a world of knowledge to discover. This book is by no means all the knowledge available. Even at the time of manuscript submission, I was discovering things I "just had to include." I would like for readers to feel free to share with me things they know, and hope that this book will trigger ideas for research projects, too!

Don't feel obligated to memorize everything in this book. My friend Chuck Lewis once told me, "Law school taught me where to look things up." In other words, there's information about this topic and this is how you find it. Use this strategy so you don't get overwhelmed by the amount of information here. This book will make you aware of information and resources out there. This way you can refer back to a page in this book, look up key words on the internet or find real experts on a topic that you find interesting and helpful.

As I mentioned in the introduction, not all excellent trainers work the same way I do. Some will even criticize my books. I take the position that there is no one style that is better than another, only a style that fits you. Just consider the Whisperers' Way one of many options. People who like a slower, thoughtful approach and have the patience should find The Whisperers' Way rewarding.

Even if my style doesn't work for you, the universal nature of The Knowledge will be useful with other styles of training. I was always taught in the traditional Chinese way that Knowledge is Power. There are people who will withhold knowledge because they want to control you.

Knowledge gives you power over your own life because you do not rely on others. You alone know what's in your best interest IF you have the knowledge. With knowledge you cannot be led astray by those who would take advantage of you.

One should not be confident that licensing is a protection for you or your loved ones. Therefore, it behooves you to do your own research whether it be health care, legal advice, remodeling projects or appliance repair. You can still hire someone with or without a license but you will have a better idea if they know what they are doing or you are being told information from those with a conflict of interest. This is called Using Discernment and Taking Personal Responsibility. Ultimately, it is Empowering.

MY SOAPBOX MOMENT: In America, there is a trend for professions to require licensing to work in our communities. As a consultant for the state veterinary board and veterinary association I witnessed how policy was developed and implemented. As a consumer, business owner and homeowner, I struggle to comply with regulations and requirements that make no sense.

Despite the original purpose to protect the consumer, in practice I have found that licensing boards, regulatory agencies and unions do not protect the public from bad actors. Worse yet, some people in positions of power will protect their friends from accountability. People in these powerful agencies will dictate how things are done regardless of the practicality or benefit to the consumer. They will punish those who challenge their authority. They are close-minded to innovation. Consequently, I have seen consumers and excellent service providers who have been harmed by regulatory boards wanting to make an example of them with charges of "practicing medicine without a license." I am only brave enough to say these things because I no longer rely on income from clinical practice to support my household.

As it stands now, these powerful agencies control our options to hire anyone we wish to help us with our animals, our children and our own bodies. It is my hope that we can regain this right to choose and not put practitioners at risk of legal sanctions. In the meantime, it behooves you to take an active role in the health and well-being of everyone you care about by being informed as much as possible.

THE MISSION

"Ask the animals, for they will teach you..."

~Job 12:7

These books are written to contribute to the mission of CETA Foundation/Phoenix Ranch, a non-profit all volunteer organization established in 2007 to help animals and people help each other. Respect, Compassion and Empowerment are the themes that underlie all that we do.

Through the years, CETA Foundation volunteers have participated in animal rescue, low cost spay/neuter, animal-assisted therapy, community events, pony parties and petting zoos, ranch visits and open houses and learning how to work with animals through caring for them at Phoenix Ranch. Happiness is seeing a need and filling it and we strive to do what we can with the resources we have.

All proceeds from the sales of these books directly benefit the animals and program of CETA Foundation/Phoenix Ranch.

It is my dream to touch more lives through this book and by partnering with others who share this vision. Donations are always greatly appreciated. Please visit our website for current offerings and contact information: www.asktheanimals.net

IN CLOSING

Please use and share all the information I've provided with my blessings to do good for others and yourself. If you have more information to add, please send it my way. I will see about including it in future articles or books. I just ask that you kindly give me credit where credit is due.

Feel free to contact me with ideas on how we can work together to implement the concepts in this book on a wider scale and through using the resources at Phoenix Ranch. My current contact information will be on the website www.asktheanimals.net. It is my goal that together we can make life better for many.

RECOMMENDED READING

H ere are a few more books and resources I find encompass the principles of The Whisperers' Way of empathetic communication and provide more practical information on how to apply these principles. Many came out about 20 years ago but their knowledge is timeless.

And of course, explore the work of those mentioned in this book. These are people who have great insights to offer in their specialties.

The Connected Child by Karyn Purvis, David Cross and Wendy Lyons Sunshine

The Best Teacher In You, by Robert Quinn Katherine Heynoski et al

Healing without Hurting: Treating ADHD, Apraxia, and Autism Spectrum Disorders Safely and Effectively without Harmful Medications, by Jennifer Giustra-Kozek"

7 Secrets of the Newborn by Dr. Robert C Hamilton

The Ultimate Horse Behavior and Training Book by Linda-Tellington-Jones

What Your Horse Wants You to Know by Gincy Self Bucklin

Resistance Free Training by Richard Shrake

No Bad Dogs by Barbara Woodhouse

Temple Grandin's Guide to Working with Farm Animals

Bud Williams Stockmanship (www.stockmanship.com)

ABOUT THE AUTHOR

D r. Sue Chan is the 3rd generation born in San Francisco from lineage out of Zhongshan District near Guangzhou China. Her undergraduate studies in Zoology and Geography (A.B.) were done at the University of California, Berkeley and her veterinary studies (D.V.M.-Food Animal Medicine, M.P.V.M.—Masters in Preventive Veterinary Medicine/Epidemiology) at the University of California, Davis.

Dr. Chan is Director of California Education Through Animals/CETA Foundation, caretaker of Phoenix Ranch and owner of Veterinary Outreach.

She is ranch mama to a herd of horses, flocks of sheep, parrots, chickens and ducks, a couple pigs, dogs and cows. Her favorite activities are making others happy and fixing things. She spends most of her time doing the latter on the ranch.

www.asktheanimals.net